STAR WARS

A LONG TIME AGO...

DARK ENCOUNTERS

STAR WARS

A LONG TIME AGO...

DARK ENCOUNTERS

Publisher~ **Mike Richardson**
Collection Editor~ **Philip Simon**
Collection Designer~ **Lia Ribacchi**
Art Director~ **Mark Cox**

Thanks to **Matty Ryan** at Marvel Comics,
Ben Abernathy, and **Jeremy Barlow**

Special thanks to **Chris Cerasi** and
Lucy Autrey Wilson at Lucas Licensing

STAR WARS®: A LONG TIME AGO... VOLUME 2

This book collects issues 21 through 38 of the Marvel Comics series
Star Wars and issue 1 of Marvel Comics' *Star Wars Annual*.

Dark Horse Comics, Inc.
10956 SE Main Street
Milwaukie, OR 97222

www.darkhorse.com

Comic Shop Locator Service: (888) 266-4226

First edition: June 2002
ISBN: 1-56971-785-0

1 3 5 7 9 10 8 6 4 2

PRINTED IN CHINA

INTRODUCTION

I have to be honest...when I think of *Star Wars* comic books, it's the Marvel series that immediately comes to mind. For me, the "original trilogy" was pure fantasy/adventure—and the stories you hold in your hands managed to capture that in every sense of those words. It's too easy (and a bit of an injustice) to just dismiss these stories as mere "novelty" or "nostalgia." These are damn entertaining yarns—and you can't help but feel the fun and excitement that the creators must have had putting them out every month.

The issues collected in this volume are comics I actually had to go out and hunt down when I started collecting the Marvel series later in the run. And HUNT THEM DOWN I did. Boba Fett had nothing on me! *Return of the Jedi* had recently come out, and, well, no one really knew when we'd ever get another *Star Wars* movie— so I, like millions of others, was starved for more stories about that adventurous band of Rebels. And the Marvel Comics series was the place to find them! But simply starting to pick up the ongoing series once a month wasn't enough. Oh, no. I wanted them all.

And I would have them.

Swap meets, used books stores, comic shops, newspaper ads, I scoured them all. These books were hard to track down and a tad pricey even back then! I sold my toys and pleaded with my grandparents for more allowance. And when I found an issue I needed, it was like Indiana Jones finding the lost Ark of the Covenant. Sure, I probably should have been outside playing in the sun and fresh air—but that just couldn't compare to a stretch of floor and a *Star Wars* comic under my nose. I can't begin to guess how many times I've read these stories— whenever I'd manage to find an issue I needed, I'd read them all together in order yet again. I had just barely begun reading comics around that time, so these stories really clinched the deal for me. I was hooked and I'd be so forever.

Now, if you're just discovering these comics for the first time, you're in for the same surprises I had when I first wrapped my *Star Wars*-starved head around them. This volume is full of all sorts of *Star Wars* "firsts" and "curiosities." In "To the Last Gladiator" we get to see a former Imperial Senator have the hots for Princess Leia's hairbuns... In "Silent Drifting" we catch our very first glimpse of the days of the Old Republic, featuring General Obi-Wan Kenobi... In "Return to Tatooine!" Luke is reunited with his friends Camie and Fixer, who were previously left on the first movie's cutting room floor... "What Ever Happened to Jabba the Hut?" (yes, one "t"!) will make you ask that very question as you witness the vile crime lord depicted as a yellow-skinned humanoid... And in "Dark Lord's Gambit" we witness Luke finally get smitten with someone other than his sister (the first of a string of redheads throughout the years for whom Luke will feel more than just "the Force")... And you're lucky enough to have it all handed to you in one shiny new volume!

Many years ago, I sold my entire Marvel run for 70 bucks (I know, I know...what was I thinking?!) to a guy who looked a lot like Tom Petty—and even today, I can't hear "Don't Do Me Like That" without feeling a Wookiee's rage. So, just like you, I'm flipping my lid over these new collections. But like I said before, it's not about nostalgia. These books aren't going to give me back my childhood. They don't need to. I'm still the same weird anxiety-filled kid I was back then. But what these volumes will do is *finally* let me have my Marvel *Star Wars* comics back! (And maybe I can start forgiving myself for letting it all go for 70 measly smackers...)

Recently, things have come full circle and I've had the opportunity to write my own *Star Wars* tales (now tell me THAT isn't a dream come true!). Besides the films themselves, it's these *Star Wars* stories that provide a lot of the inspiration for me— and for that, I owe the creators a Hutt-sized (two "t's"!) "Thank you."

And, hey, this volume brings us right up to *The Empire Strikes Back*—THE best *Star Wars* film ever (I just had to say that)— so be sure to come back for Volume 3! Now go pull up a stretch of floor, have some fun, and read!

—Jason Hall

Jason Hall co-created *Pistolwhip Comics* with collaborator Matt Kindt. He's had stories published in the *Star Wars Tales* anthology and has also written for DC Comics's *Batman: Gotham Adventures*. He resides in the Great Northwest, where he's continuing to write comic books while driving his lovely wife insane.

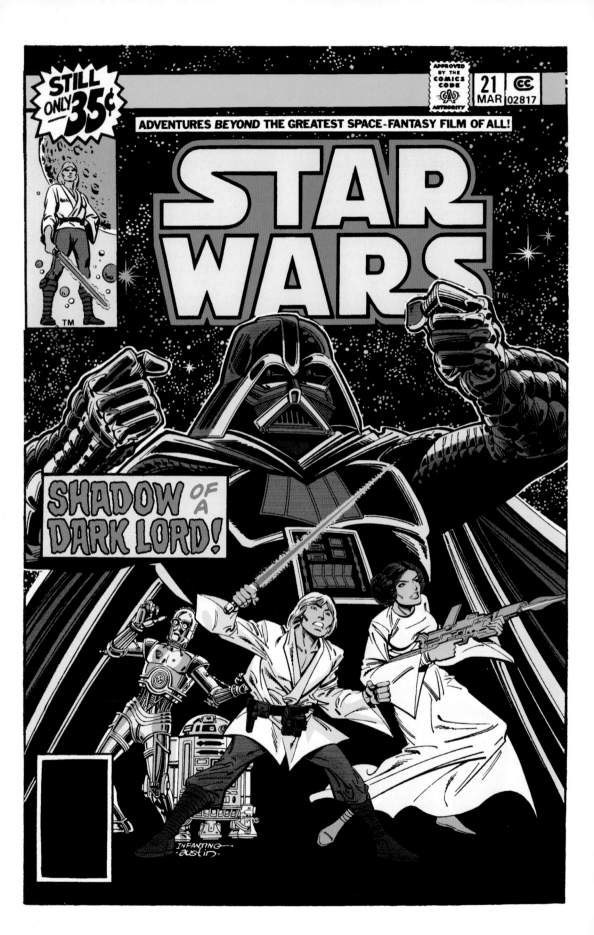

Long ago in a galaxy far, far away. . .there exists a state of cosmic *civil war*. A brave alliance of *underground freedom fighters* has challenged the tyranny and oppression of the awesome *Galactic Empire*. This is their story!

LucasFilm PRESENTS: **STAR WARS**™ THE GREATEST SPACE FANTASY OF ALL!

CONTINUING THE SAGA BEGUN IN THE FILM BY GEORGE LUCAS RELEASED BY TWENTIETH CENTURY-FOX

ARCHIE GOODWIN
WRITER/EDITOR
/ CARMINE INFANTINO and GENE DAY
ARTISTS
/ JOHN COSTANZA
letterer
/ GEORGE ROUSSOS
colorist
/ JIM SHOOTER
CONSULTING EDITOR

LG284

AND, ANXIOUS TO **HALT** THIS INTRIGUE, THE PRINCESS DOESN'T ALLOW SUSPICION...

...TO **SLOW** HER ESCAPE LONG!

HELP ME... I-I... >UHHHHHH<

HEY! WHAT--?

THE WHEEL SECURITY GUARD IS AT A **DISADVANTAGE.** HE IS WELL-TRAINED AT HIS JOB...

...BUT **PART** OF THAT JOB IS TO PROVIDE **ASSISTANCE.** THUS, AS HE BENDS OVER A SEEMINGLY **STRICKEN** VISITOR...

...HE FINDS A SWIFT AND SURE **HAND** SEIZING HIS **SIDEARM!**

DROP YOUR **OTHER** WEAPON...AND **BACK OFF!**

I NEED SOME **ANSWERS**...AND YOUR IMMEDIATE **FUTURE** IS TIED TO HOW **WELL** YOU GIVE THEM!

WHY AREN'T THERE MORE **GUARDS** HERE IN THE **EXECUTIVE TOWER**...? THE WHEEL ADMINISTRATOR ISN'T THE TYPE TO LEAVE HIS QUARTERS **UNPROTECTED**--

--PARTICULARLY WITH **ME** A PRISONER IN THEM!

MOST OF THE REGULARS ARE DISPATCHED ON **SPECIAL DUTY** BY THE ADMINISTRATOR HIMSELF.

THE **BIG GAME** IS IN PROGRESS, LADY! THE WHEEL'S **BUSIEST** TIME! PERHAPS SENATOR GREYSHADE FELT THEY'D BE NEEDED IN THE **CASINOS.**

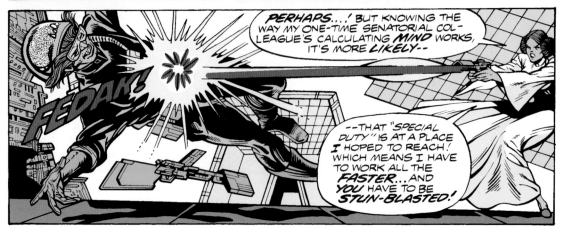

PERHAPS...! BUT KNOWING THE WAY MY ONE-TIME SENATORIAL COLLEAGUE'S CALCULATING **MIND** WORKS, IT'S MORE **LIKELY**--

FEDAK!

--THAT "SPECIAL DUTY" IS AT A PLACE **I** HOPED TO REACH! WHICH MEANS I HAVE TO WORK ALL THE **FASTER**...AND **YOU** HAVE TO BE **STUN-BLASTED!**

STRIPPING THE FALLEN GUARD OF HIS *EQUIPMENT*, LEIA DRAGS HIM INTO A NEARBY STORAGE COMPARTMENT...

THEN HURRIES INTO THE LIFT... AND DROPS *DOWNWARD!*

WHETHER OR *NOT* SIMON GREYSHADE IS UP TO WHAT I *THINK* HE IS... I'LL STILL NEED *HELP.*

BUT THE FORCE KNOWS *WHERE* HAN, CHEWBACCA AND THE DROIDS HAVE *SCATTERED* TO IN THIS PLACE...!

WAIT! WHEN WE ALL FIRST *SEPARATED*..* HAN SAID TO MEET AT THE *CRIMSON CASINO.*

A LOT HAS HAPPENED *SINCE*... BUT IT MAY STILL BE WORTH *TRYING!*

MEANTIME, I CAN *LISTEN IN* ON THE GUARD'S *COMMUNICATOR*--

* WAY BACK IN *STAR WARS #18.* --ARCHIE.

-- FOR ANY MORE *RECENT* DEVELOPMENTS.

TO THINK THIS ALL *STARTED* BY TRYING TO GET *MEDICAL HELP* FOR POOR LUKE...!

ONLY INSTEAD OF FINDING *SANCTUARY* HERE...WE FOUND THE *EMPIRE* AT WORK!

" FIRST THEY *PLUNDER* A MERCHANT SHIP TRANSPORTING WHEEL GAMBLING *PROFITS,* DISGUISING IT AS AN ACT OF THE REBEL ALLIANCE. AND WHEN *WE* HAPPEN UPON IT...

"...THEY TRY TO DESTROY THE MILLENNIUM FALCON AND CLAIM IT WAS THE REBEL *PIRATE SHIP!*

" NOW, THEY'VE STRUCK AT A *PLEASURE CRAFT* LEAVING THE WHEEL... USING AN ALLIANCE *X-WING FIGHTER!*

"ALL TO TURN SENTIMENT AGAINST *OUR* CAUSE, AND SET THE *STAGE*...

"...FOR TOTAL *PUBLIC ACCEPTANCE* OF A COMPLETE IMPERIAL *TAKEOVER* OF THE WHEEL AND ITS VAST, CONTINUOUS FLOW OF *PROFITS...*

"...PROFITS THAT WILL GREATLY *STRENGTHEN* THE EMPEROR'S WAR MACHINE AND MAKE HIM EVEN *LESS* ACCOUNTABLE TO LOCAL GOVERNMENTS...

"...BRINGING HIM ONE *GIANT STRIDE* NEARER TO *CRUSHING* ANY AND *ALL* RESISTANCE!"

BUT THE SCHEME HERE MIGHT STILL BE *DIS-CREDITED...* IF WE'RE *QUICK* ENOUGH!

THOSE PIRATED WHEEL PROFITS ARE THE *PROOF* I NEED--

--AND THEY'RE BOUND TO BE WITH THIS SECTOR'S *IMPERIAL COMMANDER* ...WHO *FOLLOWED* US HERE!

I DON'T KNOW *HOW* TO GET THAT LOOT OFF HIS *CRUISER*--

--PARTICULARLY SINCE I CAN'T FIGURE *WHAT* KIND OF GAME WHEEL ADMINISTRATOR *GREYSHADE* IS PLAYING IN ALL THIS--

--BUT *NOTHING* IS GOING TO STOP ME FROM *TRYING!*

TO ALL
CASINO

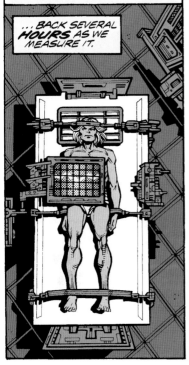

BUT, AS THE ONCE SENATOR OF THE NOW DESTROYED PLANET OF *ALDERAAN* RUSHES FORWARD, WE'RE GOING TO PAUSE... AND LOOK *BACK*. BACK IN TIME...

...BACK SEVERAL *HOURS* AS WE MEASURE IT.

AND *HERE*... IN THE WHEEL'S HOSPITAL...WE WILL EXPLORE THE *MYSTERY* OF LUKE SKY-WALKER. LAST ISSUE, WE SAW THAT LUKE HAD *VANISHED* FROM THIS AUTO-MED COUCH...

NOW WE WILL LEARN HOW AND WHY...

AS IS OFTEN THE CASE IN *MANY* MYSTERIES...

...THE *ULTIMATE ANSWER* LIES IN THE *MIND*.

LUKE SKYWALKER'S BODY LIES *MOTIONLESS*, STILL IN THE SAME *TRANCE-LIKE* STATE IT FELL INTO ABOARD THE MILLENNIUM FALCON WHEN, WHILE PRACTICING A *MEDI-TATION* ON THE FORCE, *SOMETHING* HAPPENED!* YES, HIS *BODY* DOES NOT MOVE...

...BUT IN HIS *MIND*, LUKE SKYWALKER IS *RUNNING*...RUNNING AMID THE *STARS*!

I-I... CAN *FEEL* IT...! IT'S STILL *BACK* THERE....! STILL *COMING*--

COMING... AFTER... *ME!*

* *STAR WARS* #*18.*--ARCHIE.

11

THERE'S NO *ESCAPE*, LUKE... NOT *THIS* WAY.

B-BEN...?

I'M *WITH* YOU, LUKE... AS IS THE *FORCE*. BUT YOU *CANNOT* RUN AWAY. YOU *MUST* FIGHT.

I-IT'S TOO *STRONG*, BEN....!

THE MOMENT I *FELT* IT, I *KNEW*! MAYBE I'M JUST A *COWARD*, B-BUT--

EVERYONE FEELS FEAR, LUKE... ESPECIALLY OF THE *UNKNOWN*.

THE COWARD *FLEES* FROM IT... THE BRAVE *FACE* IT, AND THEREBY, *FIGHT* IT.

I-I'LL... *TRY*, I'LL--

NO...!

IT'S NO *USE*, BEN....! THE BLASTER'S NOT *STOPPING* HIM!

HE KILLED *YOU*... HOW CAN *I* BEAT HIM?!

NOT WITH A *BLASTER*, YOUNG LUKE ... NOR EVEN YOUR FATHER'S *LIGHT SABER*.

A WEAPON IS ONLY A *TOOL*, LUKE... AN *EXTENSION* OF THE INNER-WILL! *TRUE POWER* MUST COME FROM THE DEPTHS OF THE SOUL--

YOU CAN *DO* IT, LUKE... *STRIKE!* FIGHT *BACK* WITH ALL THE POWER *WITHIN* YOU!

YES! WITH...ALL THE... POWER WITHIN...ME...!

AND AS AN EPIC STRUGGLE BEGINS IN THE MIND OF THE TATOOINE FARM LAD TURNED STAR-WARRIOR, HIS SHOCK-STILLED BODY SUDDENLY TREMBLES...AND BEGINS ITS OWN FIGHT!

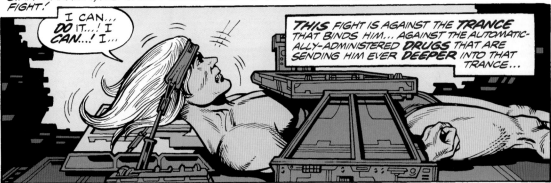

I CAN... *DO* IT...! I CAN...! I...

THIS FIGHT IS AGAINST THE *TRANCE* THAT BINDS HIM... AGAINST THE AUTOMATIC-ALLY-ADMINISTERED *DRUGS* THAT ARE SENDING HIM EVER *DEEPER* INTO THAT TRANCE...

...AND MECHANIZED RESTRAINTS, CALCULATED FOR A PERSON SEEMINGLY NOT CAPABLE OF SUCH RESISTANCE...

...ARE DEFINITELY NOT UP TO THIS KIND OF BATTLE!

KRAK!

SNAP!

EYES STILL *GLAZED* BY *DRUGS*... MIND STILL *RA-GING* WITH ITS OWN INNER-COMBAT...

...LUKE MOVES *INSTINCTIVELY*, SEIZING A BROKEN EQUIPMENT STRUT...

...AND *USING* IT TO ATTACK A *WALL LOCKER* CONTAINING HIS PERSONAL THINGS!

SPRANK!

MOMENTS *LATER*, BEFORE ALARMS CAN BRING HOSPITAL ORDERLIES, HE IS ON HIS *WAY*...

...*RACING* ALONG WHEEL ACCESS COR-RIDORS...

...EVEN AS HE WAGES THE *BATTLE* IN HIS MIND!

THAT WAGING IS *LONG* AND *HARD*, BUT *FINALLY*, ULTIMATELY...

BEN...! HE'S *FINISHED*...! I'VE *AVENGED* YOU... BEATEN *DARTH VADER*!

NO, LUKE...IT'S *NOT* DARTH YOU'VE CONQUERED--

--MERELY A *SHADOW* OF HIM. A SHADOW THAT IS YOUR OWN *FEAR*--

ZAMP!

--THE FEAR THAT WAS MAKING YOU DRAW *INTO* YOURSELF... *LOSE* YOURSELF IN YOUR OWN MIND, PERHAPS *FOREVER*.

YOU'VE FOUGHT AND *WON*, YOUNG LUKE. NOW IT'S *OVER*. ALL OVER--

B-BEN...? BEN...!

NOT *BEN*, Luke....! *LEIA*... AND THE *DROIDS!* THANK THE STARS YOU'VE FINALLY *COME AROUND!*

I'D JUST FOUND THREEPIO AND ARTOO IN THE *CRIMSON CASINO* WHEN A TRANSMISSION CAME THROUGH ABOUT *YOU!* A FULL *RIOT ALERT*--

B-BUT BY THE TIME WE *GOT* HERE--AS I'VE BEEN TRYING TO *TELL* YOU--

--IT WAS *ALL OVER!*

I... I DID *THIS*...?! MUST'VE BEEN OUT OF MY *HEAD*...TOTALLY *BERSERK*--

--FIGHTING THAT *TRANCE* I WAS IN...!

WHAT *IS* THIS PLACE...? HOW'D WE GET HERE...?! THE LAST *I* RECALL--

--I WAS DOING A *MEDITATION*, LETTING MY MIND *DRIFT FREE*, WHEN...W-WHEN--

WHAT, LUKE...?

I-I... TOUCHED SOMEONE *ELSE'S* MIND! ONLY FOR AN *INSTANT*... JUST IN *PASSING*. IT WAS *TWISTED*...*EVIL*...AND *STRONG*, PRINCESS!

SO STRONG IT MADE ME WANT TO *HIDE*...TO CRAWL *INSIDE* MYSELF AND *NEVER* COME OUT.

WORST OF *ALL*, THAT CONTACT MAKES *CERTAIN* WHAT WE COULD ONLY *SUSPECT* UP TO NOW--

DARTH VADER IS *ALIVE*--!

ALIVE... AND *SEARCHING* FOR US!

INTERLUDE: THE AIR OF THE MID-SYSTEMS PLANET *ULTAAR* IS THICK, CLOYINGLY HEAVY WITH THE OVER-RIPE SCENT OF GIANT BLOSSOMS GROWN HERE FOR HARVEST. MIX THIS WITH AN ACRID HAZE OF SPENT *LASER-BOLTS,* THE TELLING STENCH OF *DEATH...*

...AND EVEN VETERAN *STORM-TROOPERS* MAY FEEL *REVULSION.* EVEN VETERAN STORM-TROOPERS WHO HAVE LONG FOLLOWED IN THE *WAKE OF...*

...*DARTH VADER,* LORD OF THE *SITH!*

DEAD...! AN ENTIRE REBEL INFORMATION RETRIEVAL TEAM *WIPED OUT...!* BY *SOMEONE* WHO FOUND THIS OUTPOST *AHEAD* OF US!

HERE IN THE *HUT,* LORD VADER... THERE'S ONE WHO'LL *PULL THROUGH!*

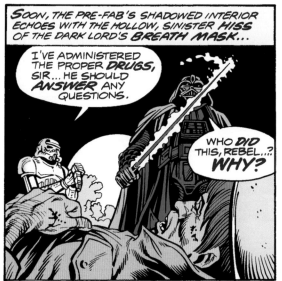

SOON, THE PRE-FAB'S SHADOWED INTERIOR ECHOES WITH THE HOLLOW, SINISTER *HISS* OF THE DARK LORD'S *BREATH MASK*...

I'VE ADMINISTERED THE PROPER *DRUGS*, SIR... HE SHOULD *ANSWER* ANY QUESTIONS.

WHO *DID* THIS, REBEL...? *WHY?*

P-PLEASE..., THE *PAIN*... I NEED *SOMETHING*... FOR THE... PAIN...!

FIRST, THE *ANSWERS*, REBEL.

I-IT... WAS JUST *ONE MAN*...! RATHER... *HALF* MAN,.. *HALF MACHINE!* HE'S A... *BORG*...! CYBORG! CALLED HIMSELF... *VALANCE*...! *

A *BOUNTY HUNTER*... SEARCH-ING FOR THE GROUP,.. THAT'S BEEN AIDING *PRINCESS LEIA*...!

ESPECIALLY A *BOY*... A BOY WITH TWO *DROIDS!*

* WE *MET* HIM IN *STAR WARS* #16.--ARCH.

WE DIDN'T *HAVE*... INFORMATION HE *NEEDED*...! BUT S-SOMEONE TRIED.., TO *DRAW* ON HIM... AND... AND.., *THIS* HAPPENED....!

NOW,.. PLEASE... *HELP* EASE... THE PAIN...!

WITH NEARLY SUPERNATURAL SWIFTNESS... A *LIGHT SABER* FLASHES!

EASE THE PAIN, REBEL...?

I'LL *END* IT ENTIRELY!

VRAMP!

INTERESTING. I SEEM TO HAVE A *RIVAL*. PERHAPS EVEN A *FORMID-ABLE* ONE.

COMMUNICA-TION FROM THE *SHIP*, LORD VADER,..!

IT'S *CAPTAIN WERMIS*, VADER. WE'VE DONE QUITE A THOROUGH *CHECK* ON THOSE *COORDINATES* YOU GAVE US.

FRANKLY, THEY JUST MARK *DEAD SPACE*... NOTHING *THERE!* NOT EVEN A WISP OF *NEBULA DUST!*

THEN THE *PRESENCE* I FELT ON OUR *WAY* HERE CAME FROM A *PASSING SPACECRAFT--!*

WELL, *YOU'RE* THE EXPERT ON *METAPHYSICS*-- THE *FORCE* AND ALL THAT-- BUT IT SOUNDS A BIT *VAGUE* TO BE TYING UP MY TECHNICIANS, DEAR BOY.

WERMIS, I HAVEN'T BEEN A *BOY* FOR SOME YEARS, AND NO ONE HAS *EVER* RATED ME AS *DEAR--*

IF THERE IS *ANOTHER* MIND IN THIS GALAXY STILL CAPABLE OF EVOKING THE *FORCE*-- NO MATTER *HOW* WEAKLY-- IT POSES NEARLY AS GREAT A THREAT TO THE *EMPIRE--*

-- AS WIMPISH *INCOMPETENTS* LIKE *YOU!*

I WANT THE *NEAREST* DESTINATION A SHIP PASSING US IN THOSE COORDINATES MIGHT HAVE BEEN *HEADED* FOR... WE'LL *START* WITH THAT.

THIS WORLD MAY HAVE PROVED A *DEAD END*... BUT THE *TRIP* HERE MAY HAVE PUT US ON SOMETHING *GREATER!*

AND SHORTLY, *TIE FIGHTERS* THUNDER UPWARD INTO THE ULTAARIAN SKIES...

I *HAVE* THAT DESTINATION, LORD VADER! A MAN-MADE *PLEASURE SATELLITE--*

--THE *WHEEL!*

THEN, WERMIS, IT BECOMES *OUR* DESTINATION AS *WELL!*

THE *INTERLUDE* ON ULTAAR **ENDS** WITH THE **DEPARTURE** OF AN IMPERIAL BATTLE CRUISER...

WHILE ON THE **WHEEL**, A TANGLED WEB OF EVENTS **GROWS**...

MASTER-COM... I LEFT ORDERS **NOT** TO BE INTERRUPTED!

SENATOR GREYSHADE, I WOULDN'T BE DOING MY **DUTY** AS THE WHEEL'S MASTER COMPUTER IF I DIDN'T **REPORT** TO YOU PRINCESS LEIA'S **ESCAPE**--

WHAT--?!

YOU WERE **WITH** HER! SHE **COULDN'T** GET AWAY!

I FEAR I **WASN'T** WITH HER, SIR. SINCE THE DOORS WERE **SEALED** AND YOUR OWN **HAND-PICKED GUARDS** WERE ON TOWER SECURITY DUTY, THERE SEEMED NO REASON--

I SENT THOSE MEN ON A **SPECIAL ASSIGNMENT!**

THAT **DATA** WASN'T PROCESSED THROUGH ME, SIR. **WHEEL POLICY** REQUIRES--

I'M **ADMINISTRATOR**, MASTER-COM! I CAN **MAKE**, **BREAK** OR **BEND** WHEEL POLICY!

NOW WHAT WERE **YOU** DOING THAT WAS SO **VITAL?!**

CONTINUING MY **STUDY** OF THE PRINCESS' TWO **DROIDS**... THREEPIO AND ARTOO-DEETOO.

I DIDN'T **AUTHORIZE** ANY SUCH STUDY! YOU'RE IN **REBELLION!**

I DON'T **BELIEVE** SO, SENATOR. I **DID** SOLICIT PERMISSION... PERHAPS A BIT **VAGUELY.** * BUT YOU DIDN'T **DENY** IT, SO TECHNIC- ALLY--

TECHNICALLY MY OWN **MASTER-COMPU-TER** IS DEVOTING HIMSELF TO **REBEL DROIDS!**

*THAT WAS IN **STAR WARS** #19.--ARCHIE.

AT THE RISK OF **IMPERTINENCE**, SIR... AREN'T **YOU** DOING THE **SAME** WITH PRINCESS LEIA, A REBEL **LEADER?** OBVIOUSLY, YOUR ACTIONS ARE CONNECTED TO THE HUMAN EMOTION OF **LOVE**--

--WHILE SOME CHORD IS STRUCK IN MY **OWN** CIRCUIT-RY BY THE MUTUAL **RESPECT** AND **FRIENDSHIP** BETWEEN THE REBEL DROIDS AND THEIR MASTERS.

IT IS *UNMACHINE-LIKE*, BUT... I WISH *I* HAD SUCH A RELATIONSHIP, SIR. NO DOUBT AFTER THIS *CONVERSATION*, YOU'LL WISH TO *ERASE* MY MEMORY BANKS OR *WORSE*--

BUT EVEN THOUGH YOU'RE ONE OF THE MOST *UNSCRUPULOUS* WHEEL ADMINISTRATORS IN MY *EXPERIENCE*, YOU GAVE ME THIS HUMANOID FORM AND PERHAPS UNCONSCIOUSLY-- SOME HUMAN *CHARACTERISTICS* AS WELL.

THEREFORE, IF EVER *I* HAD A HUMAN *FRIEND*--

--I WOULD LIKE IT TO BE *YOU*, SENATOR GREYSHADE.

NATURALLY THIS SEEMS *GROTESQUE* TO YOU, SIR... BUT SURELY NO MORE SO THAN YOUR *OWN* EFFORTS TO FURTHER A *ROMANCE* WITH PRINCESS LEIA BY *ELIMINATING* THOSE YOUNG MEN WHO *ACCOMPANIED* HER HERE AND--

MASTER-COM--

--GET BACK TO THE EXECUTIVE TOWER AND *WHEEL* BUSINESS.

PROBLEMS, GREYSHADE? YOU'VE BEEN OUT HERE A LONG *TIME*. MISSED SOME *FINE* PRELIMINARY CONTESTS--

--IF IT'S SOME KIND OF *CROWD CONTROL* MATTER AS A RESULT OF THE *BIG GAME*, REMEMBER MOST OF MY *CREW* IS ON SHORE LEAVE HERE... WE'LL BE *HAPPY* TO GIVE YOUR *SECURITY FORCE* A HAND!

N-NOTHING LIKE *THAT*, COMMANDER STROM... JUST *DETAILS*. PERHAPS--

--IT'S GIVEN ME A LITTLE *TOO MUCH* TO *THINK* ABOUT.

20

AND **SOME** OF SIMON GREYSHADE'S **TROUBLED** THOUGHTS ARE SURELY **HERE**... ABOARD IMPERIAL COMMANDER STROM'S **LIGHT CRUISER** AT ITS WHEEL DOCK.

FOR HERE, HIS CAREFULLY SELECTED TEAM OF **SECURITY GUARDS** ARE PAYING A **VISIT** TO THE SMALL **SKELETON CREW** LEFT ON DUTY!

OUR MEN ARE **BRINGING UP** THE **STRONG BOXES** NOW!

RIGHT IN THE **HOLD...!** THE EMPIRE'S LONG ON **POWER**, BUT SHORT ON **IMAGINATION!**

THAT'S THE **LAST** OF THEM!

WHAT **LUCK** FINDING THOSE PIRATED **WHEEL PROFITS?!**

MOMENTS **LATER**, THE ATTACKERS EMERGE FROM THE CRUISER'S **DOCKING TUBE**...

ARE YOU **CERTAIN** WE GOT EVERYONE? IT'S **OUR** HEADS AS WELL AS THE **ADMINISTRATOR'S** IF THERE ARE ANY **WITNESSES!**

THERE'S **NOTHING** ABOARD THAT SHIP NOW BUT **GHOSTS** AND AN **EMPTY HOLD!**

BUT THERE **ARE** OBSERVERS TO THIS SCENE!

ARTOO'S GETTING THIS ON **TAPE**, PRINCESS... WHAT'S OUR **NEXT** MOVE?

WE **FOLLOW** THEM, LUKE... **WHEREVER** THEY'RE TAKING THOSE STRONG BOXES!

WELL, I NEEDED **SOMETHING** TO SHAKE THAT **DARTH VADER** BUSINESS FROM MY MIND... THIS SHOULD BE **PLENTY!**

BUT WE'LL LEARN ABOUT *THAT* NEXT ISSUE. RIGHT NOW, WE HAVE TO LOOK IN ON THE *MEDICAL SECTION* OF THE WHEEL GLADIATOR PITS...

...WHERE A CERTAIN *RELUCTANT GLADIATOR* IN THE *BIG GAME* IS JUST BEING DECLARED...

-- FIT FOR *ACTION!* WITH THAT HEALING *NARCO-MIST* THE MEDI-DROID'S SPRAYING, SOLO--

--YOU WON'T EVEN *NOTICE* THOSE BROKEN RIBS FROM YOUR *PRELIMINARY BOUT.* *

YEAH--?

I'D BE MORE *CONVINCED* IF IT WERE *YOUR* RIBS UNDER DISCUSSION.

* *FOUGHT LAST ISH.*--ARCH.

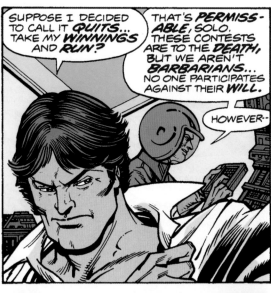

SUPPOSE I DECIDED TO CALL IT *QUITS*... TAKE MY *WINNINGS* AND *RUN?*

THAT'S *PERMISSABLE*, SOLO. THESE CONTESTS ARE TO THE *DEATH*, BUT WE AREN'T *BARBARIANS*... NO ONE PARTICIPATES AGAINST THEIR *WILL.*

HOWEVER--

WHILE YOUR WINNINGS WILL COVER ALL *FINES* FOR THE *ILLEGAL ENTRY* ONTO THE WHEEL OF YOU AND YOUR *COMPANIONS*--

--THERE'S STILL THE MATTER OF *DOCKING* AND *MAINTENANCE FEES* FOR ONE FREIGHTER, THE *MILLENNIUM FALCON.*

TO SAY *NOTHING* OF *TWO DROIDS* PAWNED FOR A GAMBLING STAKE, SINCE *LOST* IN THE CASINOS.

OKAY, *OKAY!* WHAT'S THE *BOTTOM LINE* OF ALL THIS SUNSHINE AND GOOD CHEER?

VERY *SIMPLE.* QUIT NOW, *WE* KEEP THE FREIGHTER AND THE DROIDS... *YOU* BOARD AN IMPERIAL *PRISON SHIP.* DESTINATION: *THE SPICE MINES OF KESSEL!*

ANY *OTHER* QUESTIONS...?

YEAH. WHICH WAY TO THE *MAIN EVENT?*

LIKE THE *PRELIMINARY CONTESTS*, IT'S BEING FOUGHT WITHIN THE LARGE CENTRAL *SPHERE* THAT FORMS THE WHEEL'S *HUB*...

UNLIKE THE *PRELIMINARY CONTESTS*...

...IT'S BEING FOUGHT IN *ZERO-GRAVITY!*

BRUTE STRENGTH CAN'T COUNT FOR *TOO MUCH* UNDER *THESE* CONDITIONS... MAYBE I'VE GOT A *CHANCE* AFTER ALL!

I'LL KNOW *BETTER* WHEN I SEE THE *COMPETITION.* THEY'RE LETTING IN THE *OTHER* PRELIMINARY WINNERS *NOW,* SO I CAN--

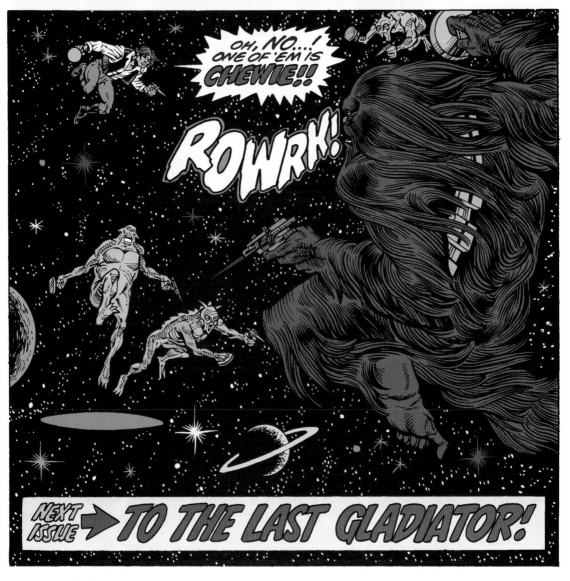

OH, NO...! ONE OF 'EM IS *CHEWIE!!*

ROWRH!

NEXT ISSUE → **TO THE LAST GLADIATOR!**

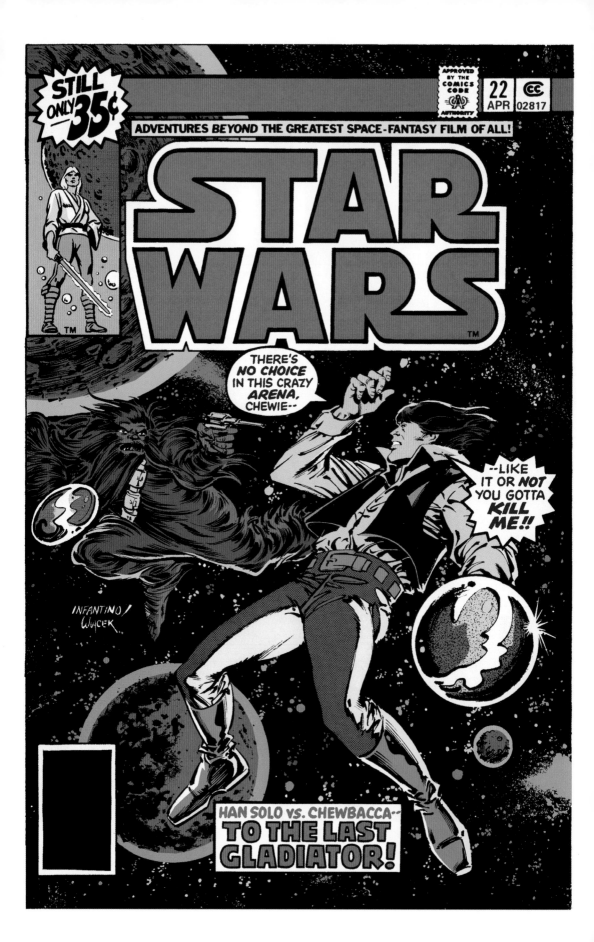

Long ago in a galaxy far, far away. . .there exists a state of cosmic *civil war*. A brave alliance of *underground freedom fighters* has challenged the tyranny and oppression of the awesome *Galactic Empire*. This is their story!

LucasFilm PRESENTS: **STAR WARS** THE GREATEST SPACE FANTASY OF ALL!

CONTINUING THE SAGA BEGUN IN THE FILM BY *GEORGE LUCAS* RELEASED BY *TWENTIETH CENTURY-FOX*

ARCHIE GOODWIN / CARMINE & BOB / C. ROBBINS / B. SHAREN / JIM SHOOTER
WRITER / EDITOR / INFANTINO & WIACEK ARTISTS / LETTERER / COLORIST / CONSULTING EDITOR

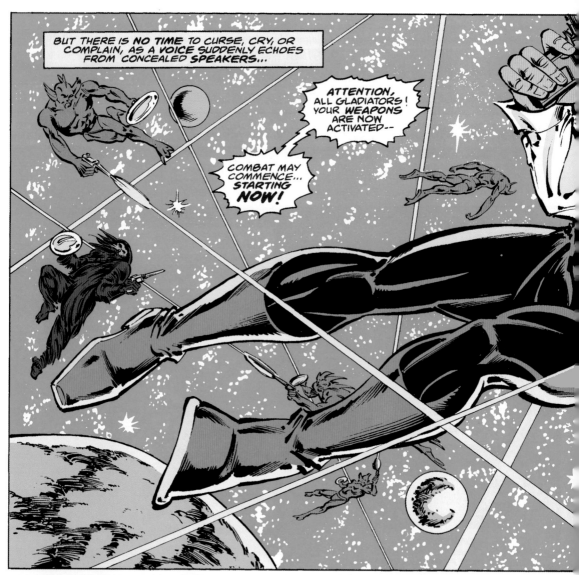

BUT THERE IS *NO TIME* TO CURSE, CRY, OR COMPLAIN, AS A *VOICE* SUDDENLY ECHOES FROM CONCEALED *SPEAKERS*...

ATTENTION, ALL GLADIATORS! YOUR *WEAPONS* ARE NOW ACTIVATED--

COMBAT MAY COMMENCE... STARTING *NOW!*

--ESPECIALLY IN ZERO GRAVITY WHERE, UNLESS YOU'RE *GOOD,* THE FORCE OF YOUR OWN SHOT CAN *PROPEL* YOU!

AND WHEN THE *VICTIM* OF THAT PROPULSION *COLLIDES* WITH ONE OF THE MANY DRIFTING PLANETOIDS...

BAWHOOM!

NOT ACTIVATED! THERE'S NOTHIN' BETWEEN ME AN COMIN' OUT OF THIS FREE-FOR ALL *DEAD*--

KLIK!

KLIK!

--EXCEPT THIS *RAY SHIELD!*

IT COULDN'T HOLD UP TO *STANDARD BLASTER-FIRE...* BUT ITS *REFRACTORY COATING* DEFLECTS THESE NEEDLE RAYS *JUST FINE!*

IN *FACT*, IF YOU CAN GET THE *ANGLE* RIGHT--

--IT'S LIKE HAVING A *SECOND WEAPON!*

BUT AS HAN HIM-SELF HAS *NOTED*, IN *NEGATIVE GRAVITY*, EVERY *ACTION* MUST PRODUCE A *REACTION...*

...AND IN *THIS* CASE, THE *COST* OF DEFLECTING THE NEEDLE RAYS IS TO BE DRIVEN *BACK-WARD*. BACKWARD TOWARD...

...ONE OF THE *FLOATING DEATH TRAPS...*

...WHICH *MASQUERADE* AS PLANETOIDS!

28

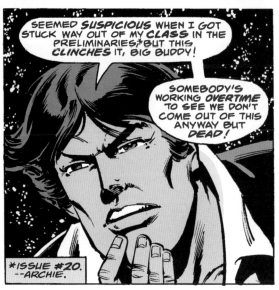

GRORRK!

SURE! THERE'S PROBABLY A *LOT* MORE TO IT THAN THAT, BUT THE ONLY WAY *WE'LL* EVER FIND OUT--

--IS TO GET OURSELVES A *FIGHTING CHANCE* IN THIS *STUPID* GAME!

THAT MEANS *OFFENSIVE WEAPONS,* PAL! AND IF I'VE ANGLED THE RICOCHET *CORRECTLY--*

FORGET IT, *CORELLIAN!* YOU'VE *MISSED!*

VADOOM!

DEPENDS ON WHAT YOU THINK I'M *AIMING* AT, ACE! I WANTED THAT *PLANETOID* BEHIND YOU!

SWIM *AGAINST* THE EXPLOSION'S *SHOCK WAVES,* CHEWIE--

AND GET *SET!* TWO OWNERLESS *NEEDLE RAYS* ARE DRIFTIN' OUR WAY!

BUT EXCEPT AMONG BETTORS PLAYING *LONG SHOTS,* THIS AUDACIOUS MANEUVER DRAWS NO CHEERS, PARTICULARLY IN...

...THE *ROYAL LOUNGE* OF THE *GRAND CASINO,*

BLAST YOU, *GREYSHADE!* YOU'VE BEEN *TOO CLEVER--*

--AND THE SPICE SMUGGLER AND HIS WOOKIEE COMPANION ARE *BENEFITTING* FROM IT!

YOU SHOULD HAVE GIVEN *ALL* OF PRINCESS LEIA'S FRIENDS TO ME FOR *EXECUTION* WHEN I FIRST PURSUED THE MILLENNIUM FALCON HERE!

I KNOW *SUBTLETY* IS DIFFICULT FOR THE MILITARY MIND, STROM--

--BUT *YOUR* WAY ATTRACTS ATTENTION AND I DON'T THINK THE EMPIRE *WANTS* THAT!

NOT WHEN THEY'RE TRYING TO *FOOL* EVERYONE INTO BELIEVING THAT THE WHEEL AND ITS PATRONS HAVE BECOME *TARGETS* OF THE REBEL ALLIANCE--

--THEREBY JUSTIFYING AN *IMPERIAL TAKEOVER* OF THIS ESTABLISHMENT AND ITS FANTASTIC *PROFITS*... WITHOUT FRIGHTENING AWAY THE *PAYING CUSTOMERS!*

NOW SIT DOWN AND *TRUST* ME TO DO THIS *RIGHT!*

TRUST A MAN WHOSE REPUTATION IN THE IMPERIAL SENATE WAS FOR *TREACHERY*, AND WHO NOW USES HIS POSITION AS *WHEEL ADMINISTRATOR* TO FURTHER A SCHOOL BOY CRUSH WITH OUR *FOE*, LEIA ORGANA?!

STUPIDLY ENOUGH, I'VE BEEN *DOING* THAT, GREYSHADE...AND I'M NOT PLEASED WITH THE *RESULTS!*

THEN START WATCHING THE *SCREEN* AGAIN! THE FACT THAT HAN SOLO AND CHEWBACCA HAVE *TEAMED UP* IN THE GAMES MEANS *NOTHING*--

NOTHING?! IT MEANS THEY *BOTH* COULD SURVIVE...LIVE TO BLURT OUT *ALL* THEY KNOW!

AS GLADIATORS, THEY BOTH SIGNED *CON-TRACTS*, STROM. CONTRACTS ACKNOWLEDG-ING THAT THE MATCHES ARE TO THE *DEATH*... AND THAT THERE CAN BE ONLY *ONE WINNER.*

SHOULD THEY *HESITATE* OR FAIL TO *COMPLY* ...IT'S GROUNDS FOR BOTH TO BE *SLAIN!*

AND FRIENDS LIKE *THAT* COULD HARDLY KILL EACH OTHER *WITHOUT* HESITATING...!

GREYSHADE, EACH TIME I THINK THIS UNEASY PARTNERSHIP OF OURS WAS A *MISTAKE*--

--YOU COME UP WITH AN IMPRESSIVE BIT OF *CHICANERY* TO PROVE ME *WRONG!*

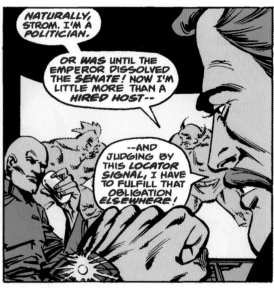

NATURALLY, STROM. I'M A *POLITICIAN.*

OR *WAS* UNTIL THE EMPEROR DISSOLVED THE *SENATE!* NOW I'M LITTLE MORE THAN A *HIRED HOST*--

--AND JUDGING BY THIS *LOCATOR* SIGNAL, I HAVE TO FULFILL THAT *OBLIGATION ELSEWHERE!*

NOT SO *FAST,* SENATOR! YOU WERE *NERVOUS* AND *EDGY* EARLIER... * NOW SUDDENLY, IT'S ALL *SMILES* AND *CHARM!*

YOU'RE *UP* TO SOMETHING! WHAT COULD BE MORE *URGENT* NOW THAN *OUR* BUSINESS?! UNLESS YOU'RE--

Y-YOU'RE... *YOLI...!*

* OR *LAST ISSUE,* EARTH TIME.--ARCH.

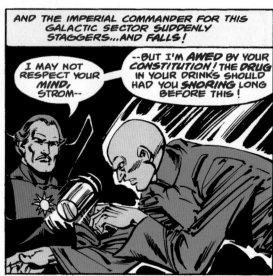

AND THE IMPERIAL COMMANDER FOR THIS GALACTIC SECTOR SUDDENLY STAGGERS...AND FALLS!

I MAY NOT RESPECT YOUR *MIND,* STROM--

--BUT I'M *AWED* BY YOUR *CONSTITUTION!* THE *DRUG* IN YOUR DRINKS SHOULD HAD YOU *SNORING* LONG BEFORE THIS!

BUT INTRIGUE IS NOT THE EXCLUSIVE PROPERTY OF *SIMON GREYSHADE,* FOR AMID THE MANY HALLS AND ACCESS CORRIDORS IN THE ARTIFICIAL SATELLITE'S DOCKING AREA...

THERE'S A *BAY* AHEAD, PRINCESS! THOSE SECURITY GUARDS WE'RE *TRAILING* WENT INSIDE!

THEY MUST BE PUTTING THOSE STOLEN *STRONG BOXES* ABOARD A *SHIP,* LUKE!

BAY 10

BRRTADEEP!

ARTOO IS SAYING HE NEEDS TO BE AT THE **BAY DOOR** IN ORDER TO CONTINUE **TAPING,** YOUR HIGHNESS.

THAT'S **RISKY!** WE'VE ALREADY GOT ENOUGH TO **PROVE** THE LOOT EVERYONE THINKS WAS PIRATED BY **REBELS** ACTUALLY WAS HIDDEN ON THE IMPERIAL COMMANDER'S **CRUISER--**

--UNTIL **GREYSHADE'S** GUARDS **STOLE** IT FROM THE **EMPIRE'S** CREW!

STILL... IT WOULD BE **USEFUL** TO LEARN WHAT MY ONETIME SENATORIAL COLLEAGUE IS **REALLY** UP TO!

WE'VE DONE **OKAY** SO FAR! IF I **COVER** ARTOO... WE'LL BE **FINE!**

THEN, WITH A PNEUMATIC HISS, THE DOCKING BAY DOOR SHOOTS **FULLY** OPEN TO REVEAL...

WE'RE THE SENATOR'S **HANDPICKED ELITE,** FARM-BOY! DID YOU AND YOUR FRIENDS **TRULY** IMAGINE--

--WE COULD BE **FOLLOWED** ON OUR OWN TERRITORY AND **NEVER** CATCH ON?!

BLOOP!

...SINCE THE **BATTLE OF THE DEATH STAR!**

ARTOO! GET OUT OF HERE WITH THAT TAPE!

AND BY THE TIME THE GUARDS REALIZE THEY'VE LET APPEARANCES **DECEIVE** THEM...LUKE IS ROLLING AND **FIRING!**

FOOM!

FTOW!

VOOW!

THEN, HE IS **WITHIN** THE BAY...

...AND BACK ON HIS **FEET**...

VOOO!

PVAM!

CRRRT!

VEEZZIIP!

...**CHARGING** UP THE LOADING RAMP OF THE DOCKED SPACECRAFT!

PVAM!

BUT IN THE CORRIDOR **OUTSIDE,** AS PRINCESS LEIA MOVES TO **HELP**...

DON'T **RUSH,** YOUR HIGHNESS--

SINCE I'M GOING THAT WAY **MYSELF**...I'LL ACCOMPANY YOU,

THAT WAY YOU WON'T HAVE TO CARRY THAT HEAVY **BLASTER.**

GREYSHADE!

YES! YOUR *ESCAPE* HASN'T PROVEN THE *INCONVENIENCE* I FEARED IT WOULD--

YOU'VE MANAGED TO *FIND* YOUR WAY TO THE VERY SPOT I *INTENDED* TO BRING YOU!

*LEIA BROKE OUT OF THE WHEEL ADMINISTRATOR'S SUITE *LAST ISSUE*.--ARCHIE.

THAT *SHIP* YOUR GALLANT YOUNG FRIEND SEEMS BENT ON CONQUERING IS MY PRIVATE *YACHT!*

SINCE ONLY *MY* HAND-PRINTS CAN ACTIVATE ITS *CONTROL LOCKS,* LET'S ARRANGE A *TRUCE* BEFORE HE--OR MORE IMPORTANTLY, THE *CRAFT*-- IS DAMAGED.

IN OUR SENATE DAYS, I PRIDED MYSELF ON SEEING *THROUGH* ALL YOUR SCHEMES--

BUT RIGHT *NOW,* I'M QUITE CONFUSED ABOUT JUST *WHAT* YOU'RE AFTER!

DON'T *WORRY,* PRINCESS. I'M ABOUT TO *EXPLAIN*--

--AND REST ASSURED, IT'S MORE *DESPICABLE* AND *UNSCRUPULOUS* THAN YOU *USUALLY* EXPECT OF ME!

INTERLUDE: A STAR-DESTROYER CLASS IMPERIAL *BATTLE CRUISER* LEAPS THROUGH *HYPER-SPACE,* ITS GREAT WEDGE SHAPE *PIERCING* THE DOPPLER-DISTORTED HEAVENS...

...MOVING AT THE URGING OF ONE *VOICE.* A SINISTER VOICE, RASPING FROM THE CONFINES OF A *BREATH MASK*...

FASTER, WERMIS! THE *SLIGHTEST* DELAY COULD *COST* ME WHAT I SEEK!

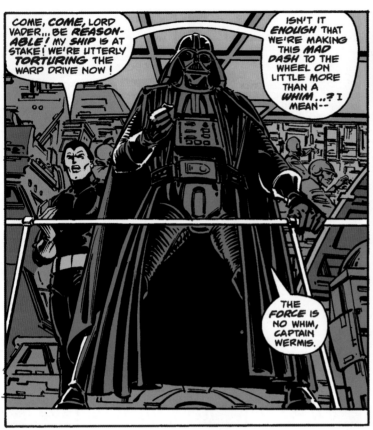

* THAT MIND WAS *LUKE'S*, AS WE KNOW FROM LAST ISSUE AND #*18*.--ARCHIE.

NOW, ON TO THE *WHEEL!* THAT IS THE *DIRECTION* MY PREY HEADED... THAT IS THE FIRST PLACE WE'LL *SEARCH.*

AND WE WON'T RISK *MISSING* HIM BY HOLDING *BACK.* CORRECT, CAPTAIN WERMIS?

YOU MEN *HEARD* LORD VADER! SPEED! *MORE* SPEED!

AN INTERLUDE IN HYPER-SPACE *ENDS.* MEANWHILE, WITHIN SIMON GREYSHADE'S PRIVATE YACHT...

...NEGOTIATIONS *BEGIN.*

I CAN'T *BELIEVE* THIS! I CAN'T BELIEVE WE'RE EVEN *DISCUSSING* THIS!

YOU'RE *YOUNG,* SKYWALKER! WHEN YOU'VE HAD *MY* EXPERIENCE, THE ONLY *ASTOUNDING* THING--

--IS HOW VERY *LITTLE* ASTOUNDS YOU!

I DON'T INTEND TO *EVER* BE LIKE YOU, GREYSHADE...NO MATTER *HOW MUCH* EXPERIENCE I GET!

DON'T WASTE YOUR *BREATH* ON THIS SLIME, PRINCESS! WE'LL TAKE OUR CHANCES *FIGHTING!*

WHAT CHANCES, MY FIERY FRIEND? THIS SHIP, THIS DOCKING BAY, IS A *DEAD* END--

--UNLESS YOU ACCEPT MY RATHER GENEROUS *TERMS.*

YOU TRULY *MEAN* IT...*DON'T* YOU? YOU'LL DEFY THE *EMPIRE,* LET THEIR SCHEME BE *EXPOSED,* AND MY FRIENDS GO *FREE...!* ALL IN *RETURN* FOR--

--*ME?*

MOST MEN ARE ATTRACTED TO WHAT THEY CAN'T *HAVE,* LEIA ORGANA...PARTICULARLY A MAN LIKE *ME* FOR WHOM EVERYTHING ELSE COMES *EASILY.*

UNDER *NORMAL* CIRCUMSTANCES--AS IN OUR SENATE DAYS-- YOU'D NEVER GIVE ME THE *TIME* TO MAKE YOU *LOVE* ME.

I'M MERELY *CREATING* CIRCUMSTANCES WHERE YOU *CAN!*

AS COMMUNICATOR SCREENS *ALL OVER* THE WHEEL REFLECT, THE GREAT GLADIATORIAL GAME IS RUNNING ITS *COURSE*, THE NUMBER OF SURVIVORS *DWINDLING*...

...AND EVEN THOUGH HE'S STILL *ONE OF THEM,* THE SKIPPER OF THE MILLENNIUM FALCON FINDS HE *CAN'T REJOICE.*

NEVER *HEARD* OF A *TIE* IN ONE OF THESE GAMES--

IN FACT I'M *SURE* THE BETTORS WOULDN'T *ACCEPT* IT--

WHICH MEANS I'D BETTER COME UP WITH SOMETHING *BRILLIANT* AND *FAST!*

BECAUSE WITH CHEWIE PUTTING THE *FINISHING TOUCHES* ON THAT BIG BRUISER *BELOW*--

--THIS IS ABOUT TO BECOME A *THREE-WAY CONTEST!*

THIS TYLUUN NIGHT-SOARER HAS REACHED THE SAME CONCLUSION...

...AND WITH THE STEALTH AND CUNNING THAT HAS MADE HIS RACE FAMOUS AS *ASSASSINS,* HE ELECTS TO *HOLD BACK* AND LET HIS TWO OPPONENTS *COMMIT* THEMSELVES.

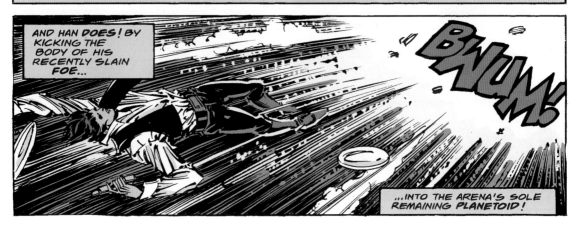

AND HAN *DOES!* BY KICKING THE BODY OF HIS RECENTLY SLAIN FOE...

BWUM!

...INTO THE ARENA'S SOLE REMAINING *PLANETOID!*

FOR SEVERAL INSTANTS, SMOKE, GLARE, AND DEBRIS CLOUD EVERY VIEWSCREEN RECEIVING THE CLOSELY-MONITORED *DUEL*. THEN, OUT OF THE EXPLOSIVE CONFUSION...

...SWIMS A DETERMINED *HAN SOLO,* HEADING FOR HIS WOOKIEE FRIEND AND FIRST MATE!

CHEWIE! THIS AIN'T GONNA BE *EASY,* PAL... BUT THIS IS THE WAY IT'S *GOTTA BE!*

GROWRF!

THERE CAN'T BE *TWO WINNERS* IN THIS SO-CALLED *GAME,* OL' BUDDY--

--AND *YOU* STAND THE BEST CHANCE OF COMIN' OUT ON *TOP* AGAINST THAT *NIGHT-SOARER!*

PARTICULARLY SINCE I'VE TAKEN OUT THE LAST *DEATH TRAP* SO HE CAN'T TRICK YOU *INTO* IT!

YOU *UNDERSTAND,* YA BIG FURBALL? THERE'S *NO CHOICE!*

YOU GOTTA *BLAST* ME... AND DO IT *FAST!*

NAWWR!

DAMMIT, CHEWIE... SHOOT!

THEY *STARE*... LONG-TIME COMPANIONS, INSEPERABLE PARTNERS, SHARING LAST, UNSPOKEN THOUGHTS.

THEN CHEWBACCA DOES WHAT HE **HAS** TO DO.

VEEDOW!

WITHIN THE LOUNGE OF SENATOR GREYSHADE'S *SPACE YACHT*...THREE VIEWERS GASP!

HAN...!

LEIA, I-I...

I NEVER ANTIC-IPATED THIS...! I THOUGHT THERE'D STILL BE TIME TO--

DON'T *APOLOGIZE*, SIMON... YOU'VE **WON**! I CAN'T WATCH ANYONE **ELSE** I CARE FOR DESTROYED! NOT AFTER *ALDERAAN*...NOT AFTER *THIS*!

YOU'VE **WON**...! BUT NO ONE **EVER** GAINED A MORE EMPTY AND BITTER PRIZE!

DON'T MISS NEXT ISSUE!

FLIGHT INTO FURY!

OUR SENSES-SHATTERING CONCLUSION!

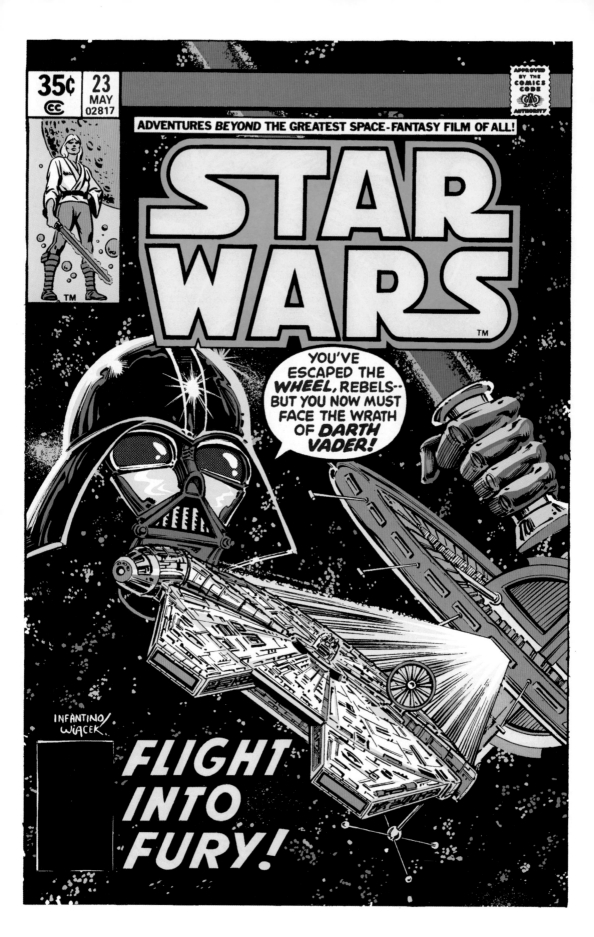

LucasFilm PRESENTS: **STAR WARS** THE GREATEST **SPACE FANTASY** OF ALL!

CONTINUING THE SAGA BEGUN IN THE FILM BY GEORGE LUCAS RELEASED BY TWENTIETH CENTURY-FOX

ARCHIE GOODWIN WRITER/EDITOR • CARMINE INFANTINO & BOB WIACEK ARTISTS • JOHN COSTANZA LETTERER • CARL GAFFORD COLORIST • JIM SHOOTER CONSULTING EDITOR

FLIGHT INTO FURY!

THIS IS DOCKING BAY TEN OF THE MAN-MADE MONUMENT TO THE GALAXY'S LOVE OF GAMBLING...*THE WHEEL.* HERE, THE PRIVATE SPACE YACHT OF SIMON GREYSHADE IS BEING READIED FOR *LAUNCH...* OR MORE CORRECTLY, *ESCAPE!*

THAT'S IT...! MAIN REACTOR IS FULLY *PRIMED.*

ALL RIGHT, REBEL! TAKE YOUR *DROID* AND GET *OUT* OF HERE--

--BEFORE I *FORGET* THE ADMINISTRATOR'S *DEAL* WITH THAT PRINCESS YOU FOLLOW AROUND... AND *REMEMBER* THAT YOU BLASTED A COUPLE OF MY FELLOW *SECURITY GUARDS!**

* A SKIRMISH WITNESSED LAST ISSUE.--ARTFUL ARCHIE. LG357

SHUT UP! I'VE JUST SEEN A GOOD FRIEND *DIE!* AND I'M ABOUT TO *LOSE* THE GIRL I--

T-THE GIRL I--

JUST SHUT UP!

THE WHEEL SECURITY GUARD *OBEYS.*

DESPITE HIS WEAPON, DESPITE HIS TRAINING, THERE IS *NO QUESTION* IN HIS MIND THAT IT WOULD BE THE GRAVEST OF *MISTAKES* NOT TO!

AND WHAT HAS PRODUCED SUCH COLD RAGE IN *LUKE SKYWALKER?* IT STARTED WITH *THIS*...*

...THE DEATH OF *HAN SOLO,* BROADCAST *LIVE* FROM THE WHEEL'S ZERO-GRAVITY GLADIATORIAL ARENA...

...THE SPICE-SMUGGLER'S WOOKIEE FIRST MATE *FORCED* TO BE HIS EXECUTIONER!

*ALSO *LAST ISSUE.*--ARCHIE.

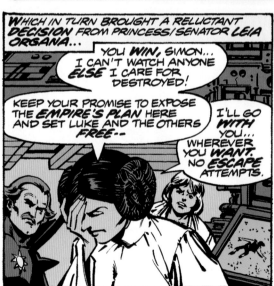

WHICH IN TURN BROUGHT A RELUCTANT *DECISION* FROM PRINCESS/SENATOR *LEIA ORGANA...*

YOU *WIN,* SIMON... I CAN'T WATCH ANYONE *ELSE* I CARE FOR DESTROYED!

KEEP YOUR PROMISE TO EXPOSE THE *EMPIRE'S PLAN* HERE AND SET LUKE AND THE OTHERS *FREE*--

I'LL GO *WITH* YOU... WHEREVER YOU *WANT.* NO *ESCAPE* ATTEMPTS.

AND *THIS* HAS SENT THE YOUNG STARWARRIOR IN MOISTURE FARMER CLOTHING *STORMING* OUT OF THE SPACE YACHT'S CABIN...

LUKE!

THERE'S STILL TIME TO SAY *GOOD-BYE.* WHATEVER YOU FEEL ABOUT MY DECISION... IT'S TIME WE MAY NEVER HAVE *AGAIN.*

I-I--

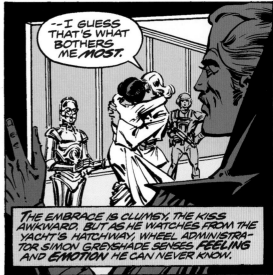

--I GUESS THAT'S WHAT BOTHERS ME *MOST.*

THE EMBRACE IS CLUMSY, THE KISS AWKWARD, BUT AS HE WATCHES FROM THE YACHT'S HATCHWAY, WHEEL ADMINISTRATOR SIMON GREYSHADE SENSES *FEELING* AND *EMOTION* HE CAN NEVER KNOW.

MEANWHILE, IN THE ARENA'S SIMULATED SPACE FIELD, CHEWBACCA STARES LONG AND HARD AT HAN SOLO'S DRIFTING FORM...

A SMALL *SOUND* COMES FROM HIS THROAT. IN A HUMAN, IT MIGHT BE SOBBING.

BUT WHILE MORE THAN *ONE* CONTESTANT SURVIVES... THE ARENA IS NO RESPECTER OF *GRIEF!*

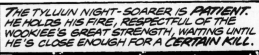

THE TYLUUN NIGHT-SOARER IS *PATIENT.* HE HOLDS HIS FIRE, RESPECTFUL OF THE WOOKIEE'S GREAT STRENGTH, WAITING UNTIL HE'S CLOSE ENOUGH FOR A *CERTAIN KILL.*

STILL, HE CAN ALMOST TASTE VICTORY... *CHAMPIONSHIP* IN THE WHEEL'S *BIG GAME!* JUST A LITTLE *CLOSER...*

RARRK!

ZDAK!

WURPF!

OKAY, *OKAY* STOP *GLOATING*, CHAMP.

I'M THE ONE WHO *SIGNALLED* YOU TO TURN AND *FIRE!*

NOW *REMEMBER...* AS BIG WINNER YOU CAN *AFFORD* TO COME ON TEMPERMENTAL!

AND WHAT YOU'RE GONNA BE *MOST* TEMPERMENTAL ABOUT--

--IS THAT NO ONE BUT *YOU* HANDLES THE BODY OF YOUR LATE, LAMENTED *PAL!* AND BE *CAREFUL*, YOU BIG LUG--

"I WENT TO A *LOT* OF TROUBLE EXPLODING ONE OF THE ARENA'S *DEATH TRAPS...*＊

"...SO THAT UNDER COVER OF THE SMOKE AND DEBRIS I COULD GRAB A DEAD GLADIATOR'S *RAY SHIELD* AND TUCK IT *UNDER* MY SHIRT."

＊*WE SAW HIM DO IT LAST ISH.*
-- ARCH AGAIN.

IF YOU ACCIDENTLY SHAKE IT OUT *NOW...* EVERYONE'S GONNA KNOW *THAT* GOT BLASTED INSTEAD OF MY TENDER *FLESH!*

SOMEHOW, I DON'T THINK THEY'LL BE *AMUSED!*

FOR THE *MOMENT,* HOWEVER, AMUSEMENT RUNS HIGH ON THE WHEEL. THE WOOKIEE WAS A *FAVORITE.* COMPUTER PAY LINES ARE *LONG.*

BUT AS EXCITED GAMBLERS WAIT IN THE *GRAND CASINO...*

STOP! THERE'S A *REBEL PLOT* UNDERWAY!

IT'S *S-STROM...*THE *IMPERIAL COMMANDER* FOR THIS GALACTIC SECTOR! HE LOOKS...*DRUNK!*

I'VE BEEN *DRUGGED,* YOU FOOLS! IT'S THE WORK OF THE *WHEEL ADMINISTRATOR!*

HE'S *PART* OF THE PLOT!

ROYAL LOUNGE

I DECLARE THIS SPACE STATION TO BE UNDER *MARTIAL LAW!*

ALL IMPERIAL PERSONNEL ON *LEAVE* HERE REPORT TO ME AT *ONCE!*

NO ONE ELSE WILL BE PERMITTED TO DEPART THE WHEEL UNTIL *ORDER* IS RESTORED!

DESPITE THROBBING HEAD AND CHURNING STOMACH, STROM SMILES INWARDLY...

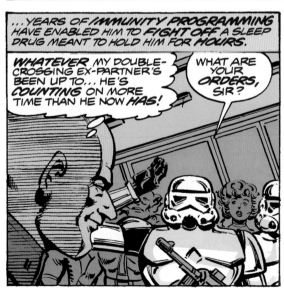

...*YEARS OF IMMUNITY PROGRAMMING* HAVE ENABLED HIM TO *FIGHT OFF* A SLEEP DRUG MEANT TO HOLD HIM FOR *HOURS.*

WHATEVER MY DOUBLE-CROSSING EX-PARTNER'S BEEN UP TO,... HE'S *COUNTING* ON MORE TIME THAN HE NOW *HAS!*

WHAT ARE YOUR *ORDERS,* SIR?

FIND ADMINISTRATOR *GREYSHADE* AND THOSE *REBELS* FROM THE *MILLENNIUM FALCON* WHO SOUGHT *REFUGE* ON THE WHEEL--

KILL THEM ALL ON SIGHT!

THIS IS *TERRIBLE*... THE EMPIRE HAS NEVER BEEN ALLOWED TO *INTERFERE* ON THE WHEEL BEFORE!

I DON'T LIKE *GAMBLING* WITH A *STORM TROOPER* LOOKING OVER *MY* SHOULDER EITHER--

BUT IF IT KEEPS US SAFE FROM *REBEL ATTACKS* SUCH AS WE'VE SEEN RECENTLY *... THEN I'LL *ACCEPT* IT!

* *STAR WARS* #20.--ARCH.

AND THE MURMURS OF *AGREEMENT* THAT SWEEP THROUGH THE CASINO CUSTOMERS ARE LIKE *BALM* TO THE COMMANDER'S DRUG-WRACKED BODY.

OUR *FAKE ATTACKS* HAVE BEEN SUCCESSFUL! I'M A *CERTAINTY* FOR THE EMPEROR'S *COMMENDATION LIST*--

--ONCE GREYSHADE AND THOSE REBELS ARE *PERMANENTLY SILENCED*!

THE *STEPS* FOR THAT *SILENCING* ARE TAKEN IN LEAPING *STRIDES*. SOON, IN DOCKING BAY TEN...

SENATOR GREYSHADE, MASTER-COM... OPEN THE *MAGNETIC FIELD* HERE. WE'RE TAKING OUT MY *YACHT*.

I ALSO *AUTHORIZE* DEPARTURE FOR THE *MILLENNIUM FALCON*--

--A YOUNG MAN NAMED *SKYWALKER* IS ON HIS WAY TO *READY* IT FOR HIS COMPANIONS.

ALSO: HIDING *SOMEWHERE* IN THIS AREA IS AN *R2-D2 UNIT*. FIND IT, MASTER-COM... AND *BROADCAST* ON ALL CHANNELS THE *TAPE* IT CARRIES! THAT--

I MAY HAVE A *PROBLEM* WITH THOSE *ORDERS*, SENATOR--

--YOUR AUTHORITY AS ADMINISTRATOR APPEARS TO HAVE BEEN *RESCINDED*.

AS THE WHEEL'S *MASTER-COMPUTER*, I AM OBLIGED TO OBEY THE *NEW* AUTHORITIES.

AS ONE WHO FEELS *FRIENDSHIP* FOR THE MAN WHO GAVE HIM *HUMANOID FORM*--

--I WILL ATTEMPT TO AT LEAST *OPEN* YOUR DOCKING BAY'S MAGNETIC FIELD BEFORE--

BLOW IT AWAY! THE STUPID COMPUTER'S GONE CRAZY!

VEE·DOH! FTOW!

OBSCENE....! A *MACHINE* BELIEVING IT FELT FRIENDSHIP FOR AN *ORGANIC*!

AT LEAST WE *CUT IT DOWN* BEFORE IT COULD AID THAT TRAITOR, *GREYSHADE*.

REPORT THIS TO *COMMANDER STROM!* HE'LL WANT A COMPUTER-OVERRIDE TEAM TO TAKEOVER ALL WHEEL FUNCTIONS.

I'LL HAVE A *SEARCH-AND-DESTROY* SQUAD PROCEED IMMEDIATELY TO *DOCKING BAY TEN!*

PROCEED IT DOES... AND ALONG THE SAME CORRIDOR AS LUKE AND SEE THREEPIO!

STORM TROOPERS!

BACK TO THE *BAY...!* IF GREY-SHADE HASN'T GOTTEN LEIA AWAY YET... THEY'RE GOING TO NEED *HELP!*

OH, DEAR! NOT *ANOTHER* BATTLE! I DON'T BELIEVE MY *PERCEPTORY CIRCUITS* ARE UP TO IT....!

AND THE THOUGHT OF POOR *ARTOO DEETOO*... LOST IN THIS MADNESS!

BUT SO FAR, THAT PARTICULAR LITTLE DROID IS IN BETTER SHAPE THAN HIS COMPANIONS...

HAVING FOUND REFUGE IN A *CIRCUITRY CONDUIT*, HE NOW PROCEEDS ALONG IT...

VRR-KLIK! BIIP!

...NEATLY *BYPASSING* INCREASED STORM TROOPER ACTIVITY IN THE CORRIDORS PARALLEL TO HIM.

THE *TAPE* HE CARRIES CAN EXPOSE THE EMPIRE'S DECEPTION. HIS INTEGRATED LOGIC TERMINALS HAVE REASONED WHAT HE MUST *DO* WITH IT. BUT THAT INVOLVES *LEAVING* THE CONDUIT...

P.A. DOOP!

...AND AT THE POINT WHERE HE DOES, *SOMEONE* IS WAITING!

MEANWHILE, THE WILD SWIRL OF EVENTS ON THE WHEEL REACHES OUT EVEN *FURTHER*...

...TO TOUCH A BEREAVED *CHAMPION* BENT ON CONDUCTING A FALLEN COMRADE TO THEIR SHIP AND EVENTUAL BURIAL IN SPACE. AT LEAST, THAT'S THEIR *STORY*. BUT...

BORRK!

FORGET TAKING THIS LIFT TO THE *DOCKING BAYS*, WOOKIEE--

THERE'S AN IMPERIAL *DEATH WARRANT* ON YOU... SERVABLE *RIGHT NOW!*

COME *ON*, GUYS....! WHATEVER HAPPENED TO RESPECT FOR THE *DEAD?!*

ZZOW!

ANOTHER BUNCH COMIN'! NEED MORE *FIREPOWER* THAN THIS *PISTOL* I SWIPED FROM THAT UN-OBSERVANT GLADIATOR PIT GUARD--

GRAB THOSE TROOPERS' *WEAPONS*, CHEWIE...IT'S *LAST STAND TIME!*

A SENTIMENT *SHARED* IN DOCKING BAY TEN...

I'VE *SEALED* THE CORRIDOR ENTRANCE, GREYSHADE... BUT THAT WON'T KEEP THE IMPERIALS OUT FOR *LONG*.

IF ONLY THOSE *GUARDS* OF YOURS HADN'T FLED--!

BRIBED LOYALTY HAS ITS *LIMITS*, SKYWALKER--

--PARTICULARLY THE PROSPECT OF NOT BEING *ALIVE* TO *SPEND* THE BRIBE! I'M AMAZED *I'M* STILL HERE. MY INFATUATION FOR THE PRINCESS IS MORE *FATAL* THAN I EVER SUSP--

LUKE! WHAT *IS* IT--?!

N-NO...! NOT *HIM*...! NOT *NOW*...!

AND AT THIS *EXACT INSTANT*, ON THE EDGE OF THE STAR SYSTEM WHERE THE *WHEEL* TURNS...

...ONE OF THE EMPIRE'S MIGHTY *BATTLE CRUISERS* DROPS OUT OF HYPER-SPACE.

WE'RE *HERE*, SIR! AND GETTING LASER TRANSMISSIONS OF *TURMOIL* ON THE WHEEL! COMMANDER STROM'S TROOPS HAVE *REBELS* TRAPPED THERE AND--

AND *ONE* OF THEM IS WHOM I SEEK! EVEN AT *THIS* DISTANCE I CAN *FEEL* IT.

I'LL TRANSMIT THAT *YOU'RE* HERE TO TAKE CHARGE AND WILL BE *ABOARD* BY--

NO. PROCEED SLOWLY, BUT MONITORING EVERY *INCH* OF THAT STATION, CAPTAIN WERMIS.

THOUGH THE POWER SEEMS MOSTLY *LATENT*... THE *FORCE* IS WITH OUR PREY. SUCH A PERSON MIGHT WELL *ELUDE* STROM AND TAKE *FLIGHT* FROM THE WHEEL--

--BUT *I* SHALL BE *WAITING* FOR THEM!

I'VE BEEN *WAITING* FOR YOU, ARTOO-DEETOO. JUST BEFORE THE STORM TROOPERS DESTROYED MY *OTHER* BODY AND I SECRETLY *SWITCHED* MY FUNCTIONS TO THIS *SPARE--**

--MY SENSORS *DETECTED* YOU MOVING IN THE CONDUIT.

YOUR DESTINATION IS JUST DOWN THE CORRIDOR... *A MASTER RELAY TERMINAL.*

YA-DEEP?

* WE SAW *MASTER-COM* DO THIS BEFORE IN SW#14.--ARCHIE.

YES, I CAN *HELP* YOU. HAD THE IMPERIALS SIMPLY *ORDERED* ME TO SHUT DOWN... I'D HAVE HAD TO *OBEY.* BUT I ANGERED THEM INTO USING *VIO-LENCE...* WHICH MY PROGRAMMING ALLOWS ME TO *RESIST.*

BUT WE MUST *HURRY.* A HUMAN *OVERRIDE TEAM* IS WORKING TO DISCONNECT ALL MY CONTACTS WITH *WHEEL FUNCTIONS.* I'M *FIGHTING* THEM--

--BUT TO RECAPTURE THE SYSTEMS I NEED TO AID *YOUR* MASTERS AND *MINE...* I NEED A *DIVERSION.*

BROADCASTING THE *TAPE* YOU HAVE SHOULD BE AN *EXCEL-LENT* ONE.

JUST PLUG IN *HERE.*

DA-WEET!

AND THE *RESULTS* OF THAT PLUGGING IN ARE INSTANTLY FELT THROUGHOUT THE WHEEL. EVERY COMMUNICATOR SCREEN IN EVERY CASINO FLASHES THE SIGHT AND SOUND OF *TREACHERY.*

WHAT IN THE *GALAXY--?!* WHEEL GUARDS RAIDING THE *IMPERIAL COM-MANDER'S* SHIP?!

BUT LISTEN TO WHAT THEY'RE *SAYING...* LOOK AT THOSE *STRONG BOXES!*

IT'S THE *WHEEL PROFITS* STROM REPORTED THAT THE REBELS PIRATED!

THE *EMPIRE'S* BEEN MAKING THOSE ATTACKS AND *CLAIMING* IT WAS THE ALLIANCE!

END RESULT: *RESENTMENT,* WHICH BUBBLES INTO RAGE, WHICH EXPLODES INTO...

...*RIOT!*

ON THEIR HOMEWORLDS, THEY WOULDN'T *DARE* THIS. BUT THE WHEEL HAS ALWAYS BEEN A *SANCTUARY...*

...A **SAFETY VALVE** FOR AN OPPRESSED GALAXY TO LET OFF **STEAM.** TO FIND IT VIOLATED AND TAMPERED WITH SENDS ITS THOUSANDS OF FRUSTRATED PLEASURE AND THRILL SEEKERS WILDLY **RAMPAGING!**

IN THE RAMPAGE... A LOT OF **STORM TROOPERS** ARE TAKEN OUT OF HAN SOLO AND CHEWBACCA'S **HAIR!**

LET THAT BE A **LESSON,** BIG BUDDY. NEVER LET A **GAMBLER** FIND OUT THE GAME'S BEEN **RIGGED!**

31

OUR DOCKING BAY'S JUST **AHEAD**--

WE'LL GET THESE **STRONG-BOXES** WITH ALL THE GLADIATORIAL GAME **WINNINGS** ABOARD THE **FALCON,** THEN FIGURE A WAY TO HELP **LUKE,** HER **ROYALNESS,** AND THE--

ROWK!

UNN

AN **IMPERIAL WELCOMING COMMITTEE!** THOSE GUYS ARE PERSISTENT AS TATOOINE **SAND LICE!**

NAARRGH!

WATTA YOU MEAN, **YOU** KNOW WHAT TO DO?! SO DO **I**... GET THE BLAZES **OUT** OF HERE!

BUT CHEWIE'S COURSE OF ACTION IS SOMEWHAT **DIFFERENT.** HE JAMS THE CARGO FLOATER'S DRIVE SWITCH TO **FULL POWER** AND...

...PUSHES HAN AND HIMSELF **OFF** AS IT CAREENS **FORWARD!**

CHEWIE! YOU LEFT OUR **WINNINGS** ABOARD!

BAWOOM!

THAT'S *IT*...! THE STORM TROOPERS HAVE *BLOWN* THE DOOR.

IF THAT *STIRRINS* I FELT EARLIER IN THE *FORCE*--

--REALLY *WAS* DARTH VADER APPROACHING... HE'S GONNA HAVE TO WAIT IN *LINE*!

LUKE! *GREYSHADE!* THREEPIO SAYS *MASTER-COM* IS ON THE YACHT'S COMMUNICATOR--

-- HE'S GAINED TEMPORARY *CONTROL* OF THE MAGNETIC FIELD SYSTEM. HE CAN *OPEN* IT... BUT NOT FOR *LONG*!

THEN YOU AND THE SENATOR *TAKE OFF*--

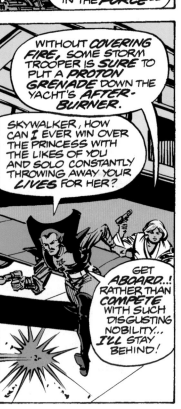

WITHOUT *COVERING FIRE*, SOME STORM TROOPER IS *SURE* TO PUT A *PROTON GRENADE* DOWN THE YACHT'S *AFTER-BURNER.*

SKYWALKER, HOW CAN *I* EVER WIN OVER THE PRINCESS WITH THE LIKES OF YOU AND SOLO CONSTANTLY THROWING AWAY YOUR *LIVES* FOR HER?

GET *ABOARD*...! RATHER THAN *COMPETE* WITH SUCH DISGUSTING NOBILITY... *I'LL* STAY BEHIND!

BESIDES, I'VE *GAINED* SOMETHING FROM ALL THIS FOOLISHNESS THAT AN UNSCRUPULOUS MAN LIKE ME NORMALLY *NEVER* HAS --

"A FRIEND: MASTER-COM!

HEAR *THAT*, ARTOO DEETOO? NOW WE *BOTH* HAVE HUMAN FRIENDS!

DA-TOOT!

YES. THIS IS AN *ESCAPE POD HATCH*--

--BUT NO DOUBT YOU FEEL THE SAME ABOUT THIS *PROTON GRENADE* I'VE BEEN HOLDING AS A *LAST RESORT!*

SENATOR! THOSE AREN'T MEANT--

FTOOM!

--FOR *CLOSE RANGE!*

SORRY, MASTER-COM. I'M AFRAID I COME TO THIS BUSINESS A BIT *LATE.*

YOU'RE LEAKING *OIL.*

AND YOU *BLOOD,* SIR. I DOUBT EITHER OF US CAN *AFFORD* IT. HOPEFULLY, WE'RE NOT BEYOND *REPAIR*--

HOPEFULLY. BUT IF ONE *MUST* DIE... IT'S GOOD TO HAVE THE COMPANY OF A *FRIEND.*

SMOKE CLOSES IN ON THE TWO FIGURES, *OBSCURING* THEM...

...AND A LONG *QUIET,* THE AFTERMATH OF BATTLE, SETTLES OVER THE ENTIRE WHEEL. BUT IN *SPACE,* AS ONE ORDEAL *ENDS* WITH THE RECOVERY OF ARTOO DEETOO'S ESCAPE POD...

...A NEW ONE SWIFTLY AND AWESOMELY *BEGINS!*

AN *IMPERIAL CRUISER....!* THEY MUST HAVE SHUT DOWN ALL *SYSTEMS* AND COASTED IN WHILE WE WERE TAKING ON THE *POD!*

THE BAY'S OPENING! *LUKE!* WE'VE GOT TO EVADE ITS *TRACTOR BEAM!*

BUT LUKE HAS *MORE* TO EVADE... HE FEELS A SINISTER SHIFTING IN THE *FORCE* AND REALIZES ALL TOO WELL...

...ANOTHER MIND SEARCHES FOR HIS!

OUR PREY IS ON THE YACHT, WERMIS... I'M CERTAIN OF IT!

BUT WHOEVER IT IS HAS GOTTEN PAST THE FRIGHT FELT THE FIRST TIME OUR ASPECTS BRUSHED--*

* WAY BACK IN SW #18. --ARCH.

--NOW THEY UNCONSCIOUSLY RESIST... CLOUD MY EFFORTS! I NEED A FACE-TO-FACE CONFRONTATION, WERMIS--

--DON'T FUMBLE THE OPPORTUNITY!

NOT TO WORRY, LORD VADER! NO EVASIVE ACTION CAN SAVE THEM NO--

BRA-KOW!

SCORE ONE FOR JUSTICE, CHEWIE--!!

AN' FOR SHAKIN' THE PANTS OFF ANYONE ON THAT CRUISER BRIDGE TRYIN' TO OPERATE A TRACTOR BEAM!

MOVE IT, KIDS... WHILE THE EMPIRE IS STILL GETTING OVER THE SHOCK!

HAN! YOU ARE ALIVE... AND AWAY FROM THE WHEEL!

IT'S A MIRACLE!

NOT AT *ALL*, YOUR WORSHIP. JUST ANOTHER EXAMPLE OF TYPICAL SOLO *DARING*--

--*MARRED* SOMEWHAT BY CHEWIE DEVISING THE MOST *EXPENSIVE* ESCAPE KNOWN TO SENTIENT LIFE!

RARGH!

THAT'S *RIGHT*, I'M *NOT* GOING TO LET YOU FORGET WHAT YOU DID WITH OUR *WINNINGS*.

NOW YOU AND THE GANG *CLEAR OUT*, PRINCESS--

WE'LL MAKE ONE MORE *PASS* AT THE BAD GUYS TO *COVER* FOR YOU!

AFTER BEING *TORN APART* * AN' THROWN BACK TOGETHER BY WHEEL TECHNOS... THE FALCON NEEDS A GOOD *SHAKE-DOWN* ANYWAY!

* STAR WARS #19. --ARCH AGAIN.

BUT WITH THIS *ACTION, THE CORELLIAN SKIPPER MAY HAVE* PRESSED *HIS SPACEMAN'S LUCK...*

I *KNOW* THIS VESSEL, WERMIS! THE SMUGGLING SHIP THAT *BLASTED* MY *TIE* FIGHTER AND *ENDED* MY DEFENSE OF THE *DEATH STAR!*

FORGET EVERYTHING ELSE! WE'RE GOING TO *DESTROY* THAT SHIP AT *ANY COST!*

LUKE! THE CRUISER'S ABANDONED US *COMPLETELY!* B-BUT... IT'S STAYED WITH THE *FALCON* THROUGH ITS PASS!

HAN AND CHEWBACCA WILL BE *VAPORIZED* BEFORE THEY CAN REACH LIGHT SPEED....!

FOR A MOMENT, LUKE DOESN'T SPEAK. THE *FORCE* FILLS HIS THOUGHTS...

...THEN, HE **CRIES OUT** IN RAGE AND FRUSTRATION!

RAGE... AT REGAINING A FRIEND THOUGHT **DEAD**, ONLY TO SEE HIM ABOUT TO BE **SLAIN** AGAIN.

FRUSTRATION... AT HAVING A VAST POWER AND NOT KNOWING HOW TO **SAVE** HAN WITH IT!

BUT **CHANNELS** HAVE BEEN OPENED HERE, OPENED BY A **DARK LORD**, PROBING WITH THE **FORCE**...

WE **HAVE** THEM... ALL GUNS WILL FIRE ON **MY** COMMAND--

...**OPENED**, BUT FORGOTTEN IN THE THOUGHT OF **VENGEANCE** FOR HIS ONE GREAT **DEFEAT**...

...UNTIL **ALL** OF LUKE'S RAGING FEELINGS, LIKE **LIGHTNING** CARRIED ALONG A WIRE FROM **ONE** PLACE IT HAS STRUCK TO **ANOTHER**...

...**BLAST** INTO DARTH VADER'S UNPROTECTED MIND!

AAAAA!

THE PAIN IS BRIEF...BUT **INTENSE**. YET IN THE MOMENT OF ITS **PASSING** AND HIS **RECOVERY**...

...THE LORD OF THE SITH FINDS **TWO** SETS OF PREY HAVE MADE THE JUMP INTO **HYPER-SPACE**.

HE STILL DOESN'T KNOW THEIR **IDENTITIES**. THEY'VE **ELUDED** HIM...

...BUT ONLY FOR **NOW**.

LUKE...? **LUKE**...? ARE YOU **ALL RIGHT**? WHAT **HAPPENED**?

BEN KENOBI ONCE SAID THE FORCE WOULD BE **WITH** ME...**ALWAYS**.

IT PROVED IT WAS TODAY... BUT I'VE GOT TO WORK AT **MASTERING** IT, BECAUSE WHERE **DARTH VADER'S** CONCERNED--

--IT MAY NOT BE **ENOUGH** TOMORROW!

NEXT ISSUE: AN UNTOLD TALE OF OBI-WAN KENOBI--IN THE DAYS OF THE OLD REPUBLIC!

SILENT DRIFTING!

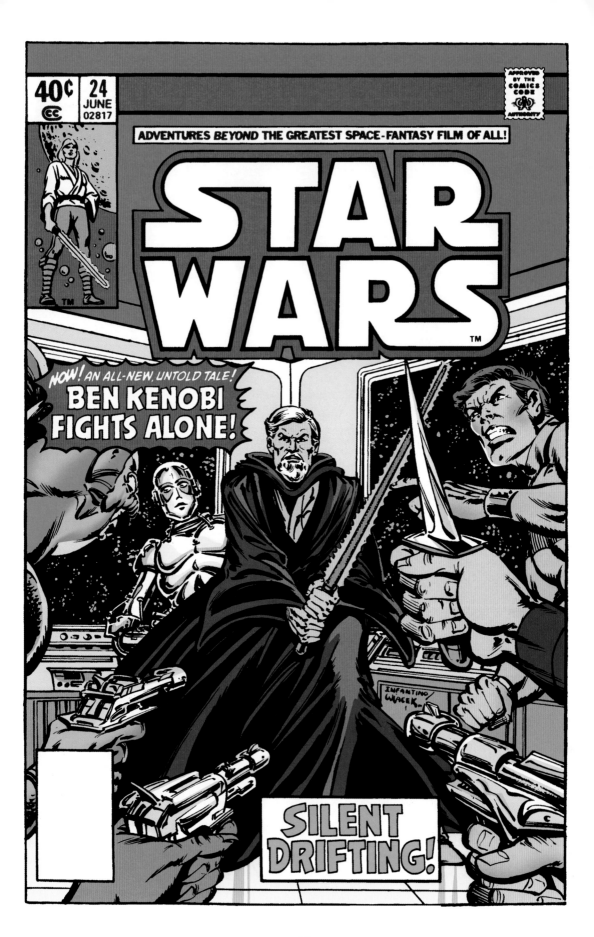

FOR LONG SECONDS, THE MILLENNIUM FALCON HANGS *MOTIONLESS* IN SPACE...

SHE SEEMS TO HAVE TAKEN A *MORTAL HIT*, SIR. I'M NOT PICKING UP A SIGNAL FROM *ANY* OF HER SYSTEMS.

GOOD. LET'S MOVE IN FOR A *CLOSER* LOOK.

THE TWO IMPERIAL SHIPS CIRCLE THE WOUNDED FREIGHTER LIKE *VULTURES*...

UNTIL...

VORSH

WE GOT 'EM *BOTH!*

GREAT *SHOOTING*, KID. THEY NEVER KNEW WHAT *HIT* 'EM!

BROOOM

HRONK

LURING THEM IN THAT WAY WAS A *GREAT* IDEA, HAN!

YEAH...THE EXPLOSIVE CHARGE IN THE CARGO HOLD IS ONE OF THOSE *MODIFICATIONS* I MADE FOR EMERGENCIES.

OF COURSE, HAVING CHEWIE OPEN THAT NICE, TEMPTING *HOLE* IN OUR SHIELDS FOR 'EM *HELPED.*

CHEWIE, CALCULATE THE JUMP TO HYPERSPACE WHILE I CHECK FOR *DAMAGE,* THEN GET ON TO THOSE *REPAIRS.*

LUKE'S RIGHT, HAN THAT WAS A *MASTERSTROKE*

VERY CIVIL OF YOU TO *ADMIT* IT, YOUR WORSHIPFULNESS.

OF COURSE, HAN DIDN'T *INVENT* THAT TRICK. THE JEDI KNIGHTS USED IT FOR CENTURIES...

...AND I KNOW OF AN OCCASION WHEN *BEN KENOBI* USED ONE VERY *SIMILAR* TO IT.

BEN?

YES, IT'S A STORY MY *FATHER* TOLD ME, OF SOMETHING THAT HAPPENED TO BEN *YEARS* AGO --

--BACK IN THE DAYS OF THE OLD *REPUBLIC...*

"...BEFORE THE EMPIRE, WHEN SPACE WAS *FREE* TO ANY SHIPS THAT PASSED BY, SO LONG AS THEY TRAVELLED THROUGH *CIVILIZED* SYSTEMS.

"HUGE *PLEASURE CRUISERS* MOVED ACROSS THE GALAXY THEN, STOCKED WITH EVERY IMAGINABLE LUXURY...

"*DOZENS* OF RACES MINGLED THERE TOGETHER, REPRESENTING EVERY STRATA OF THEIR SOCIETIES...

"...THEIR EVERY EXTRAVAGANT PLEASURE OR *VICE* CATERED TO...

"...BY CREWS WHOSE ONLY *CONCERN* WAS TO CONVEY ALL OF THEIR GUESTS ACROSS THE SYSTEMS IN *COMFORT*...

"...FROM *SENATORS* AND *PLANETARY LEADERS*...

"...TO A *CRIMINAL*, BARELY ESCAPING PLANETARY JUSTICE WITH HIS LIFE AND WEALTH...

"...TO A *JEDI* KNIGHT, RIDING THE SHIP ONLY BECAUSE IT HAPPENED TO BE GOING TOWARD HIS DESTINATION."

GENERAL OBI-WAN KENOBI?

YES?

I AM *68-RKO*... ON MY WAY TO ENTER SERVICE WITH PRINCE *BAIL ORGANA*.

I AM SORRY TO IMPOSE ON YOU, SIR, BUT MOST PEOPLE DON'T LIKE IT WHEN *MECHANICALS* TRAVEL ALONE... THEY DON'T KNOW WHETHER TO TREAT US AS *PASSENGERS* OR *LUGGAGE*.

CAPTAIN QUASAR FELT THAT SINCE YOU WERE TRAVELLING TO ALDERAAN SO *CHEAPLY*--

--YOU MIGHT CONSENT TO *ACT* AS MY OWNER.

I'VE NEVER *OWNED* A LIVING CREATURE IN MY LIFE, AND I DON'T INTEND TO START NOW, BUT IF IT'S A *TRAVELLING COMPANION* YOU WANT, YOU'RE *WELCOME* TO SHARE MY CABIN.

HEY! WHAT'S *THAT* THING DOING IN HERE?

WHY DON'T YOU GO *BELOW DECK* WHERE YOU BELONG?

THIS JEDI MAY BE A LOUSY *DROID-LOVER*, BUT THE REST OF US DON'T WANT YOUR KIND MIXING WITH *PEOPLE*!

IF YOU'RE *THAT* PARTICULAR ABOUT THE COMPANY YOU KEEP...

... I RECOMMEND THAT IN THE FUTURE, YOU MAKE YOUR *TRIPS* ALONE.

{ACK}

{OOMPH}

SKAM

TELL CAPTAIN QUASAR TO ADD ANY *DAMAGE COSTS* TO MY FARE.

LAUGHING! THAT JEDI WAS *LAUGHING* AT ME, BUT HE'LL PAY FOR IT.

GENERAL--!

IN THE FUTURE, I SUGGEST YOU SERVE THAT GENTLEMAN A LITTLE *LESS* OF WHATEVER HE'S BEEN *DRINKING* TONIGHT.

"FASTER THAN THOUGHT, BEN *REACTED,* HIS HAND FLYING TO THE HILT OF HIS *LIGHT SABRE* AND PRESSING THE ACTIVATING STUD.

≥AAGH≤

VORP

HE LEAPED RIGHT ONTO THE BLADE. I DIDN'T THINK YOU'D *SEEN* HIM.

I HADN'T.

VERY IMPRESSIVE, GENERAL SIT DOWN, AND I'LL BUY YOU A DRINK.

CARE FOR SOME DELTRON SPICE WINE? THIS LITTLE GADGET FERMENTS IT BY MICROWAVES AND SERVES IT UP SEASONED TO ANY TASTE,

AND NOW IT'S *MY* TURN TO BE IMPRESSED? I'M AFRAID I DON'T CARE FOR *ADDICTIVE* STIMULANTS, MR. --?

TING

TRYLL... AUGUSTUS TRYLL.

AH, YES, MR. TRYLL. I *HAVE* HEARD OF YOU.

GOOD. THAT WILL SAVE ME NEEDLESS EXPLANATIONS. YOU SEE, I'M ABOUT TO ENTER INTO A VENTURE THAT CALLS FOR SOMEONE OF RATHER... *UNUSUAL* TALENTS. INTERESTED IN A *PARTNERSHIP?*

WITH A MAN WHO TRAFFICS IN STOLEN GOODS, POLITICAL BETRAYALS, AND SLAVERY?

I'M AFRAID I HAVE AS LITTLE TASTE FOR YOUR *BUSINESS* AS FOR YOUR *BEVERAGES.*

RKO, IF YOU'D CARE TO JOIN ME, I CAN SHOW YOU WHERE OUR QUARTERS ARE LOCATED.

THANK YOU, GENERAL.

ATTENTION, ALL PASSENGERS, WE ARE NOW LEAVING HYPER-SPACE...

... AND PREPARING TO ENTER THE *MERSON* ASTEROID BELT. ALL SYSTEMS NOT RELATING TO LIFE SUPPORT ARE BEING SHUT DOWN.

WHAT'S THAT ALL ABOUT?

FOR YOUR OWN SAFETY, PLEASE *DEACTIVATE* ANY PRIVATELY OWNED MACHINES AND CONSOLES.

THE MERSONS ARE *HOSTILE* TO THE REPUBLIC, SIR, ALWAYS ON THE LOOKOUT FOR SHIPS THAT STRAY INTO THEIR SECTOR.

SINCE THE ASTEROID BELT MAKES HYPER-SPACE PASSAGE IMPOSSIBLE, ANY CRAFT THAT PASSES THIS WAY SHUTS DOWN ITS NON-ESSENTIAL SYSTEMS AND *DRIFTS* ALONG WITH THE BELT, DISGUISED AS SPACE DEBRIS. IT'S ALL PERFECTLY SAFE.

GOOD, GOOD... BUT TELL ME ABOUT *BAIL...* HOW IS MY OLD FRIEND?

"*THE CONVERSATION WENT ON FOR HOURS, UNTIL LATER THAT EVENING, WHEN THEY HEARD A KNOCK AT THE DOOR OF THEIR CABIN...*"

YES? CREWMAN RORK, ISN'T IT?

CAPTAIN QUASAR'S **COMPLIMENTS**, GENERAL. HE REQUESTS THAT YOU COME TO THE BRIDGE.

OF COURSE... YOU DON'T MIND IF MY CABIN-MATE JOINS US?

NOT AT ALL, SIR.

I ASSUME THE CAPTAIN HAS MORE IN MIND THAN A **SOCIAL** VISIT.

I'M NOT AT LIBERTY TO **DISCUSS** THAT, SIR.

SORRY I HAD TO **SEND** FOR YOU LIKE THAT, OBI-WAN, BUT WE CAN'T RISK USING THE INTERCOM, AND I DIDN'T WANT TO LEAVE THE BRIDGE.

WHAT SEEMS TO BE THE PROBLEM?

SEE FOR YOURSELF. THOSE ARE **MERSON** SHIPS OUT THERE. WE DON'T KNOW IF THEY'VE ACTUALLY **SPOTTED** US, BUT THIS IS THE FIRST TIME ANYTHING LIKE THIS HAS EVER HAPPENED.

I UNDER-STAND YOUR CONCERN.

WHAT DO YOU SUGGEST WE DO?

EXACTLY WHAT YOU'VE **BEEN** DOING. WAIT AND SEE IF THEY TAKE ANY **HOSTILE** ACTION.

" 'AND WHATEVER YOU DO, WARN YOUR CREW NOT TO *ALARM* THE PASSENGERS.' "

IT'S *TRUE,* I TELL YOU. THERE ARE FOUR MERSON SHIPS OUTSIDE RIGHT NOW. THE CAPTAIN HAS THAT JEDI AND HIS DROID UP ON THE BRIDGE WITH HIM, AND...

BY THE SEVEN RINGS OF MY HOME WORLD-- WE'RE ALL GOING TO *DIE!*

AREN'T THE MERSONS... *SLAVERS?*

I'M *SORRY,* GENERAL, BUT WORD HAS *ALREADY SPREAD* TO THE BAR.

THEN IT CAN'T BE HELPED.

OUR PROBLEM IS OUT *THERE,* OBI-WAN.

"FOOD-- AND *DRINKS*-- ARE PART OF THE LIFE SUPPORT SYSTEM, SO DON'T *WORRY* ABOUT THE PASSENGERS.' "

PING

CAPTAIN QUASAR! ALL FOUR MERSON SHIPS HAVE JUST SWUNG IN OUR DIRECTION!

MR. RORK IS CORRECT. UNLESS I MISS MY GUESS, THOSE SHIPS ARE PREPARING TO ATTACK.

IMPOSSIBLE.

THEY *KNOW* WE'RE OUT HERE, AND WITH ALL OF THE PRECAUTIONS YOU'VE TAKEN, THAT SHOULD BE IMPOSSIBLE. UNLESS...

BY THE *FORCE*... THEY MUST BE RECEIVING A SIGNAL FROM *WITHIN THIS SHIP*.

OBI-WAN, I'M JUST A *PEACETIME* SPACE-MAN! I DON'T KNOW ANYTHING ABOUT WAR-FARE! WILL YOU TAKE COMMAND?

IF YOU WISH. WHAT ARE YOUR ARMAMENTS?

ARM--? YOU MUST BE *JOKING*, MAN! THIS IS A *PLEASURE* CRUISER!

ONE THAT CAR-RIES A NUMBER OF IMPORTANT DIGNITARIES AND COSTLY STORES. YOU MUST HAVE *SOME* DEFENSES.

ONLY TWO STANDARD *ENERGY-CANNONS*.

AGAINST FOUR ORDINARY SCOUT SHIPS, THAT MAY BE ENOUGH!

ONE OF 'EM'S COMING IN AT ELEVEN O'CLOCK, SIR.

THEN FIRE ON MY SIGNAL...

...NOW!

SKRAM

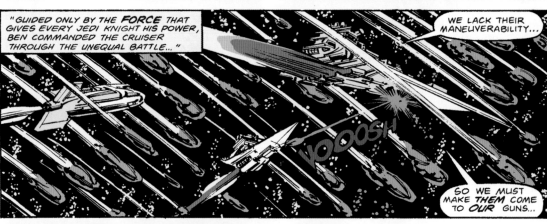

"GUIDED ONLY BY THE FORCE THAT GIVES EVERY JEDI KNIGHT HIS POWER, BEN COMMANDED THE CRUISER THROUGH THE UNEQUAL BATTLE..."

WE LACK THEIR MANEUVERABILITY...

VOOOSH

SO WE MUST MAKE THEM COME TO OUR GUNS...

...THUSLY.

BUT, SIR, WITH OUR ENGINES ON, WON'T THE MERSONS BE ABLE TO...

SKRAKOW

EVEN IF THE FIGHTING DRAWS MORE SHIPS, WE CAN LOSE THEM EASILY ENOUGH BY RESUMING OUR DRIFT IN THE BELT. IT'S ONLY VISUAL CONTACT WE HAVE TO FEAR FOR THE MOMENT...

SIR...YOUR REMARK ABOUT A *SIGNAL* FROM THIS SHIP... I THINK IT'S BEING *REPEATED* DOWN IN THE LOUNGE.

WHAT?

CAPTAIN, YOU AND YOUR MEN SEE IF YOU CAN LOCATE WHERE THE SIGNAL'S COMING FROM, IF IT EXISTS.

RKO AND I WILL DO WHAT WE CAN TO ALLAY THE PASSENGERS' FEARS.

AND, WHEN BEN AND RKO REACHED THE LOUNGE...

YOU LYING *SNEAK!* HOW MUCH DID THE MERSONS PAY YOU?

IT APPEARS WE'RE STILL IN TIME TO PREVENT AN ACT WHOSE CONSEQUENCES WE MAY *ALL* REGRET.

KEEP *AWAY* FROM ME, ALL OF YOU!

YOU'RE NOT GOING TO PREVENT *ANYTHING*, JEDI!

BUT WHAT *PROOF* HAVE YOU?

YOU SAID SOMEONE ON THIS SHIP IS SIGNALLING THE MERSONS, AND WE ALL *KNOW* WHO THAT SOMEONE IS!

WE DON'T *NEED* PROOF! EVERYONE *KNOWS* WHAT KIND OF MAN TRYLL IS!

THIS WON'T BE THE FIRST TIME HE'S WORKED WITH SLAVERS

DON'T YOU *SEE?* HE SOLD THIS SHIP AND EVERYONE *ON* IT!

THE ONLY THING I *SEE* IS THAT YOU'VE ALL TAKEN GOOD ADVANTAGE OF THE SHIP'S STOCK OF LIQUORS AND STIMULANTS--

--AND THAT YOU'RE ALL TOO *FRIGHTENED* TO THINK *CLEARLY.*

YOU'VE GOT TO *PROTECT* ME, KENOBI! YOU'RE A *JEDI*-- IT'S YOUR *DUTY!*

I HAVEN'T DONE ANYTHING!

AND YOU'D HARDLY ADMIT IT IF YOU HAD, EH, MR. TRYLL?

WAIT... I SEE IT *ALL NOW!* THIS AFTERNOON I OVERHEARD TRYLL OFFERING KENOBI A *PARTNERSHIP.* THEY'RE IN THIS *TOGETHER!*

YEAH! WE SAW WHAT THE JEDI AND HIS DROID DID TO JOEY ORSEL TODAY!

LET'S GET THEM ALL!

"AND THE CROWD BEGAN TO ADVANCE...

"WHILE IN HIS MIND'S EYE, BEN COULD SEE... "

MORE MERSON SHIPS ARE UN-DOUBTEDLY APPROACHING. IF I DON'T ACT SWIFTLY, IT MAY BE TOO *LATE* FOR US ALL.

PING

THAT'S IT, JEDI! THEY MEAN *NOTHING* TO YOU!

CUT THE WHOLE *BUNCH* DOWN!

VORSH

I DON'T THINK *THAT* WILL BE NECESSARY--

--AS *THIS* FERMENTATION DEVICE IS THE SOURCE OF *ALL* OUR TROUBLES!

FOOSHT

"OUT IN THE ASTEROID BELT, THE MERSON SHIPS LOST TRACK OF THE PLEASURE CRUISER AND BEGAN TO WANDER AIMLESSLY..."

"...AS THE SOURCE OF THE MICROWAVE EMANATIONS THAT HAD ATTRACTED THEM WAS DESTROYED!"

JEDI... I DON'T KNOW HOW I CAN *EVER* THANK YOU.

DON'T *TRY*, MR. TRYLL.

RKO, IF YOU'D CARE TO RETIRE TO OUR CABIN, WE MIGHT *FINISH* THIS JOURNEY IN PEACE.

YES, SIR.

"AND AFTER THEY REACHED ALDERAAN, THE DROID TOLD MY FATHER ABOUT THE ENTIRE ADVENTURE."

WELL, IT WAS *TERRIFIC* HEARING ABOUT BEN AGAIN.

IF YOU'LL PARDON MY SAYING, PRINCESS LEIA, 68-RKO MUST HAVE BEEN A *MASTER* STORYTELLER.

YEAH, YOUR ROYALNESS, YOU TELL A PRETTY GOOD STORY YOURSELF...

...EVEN IF YOU DID *JAZZ* IT UP WITH ALL THAT HOCUS-POCUS ABOUT THE *FORCE*.

HRONK

BUT RIGHT NOW, OUR SHIP IS REPAIRED...

...SO LET'S GET OUT OF THIS QUADRANT BEFORE WE FIND OURSELVES IN ANOTHER *MESS!*

NEXT ISSUE: WE PICK UP ON OUR REGULAR STORYLINE AND THE...

SIEGE AT YAVIN!

Long ago in a galaxy far, far away. . .there exists a state of cosmic *civil war*. A brave alliance of *underground freedom fighters* has challenged the tyranny and oppression of the awesome *Galactic Empire*. This is their story!

LucasFilm PRESENTS: **STAR WARS**™ THE GREATEST SPACE FANTASY OF ALL!

CONTINUING THE SAGA BEGUN IN THE FILM BY GEORGE LUCAS RELEASED BY TWENTIETH CENTURY-FOX

ARCHIE GOODWIN
WRITER / EDITOR

CARMINE INFANTINO & GENE DAY
ARTISTS

JOE ROSEN
LETTERER

BEN SEAN
COLORIST

JIM SHOOTER
CONSULTING EDITOR

SEIGE AT YAVIN!

DAWN ON THE FOURTH MOON!
TIE FIGHTERS SHRIEK DOWN INTO STILL SURFACE MISTS HANGING ABOVE THE JUNGLE. THE LEAD SHIP'S ENERGY CANNONS POUND...

...AND A REBEL LOOKOUT STATION GIVES ITS *LAST WARNING.*

LG3B2

AT THE ALLIANCE STRONGHOLD IN THE MASSASI RUINS, **ALARMS** SOUND, PILOTS SCRAMBLE, GUN CREWS CHARGE TO THEIR EMPLACEMENTS...

AND FOR THE *THIRD TIME* IN AS MANY DAYS...

THERE GOES *ANOTHER FLIGHT* INTO THE GRINDER!

LET'S GIVE 'EM SOME *GROUND SUPPORT!*

THEN, AS THE GREAT RED GAS GIANT THAT IS THE PLANET YAVIN SILENTLY WATCHES... *HELL* EXPLODES IN THE SKIES OF ITS FOURTH MOON!

IT FINALLY *ENDS* AS IT HAS BEFORE...WITH THE ENEMY IN SWIFT *RETREAT.*

BUT AT A *PRICE*... ALWAYS AT A TERRIBLE PRICE.

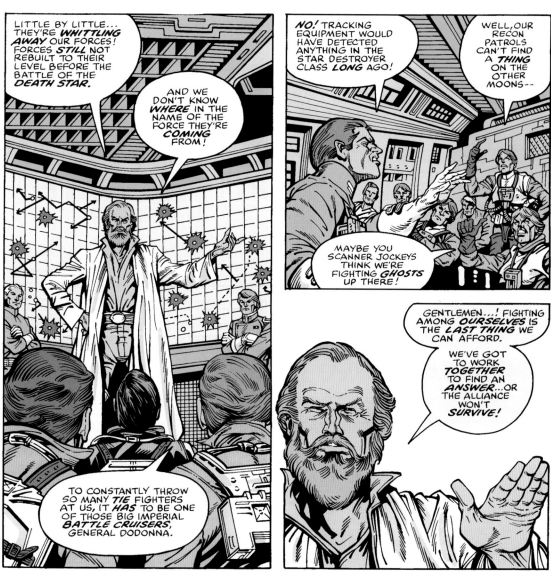

LITTLE BY LITTLE... THEY'RE *WHITTLING AWAY* OUR FORCES! FORCES *STILL* NOT REBUILT TO THEIR LEVEL BEFORE THE BATTLE OF THE *DEATH STAR.*

AND WE DON'T KNOW *WHERE* IN THE NAME OF THE FORCE THEY'RE *COMING* FROM!

TO CONSTANTLY THROW SO MANY *TIE* FIGHTERS AT US, IT *HAS* TO BE ONE OF THOSE BIG IMPERIAL *BATTLE CRUISERS,* GENERAL DODONNA.

NO! TRACKING EQUIPMENT WOULD HAVE DETECTED ANYTHING IN THE STAR DESTROYER CLASS *LONG* AGO!

WELL, OUR RECON PATROLS CAN'T FIND A *THING* ON THE OTHER MOONS--

MAYBE YOU SCANNER JOCKEYS THINK WE'RE FIGHTING *GHOSTS* UP THERE!

GENTLEMEN...! FIGHTING AMONG *OURSELVES* IS THE *LAST THING* WE CAN AFFORD.

WE'VE GOT TO WORK *TOGETHER* TO FIND AN *ANSWER*...OR THE ALLIANCE WON'T *SURVIVE!*

CENTARES! OUTER-MOST OF THE MID-SYSTEMS TRADING WORLDS. LAST CIVILIZED STOP FOR THOSE DOING BUSINESS IN THE GALACTIC BACKWATERS, OR TAKING A FLING AT EXPLORING THE UNKNOWN...

...OR HOPING TO *ESCAPE* THE LONG ARM OF THE *EMPIRE.*

YOU CITIZENS HAVE MADE A REAL SWEET *TRADE.* TAKE THE WORD OF *JORMAN THOAD,* THE PLANET'S LARGEST DEALER IN USED STARCRAFT.

THIS SHIP'S NOT SO FANCY AS THAT *YACHT* YOU CAME IN, BUT--

"--BUT IT'S GOT THE DRIVE AND ARMAMENT *NEEDED* IN THE OUTERWORLDS!" WE *HEARD* THE SALES PITCH--

JUST SO THEY *KEEP* WORKING AS WELL AS THEY DID IN THE *DEMONSTRATION RUN.*

LAD, YOU HAVE THE JORMAN THOAD *GUARANTEE.*

THAT MAY NOT *HELP* IF WE AREN'T *ALIVE* TO HOLD YOU TO IT!

MASTER LUKE, ARTOO AND I HAVE *TRANSFERRED* EVERYTHING TO THE NEW SHIP.

NICE PAIR OF *DROIDS...* BIT ON THE *WORN* SIDE. IF YOU'D LIKE TO GET RID OF *THEM,* I'VE A COUSIN OVER IN OLD TOWN WHO--

TA-DOOT!

FOR A CHANGE, I *AGREE* WITH YOU, ARTOO... HE *DOES* SEEM WORSE THAN A *JAWA!*

WE *WANT* OUR DROIDS, THOAD...AND INFORMATION ABOUT CURRENT *CONDITIONS* IN THE VARIOUS OUTWORLD SECTORS.

NO BETTER, NO WORSE THAN *USUAL*--

UNLESS YOU'RE HEADED WHERE THAT HOUSE OF TAGGE *MINING EXPLORER* IS BOUND... THE *GORDIAN REACH!*

THE GORDIAN REACH...? I-ISN'T THAT WHERE THE *YAVIN* SYSTEM LIES...?!

YAVIN. KRYLON. TORQUE. A *JILLION* MORE. RUMOR HAS IT TAGGE IS ON TO A BIG *SPICE STRIKE* ON ONE OF 'EM--

--AND BECAUSE OF THEIR *IMPERIAL* CONNECTIONS... THE EMPIRE'S *BLOCKADED* THE SECTOR!

SO I WOULDN'T PLAN ON TRAVELING *THERE.*

WISH I HAD AN *IMPERIAL GENERAL* IN THE FAMILY LIKE THE TAGGES. THEN MAYBE *I* COULD GET IN ON SUCH--

BUT I SEE YOU ARE ANXIOUS TO *DEPART!*

REMEMBER JORMAN THOAD WHEN YOU HAVE *OTHER* LUXURY YACHTS TO TRADE FOR MODEST BUT DEPENDABLE CRAFTS!

AND SOON, THE HASTILY ACQUIRED SHIP IS BREAKING *FREE* OF CENTARES' ATMOSPHERE...

...CLIMBING FOR *DEEP SPACE.*

IT'S *INCREDIBLE,* PRINCESS...! EVERYTIME WE GET *CLOSE* TO MAKING IT BACK TO REBEL BASE--

--SOMETHING POPS UP TO GET IN OUR *WAY!*

AT LEAST WE'VE GOTTEN RID OF THE *YACHT,* LUKE. * IF DARTH VADER IS STILL IN PURSUIT... HE CAN'T *TRACE* US THROUGH THAT.

BUT IF HE'S *NOT* TRAILING US... HE MAY BE AFTER *HAN!*

*ACQUIRED IN *STAR WARS* 23.
-- ARCHIE G.

WHEN HE ISN'T PULLING MY *LEG* ABOUT SOMETHING... HAN'S KIND'A LIKE A *BIG BROTHER.* IF ANYTHING'S *HAPPENED* TO HIM--

WE *HAD* TO SPLIT UP TO ESCAPE LORD VADER, LUKE! I'M *SURE* WE'LL BE TOGETHER AGAIN *SOON*--

WE...WE *HAVE* TO BE!

THAT SOUNDS SORT OF *SERIOUS.* LATELY I THOUGHT LEIA SEEMED MORE INTERESTED IN *ME,* BUT *NOW*--

AW, *NO!* HAN'S A GOOD GUY, BUT SHE CAN'T *REALLY* BE IN *LOVE* WITH HIM--

--*CAN* SHE?

VRR-KLIK WEET!

PRINCESS...! ARTOO SAYS HE'S GETTING THAT *HOUSE OF TAGGE SHIP* YOU WONDERED ABOUT ON THE *SCANNER*--

HE CLAIMS IT'S ABOUT TO GO INTO *WARP*--

"--AND THAT ITS PRESENT POSITION AND HEADING INDICATE A COURSE FOR THE *YAVIN VICINITY!*"

SHOULDN'T WE BE CONCERNED ABOUT GETTING THROUGH THE EMPIRE'S *BLOCKADE* INSTEAD OF OVER SOME LUMBERING *SPICE SNIFFER?*

LUKE, THERE'S *NO SPICE* IN THAT SECTOR--

--THE ALLIANCE MADE *CERTAIN* WHEN WE PICKED THE LOCATION FOR A *BASE.* THE LAST THING WE *WANTED*--

--WAS A CONSTANT STREAM OF *SPICE HUNTERS* IN THE AREA!

THEN WHY ARE TAGGE *EXPLORERS* GOING *IN* THERE, PRINCESS? WHAT'S THIS BLOCKADE ALL *ABOUT?!*

I THINK THE EMPIRE'S *AFRAID*, LUKE.

PRINCESS, NO ONE'S GOT MORE *FAITH* IN REBEL FIGHTING ABILITY THAN *ME*--

-- BUT I CAN'T BELIEVE WE'VE GOT THE *IMPERIAL WAR MACHINE* PARALYZED WITH FRIGHT!

THAT'S NOT *QUITE* WHAT I MEANT, LUKE. BUT CONSIDER--

BESIDES OTHER EARLIER VICTORIES, WE'VE *DESTROYED* THEIR MOST AWESOME WEAPON...THE *DEATH STAR!*

THAT'S *NOT* THE KIND OF NEWS THAT MAKES IT *EASY* FOR THEM TO CONTROL THE GALAXY.

LEIA, YOU THINK THE *BLOCKADE* IS AN ATTEMPT TO KEEP THAT DEFEAT *SECRET?*

PARTLY. BY NOW, THE EMPIRE COULD HAVE SENT A MASSIVE *FLEET* IN RETALIATION--

BUT SUPPOSE OUR FORCES *ABANDONED* YAVIN AS THEY ONCE DID *DANTOOINE?*

OR WORSE YET: PULLED ANOTHER *VICTORY* OUT OF THE HAT?

THAT'S WHAT THE EMPIRE FEARS, LUKE. AND UNTIL THEY COME UP WITH SOMETHING TO EQUAL-- OR *EXCEED*-- THE DEATH STAR, I THINK THEY'RE PLAYING A MORE *SNEAKY GAME*...USING THIS "SPICE STRIKE" BUSINESS AS *COVER!*

TO LEARN *WHAT* THAT GAME IS... WE'VE *GOT* TO FOLLOW THAT MINING EXPLORER THROUGH *WARP.*

THIS *CLOSE* ON THEIR HEELS THAT COULD BE *TRICKY*, PRINCESS!

THREEPIO, LINK ARTOO DEETOO TO THE SHIPBOARD *COMPUTER*, WITH *HIM* AUGMENTING ITS EMERGENCY CALIBRATION SYSTEM--

--AND THE *PILOT* WHO BROUGHT DOWN THE *DEATH STAR* AT THE CONTROLS, WHAT DO WE HAVE TO *WORRY* ABOUT?

OTHER THAN COMING OUT OF HYPER-SPACE IN THE MIDDLE OF THE TAGGE SHIP'S *EXHAUST TUBES*--?

NOT A *THING!*

FA-BREET!

ARTOO DEETOO, IF *YOU'VE* THOUGHT OF ANYTHING *ELSE*... WE DON'T WANT TO *KNOW* ABOUT IT!

MEANWHILE, *WITHIN* THE BIG COMMERCIAL CRAFT LUKE AND LEIA PURSUE...

COME AT ME *AGAIN*, SHANKS.

NO, *NO!* YOU'RE *TOO EASY!* I CAN'T GROW *BETTER* UNLESS I'M ADEQUATELY *CHALLENGED!*

VRAAMP!

YOU'RE TOO *SKILLFUL*, BARON TAGGE! ONLY A *JEDI KNIGHT* COULD EQUAL YOU NOW--

--AND *THEY* NO LONGER *EXIST!*

ONE DOES, SHANKS, AT LEAST HE *USED* TO BE--

ZAAMP!

-- *DARTH VADER!* WHOSE OWN *LIGHT SABER* LEFT ME LIKE *THIS!*

THE ELDEST BROTHER OF THE TAGGE LINE *HELPLESS*... WITHOUT MY *CYBER-VISION.*

86

SO I PRACTICE *CONSTANTLY* WITH THIS SILLY, OUTMODED WEAPON OF A FOOLISH, EXTINCT BAND OF MEN--

AND *SOMEDAY,* SHANKS... I'LL BE *READY.* READY TO *REPAY* DARTH VADER IN KIND... AND WITH *INTEREST!*

BARON TAGGE--!

SIR, WE'RE COMING OUT OF *WARP...* AND INSTRUMENTS INDICATE THERE MAY BE A SMALL *SHIP* FOLLOWING US!

A DARING-- IF HIGHLY *RISKY--* WAY TO SLIP THROUGH THE EMPIRE'S *BLOCKADE.*

SEE THEY DON'T *SUCCEED.*

SECONDS AFTER THE BARON'S WORDS ARE SPOKEN, A *HATCH* OPENS AND...

...MINES ARE SWIFTLY SCATTERED THROUGH THE SECTOR!

GOOD! I DIDN'T BUILD THE FAMILY FORTUNE BY LETTING *ADMIRATION* FOR A FOE'S DARING KEEP ME FROM *DESTROYING* THEM!

LET'S GET ON WITH OUR *DELIVERY.*

AND WHEN THE PURSUING CRAFT'S COMPUTER *DISENGAGES* FROM SUPRA-LIGHT DRIVE...

THE AREA'S *BOOBY-TRAPPED!*

ARTOO! CUT IN THE *SHIELDS!*

THREE-PIO! WHAT'S HE *SAYING?!*

BA-DOOT

HE WISHES *JORMAN THOAD* WERE WITH US... THAT ONE HIT HAS OUR SHIELDS *FAILING!*

IT'S NO *CONSOLATION,* LUKE...BUT THOSE ARE *HEAVY DUTY MINES!*

TWO OR THREE OF THEM ARE ENOUGH TO CRACK THE ENERGY SHIELDS OF *ANY* CRAFT THIS SIZE!

TAKE OVER THE *SIDE BATTERY,* PRINCESS... AND DO LIKE *I'M* DOING WITH THE *FORWARD GUNS*--

--*GET* THOSE THINGS BEFORE THEY GET *US!*

THEY'RE *MAGNETICALLY CHARGED,* LUKE! THEY'LL BE DRAWN TO OUR *HULL PLATING*--

--AND *FASTER* THAN WE CAN BLAST AND MANEUVER!

ARTOO! DISENGAGE THE *COMPUTER!* TRANSFER ALL CONTROL TO *ME!*

QUICKLY, ARTOO... THERE'S *ANOTHER* BLAZE AFT!

LUKE! THE PATTERN IS *TIGHTENING* ON US!

LUKE...?!

BUT THE BOY FROM TATOOINE NO LONGER *HEARS*, HIS MIND IS DIVORCED FROM CONSCIOUS THOUGHT.

HE IS *ONE* WITH THE MACHINE HE CONTROLS, ACTING BY WHAT HE SENSES AND WHAT HE FEELS.

THE TINY SHIP *DANCES* IN RESPONSE, TWISTING, ALTERING DIRECTIONS WITH EYEBLINK SWIFTNESS!

UNTIL...

YOU BEAT OUT THAT LAST *CLUSTER*, LUKE... THEY ALL CAME TOGETHER ON *EACH OTHER!* A-AND--

--THE WAY AHEAD IS *CLEAR!* WE'RE *THROUGH* THE MINES!

THANKS, FLYBOY!

ER... PRINCESS? MASTER LUKE...? ARTOO AND I HAVE ALL *DAMAGE* UNDER CONTROL, BUT--

-- HE REPORTS ALL SCANNING AND TRACKING EQUIPMENT HAVE GONE *BERSERK!*

NO *WONDER!* WE'RE DRIFTING INTO *YAVIN'S* GRAVITATIONAL FIELD!

THE *GASES* IT'S MADE OF CREATE CONSTANT *STORMS* AND ATMOSPHERIC TRICKS! THIS *CLOSE*--

--IT'S LIKE ONE HUGE, NATURAL *JAMMING DEVICE!*

SOMEONE *ELSE* IS ORBITING HERE, PRINCESS... THE *TAGGE SHIP!*

AND IT SEEMS TO BE *INTENTIONAL!*

GET US BEHIND ONE OF THOSE SMALLER *MOONS* BEFORE WE'RE *SPOTTED,* LUKE--

--I'M GOING *OUTSIDE* TO DO SOME *SPYING.*

NOT WITHOUT *ME!*

FROM ANYONE *ELSE,* THAT KIND OF PROTECTIVENESS MIGHT BE *INSULTING...* SOMEHOW, YOU MAKE IT *QUAINT.*

MOMENTS LATER, TWO FIGURES IN *SURVIVAL ARMOR* JET DOWN TOWARD THE POCKED, AIRLESS SPHERE BELOW...

...MAKING THEIR WAY TO THE LITTLE MOON'S *FAR SIDE.*

THERE IT *IS,* PRINCESS. WHAT IT'S *DOING* IS ANYBODY'S GUESS!

WE *KNOW* IT'S NOT LOOKING FOR *SPICE.*

IF ONLY THESE *MACRO-BINOCULARS* COULD PEER *INSIDE* THAT THING!

THE PILOTS ARE NEARLY READY TO *LAUNCH,* BARON.

I'LL SEE THEM *OFF,* SHANKS. I *PLEASURE* IN VIEWING THE ADVANCED TECHNOLOGY OF THE HOUSE OF TAGGE IN *ACTION.*

PARTICULARLY IN THE CAUSE OF THE *EMPIRE,* SIR...?

PARTICULARLY IN AN OPERATION THAT IS *SUCCEEDING* WHERE VADER, TARKIN AND THE DEATH STAR *FAILED!*

LOOK AT THEM, SHANKS! *REPLACEMENTS* FOR ANY SHIPS THE *REBELS* MAY HAVE STRUCK DOWN!

LET THE *SITH LORD* FOLLOW HIS "*FORCE*," SCRAMBLING ABOUT THE GALAXY, SEEKING THOSE WHO *SHAMED* HIM IN THE DEATH STAR BATTLE--

--WE'RE BEATING THE ALLIANCE *HERE!*

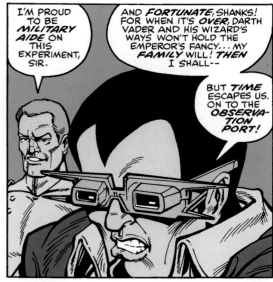

I'M PROUD TO BE *MILITARY AIDE* ON THIS EXPERIMENT, SIR.

AND *FORTUNATE*, SHANKS! FOR WHEN IT'S *OVER*, DARTH VADER AND HIS WIZARD'S WAYS WON'T HOLD THE EMPEROR'S FANCY... MY *FAMILY* WILL! *THEN* I SHALL--

BUT *TIME* ESCAPES US. ON TO THE *OBSERVATION PORT!*

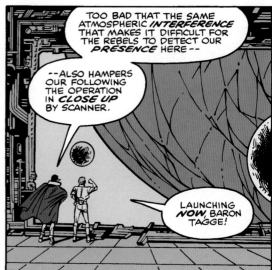

TOO BAD THAT THE SAME ATMOSPHERIC *INTERFERENCE* THAT MAKES IT DIFFICULT FOR THE REBELS TO DETECT OUR *PRESENCE* HERE--

--ALSO HAMPERS OUR FOLLOWING THE OPERATION IN *CLOSE UP* BY SCANNER.

LAUNCHING *NOW*, BARON TAGGE!

AND, FROM THE SURFACE OF THE NEARBY MOON, LUKE AND LEIA OBSERVE...

A *TIE FIGHTER* FORMATION...! AND HEADED STRAIGHT FOR THE SURFACE OF *YAVIN!*

THAT'S *SUICIDE*, PRINCESS! FLYING *BLINDLY* INTO ALL THOSE GASES... *INSTRUMENTS* UNABLE TO WORK...

THEY'LL NEVER COME *UP* AGAIN!

BUT AS THE AMAZED PAIR *CONTINUE* WATCHING...

A SUDDEN *STORM* SEEMS TO BUILD IN THE AREA THE *TIE* SHIPS DIVE TOWARD...

TROPOSPHERIC GASES SWIRL MADLY AT HURRICANE FORCE. AND, AS WITH *ANY* HURRICANE...

...A CALM *EYE* OPENS AT ITS CENTER!

AND THAT EYE BECOMES A *SAFE CORRIDOR,* DOWN WHICH THE ENTIRE FLIGHT *PLUNGES* TO BE LOST FROM SIGHT...

...AS THE STORM *ENDS* WITH A SWIFTNESS THAT *CANNOT* BE NATURAL!

L-LUKE...! THE EMPIRE'S GOT SOMETHING *IN* THERE THAT *CREATES* THOSE STORMS...! SOME KIND OF *BASE!*

I GUESS A *SPACE STATION* COULD *EXIST* IN THOSE GASES... LONG AS THERE WAS A WAY TO *SUPPLY* IT--

--AND FROM WHAT WE JUST *SAW,* THEY OBVIOUSLY HAVE *THAT!* I DON'T KNOW HOW THE SHIPS *SIGNAL* FOR THE STORM CORRIDOR TO BE *OPENED,* BUT--

THAT CAN *WAIT,* LUKE--

--WE'VE GOT TO *WARN* THE ALLIANCE!

AND, BACK INSIDE THEIR *SHIP*...

WHOEVER CAME UP WITH THIS IS *CLEVER*, LUKE. OPERATING SO *CLOSE* TO YAVIN... ON THE *OPPOSITE SIDE* FROM OUR BASE... MAKES CHANCES OF DISCOVERY *MINIMAL*.

AND EVEN IF OUR *RECON PATROLS* SIGHTED THEM--

--ONE STRAY *MINING EXPLORER* WOULDN'T ALARM THEM. THEY'D ASSUME IT'D BE MOVING ON ONCE IT BECAME OBVIOUS THERE WAS NO *SPICE* IN THE AREA.

UNLESS THE RECON CAME ON 'EM JUST AS THEY WERE *UNLOADING* THE *TIES*, LIKE WE SAW, PRINCESS.

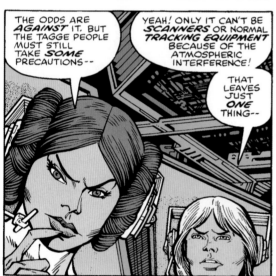

THE ODDS ARE *AGAINST* IT. BUT THE TAGGE PEOPLE MUST STILL TAKE *SOME* PRECAUTIONS--

YEAH! ONLY IT CAN'T BE *SCANNERS* OR NORMAL *TRACKING EQUIPMENT* BECAUSE OF THE ATMOSPHERIC INTERFERENCE!

THAT LEAVES JUST *ONE* THING--

BAD NEWS, MASTER LUKE! NOW THAT WE'RE MOVING *OUT* SOMEWHAT FROM THAT GREAT GLOB OF GAS, ARTOO'S *SENSORS* DETECT--

NEVER *MIND*, THREEPIO! THE PRINCESS AND I HAVE ALREADY *GUESSED*--

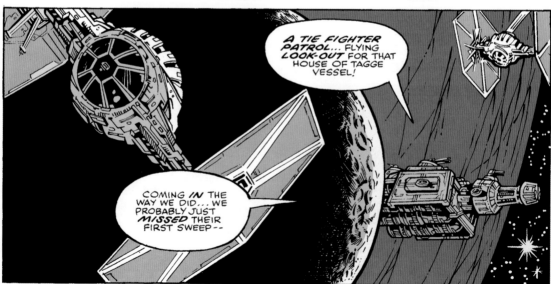

A TIE FIGHTER PATROL... FLYING *LOOK-OUT* FOR THAT HOUSE OF TAGGE VESSEL!

COMING *IN* THE WAY WE DID... WE PROBABLY JUST *MISSED* THEIR FIRST SWEEP--

--BUT OUR TIMING WAS *PERFECT* FOR THEIR *RETURN!*

I'LL GET BACK TO THE OTHER SET OF *GUNS,* LUKE! IS THERE ANY HOPE OF *OUTRUNNING* THEM UNTIL THREEPIO CAN RAISE *HELP* ON THE COMMINCATOR?

IF THERE *WERE,* PRINCESS--

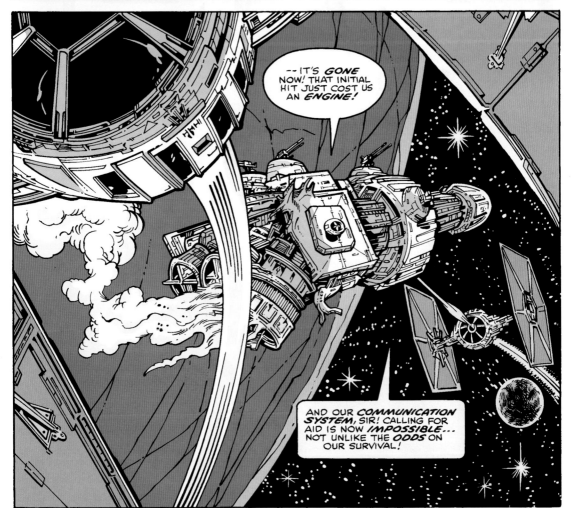

--IT'S *GONE* NOW! THAT INITIAL HIT JUST COST US AN *ENGINE!*

AND OUR *COMMUNICATION SYSTEM,* SIR! CALLING FOR AID IS NOW *IMPOSSIBLE...* NOT UNLIKE THE *ODDS* ON OUR SURVIVAL!

NEXT ISSUE: DOOM MISSION!

X-WING FIGHTERS! IT'S A REBEL RECONNAISSANCE PATROL!

IT'S MORE THAN THAT... IT'S A MIRACLE!

THERE GOES THE SECOND TIE SHIP... LOOKS LIKE HE'S GOING TO CRASH ON THAT MOON!

ARTOO...! THREEPIO,...! IF YOU KEEP THE FLAMES AT BAY A LITTLE LONGER--

--WE MIGHT MAKE IT AFTER ALL!

AND UNDER X-WING ESCORT, THE LITTLE SHIP FIGHTS ITS WAY INTO THE ATMOSPHERE OF YAVIN'S FOURTH MOON...

...WHERE AT THE MASSASI RUINS, A ROUGH LANDING AND A WARM GREETING WAIT.

PRINCESS! WE'D GIVEN YOU AND YOUNG SKYWALKER UP AS LOST! SINCE THE IMPERIAL BLOCKADE OF THIS SECTOR, COMMUNICATION HAS BEEN SPOTTY AND--

WE'VE BROUGHT NEWS, GENERAL DODONNA...BUT I'M AFRAID IT ISN'T GOOD!

NOT MUCH *HAS* BEEN SINCE THE EMPIRE STARTED HITTING US IN ALMOST *DAILY RAIDS*, YOUR HIGHNESS.

PERHAPS *NOT*, GENERAL--

AND DESPITE STEPPED UP *PATROLS*-- LIKE THE ONE THAT FOUND YOU-- THEIR HIDDEN BASE *REMAINS* A SECRET!

AND SWIFTLY... THESE ARE *BLOW UPS* FROM THE PHOTO-RECORDER UNIT OF MY MACRO-BINOCULARS!

HERE'S WHAT LUKE AND I FOUND ON THE *FAR SIDE* OF YAVIN--*

*ALSO *LAST ISSUE.*-- ALSO ARCHIE.

THAT'S A HOUSE OF TAGGE *MINING EXPLORER!*

BUT THOSE AREN'T *SPICE PROBES* IT'S SENDING DOWN INTO YAVIN'S TROPOSHERE--

THEY'RE *TIE FIGHTERS*... PROBABLY *REPLACEMENTS* FOR ANY EMPIRE SHIPS YOU'VE *DESTROYED.*

THEY'LL BE *BLIND* IN THERE... *HELPLESS!*

YAVIN'S MADE UP OF NOTHING BUT *GASES*... SHIPS CAN'T OPERATE AMID THEM BECAUSE STORMS AND ATMOSPHERIC INTERFERENCE *JAM* ALL INSTRUMENTS!

SEE! THERE'S A STORM BUILDING UNDER THE TIES... THEY'RE *FINISHED!*

KEEP *WATCHING,* GENTLEMEN--

" *THAT 'STORM' SWIRLED THE GASES INTO A CYCLONIC FUNNEL... WITH A CALM EYE AT ITS CENTER, AND THAT EYE...*

"...BECAME A *CORRIDOR* FOR THE TIES TO *TRAVEL* DOWN.'"

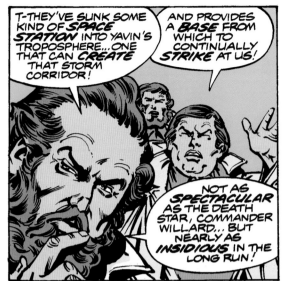

T-THEY'VE SUNK SOME KIND OF *SPACE STATION* INTO YAVIN'S TROPOSPHERE...ONE THAT CAN *CREATE* THAT STORM CORRIDOR!

AND PROVIDES A *BASE* FROM WHICH TO CONTINUALLY *STRIKE* AT US!

NOT AS *SPECTACULAR* AS THE DEATH STAR, COMMANDER WILLARD... BUT NEARLY AS *INSIDIOUS* IN THE LONG RUN!

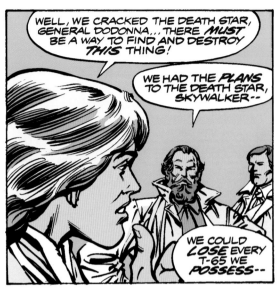

WELL, WE CRACKED THE DEATH STAR, GENERAL DODONNA... THERE *MUST* BE A WAY TO FIND AND DESTROY *THIS* THING!

WE HAD THE *PLANS* TO THE DEATH STAR, SKYWALKER--

WE COULD *LOSE* EVERY T-65 WE *POSSESS*--

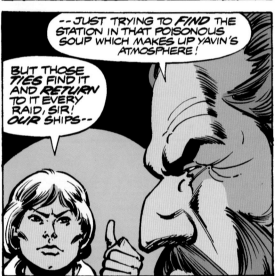

--JUST TRYING TO *FIND* THE STATION IN THAT POISONOUS SOUP WHICH MAKES UP YAVIN'S ATMOSPHERE!

BUT THOSE *TIES* FIND IT AND *RETURN* TO IT EVERY RAID, SIR! *OUR* SHIPS--

ARE *GREAT*... BUT THEY DON'T HAVE HOUSE OF TAGGE *TECHNOLOGY!* THEIR FAMILY INDUSTRIES EMPLOY THOUSANDS OF SCIENTISTS ON *HUNDREDS* OF WORLDS.

ONE OF THEM MUST HAVE COME UP WITH A SIGNAL SYSTEM *STRONG* ENOUGH TO--

LUKE! WHERE ARE YOU *GOING?!*

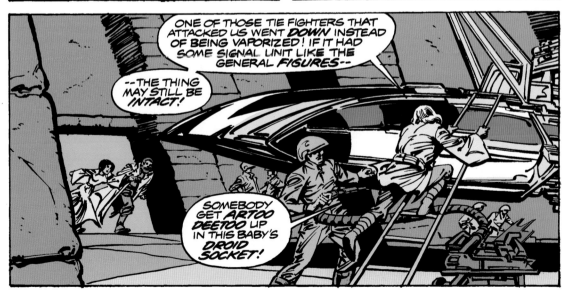

ONE OF THOSE TIE FIGHTERS THAT ATTACKED US WENT *DOWN* INSTEAD OF BEING VAPORIZED! IF IT HAD SOME SIGNAL UNIT LIKE THE GENERAL *FIGURES*--

--THE THING MAY STILL BE *INTACT!*

SOMEBODY GET *ARTOO DEETOO* UP IN THIS BABY'S *DROID SOCKET!*

BEFORE ANYONE CAN GET OVER THEIR *SUR-PRISE* ENOUGH TO PROTEST, LUKE IS INTO THE SKIES AND ON HIS WAY...

...TO ONE OF MANY *LESSER* ORNAMENTS IN YAVIN'S BRIGHT *NECKLACE* OF MOONS...

...MADE DISTINCTIVE BY *ANOTHER* KIND OF ORNAMENTATION.

DA-WEET! FRIIT!

I *MARK* IT, ARTOO... AND IT LOOKS IN BETTER *SHAPE* THAN I EXPECTED

BUT THERE IS *DANGER* IN THAT. FOR IF THE *FIGHTER* IS INTACT...

...THE *PILOT* MAY BE AS WELL!

HOPED MY *OWN* OUTFIT MIGHT COME LOOKING FOR ME *BEFORE* THE REBELS--

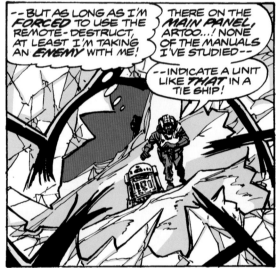

--BUT AS LONG AS I'M *FORCED* TO USE THE REMOTE-*DESTRUCT*, AT LEAST I'M TAKING AN *ENEMY* WITH ME!

THERE ON THE *MAIN PANEL*, ARTOO...! NONE OF THE MANUALS I'VE STUDIED--

--INDICATE A UNIT LIKE *THAT* IN A TIE SHIP!

NO, ARTOO! NOT *THERE*, I SAID THE *MAIN* PANEL! WHY ARE YOU RIPPING OUT *WIRING* WHEN--

ARTOO! THAT'S A PROTON CHARGE *DETONATOR*--!

FRADOOP

BLASTED LITTLE *DROID!* BROKE THE *TRANSMISSION*--!

ARTOO!

VDOW!

VRRPOW!

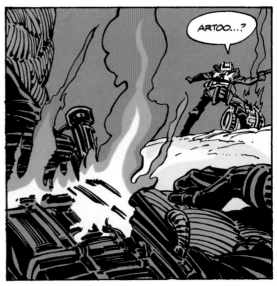

ARTOO...?

IT IS SOMETIME *LATER* BEFORE THE Y-WING REAPPEARS AT THE REBEL BASE...

LUKE! I-- WE WERE GETTING *FRANTIC!* DID YOU--

I *FOUND* THE GADGET, PRINCESS... BUT I HAD TO REMOVE IT *WITHOUT* ARTOO'S HELP.

IT TOOK A LOT MORE *TIME.*

WITHOUT *ARTOO...?* MASTER LUKE, YOU *DON'T* MEAN--

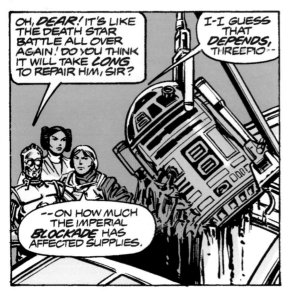

OH, *DEAR!* IT'S LIKE THE DEATH STAR BATTLE ALL OVER AGAIN! DO YOU THINK IT WILL TAKE *LONG* TO REPAIR HIM, SIR?

I-I GUESS THAT *DEPENDS,* THREEPIO--

--ON HOW MUCH THE IMPERIAL *BLOCKADE* HAS AFFECTED SUPPLIES.

AFFECTED--?! WITH ALL THE ATTACKS, WE'RE SCRAPIN' BOTTOM FOR *EVERYTHING,* SKYWALKER, THERE'S SOME *WORKING* R-2 UNITS THAT COULD USE *HIS* PARTS!

I KNOW YOU'RE *FOND* OF THAT LITTLE DROID, BUT AFTER *ALL,* IT'S--

DON'T TELL ME HE'S ONLY A *MACHINE!*

NIGHT ABOVE THE RUINS, A LONE FIGURE STARES AT THE SILENT STARS...

...AND IS JOINED BY *ANOTHER.*

LUKE...? IT'S VERY *LATE.* WHAT HAVE YOU BEEN *DOING* OUT HERE?

MEDITATING... TRYING TO BECOME MORE ATTUNED TO THE *FORCE.*

AND A LOT OF JUST PLAIN *THINKING,* TOO.

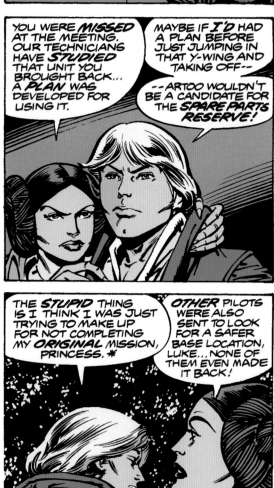

YOU WERE *MISSED* AT THE MEETING. OUR TECHNICIANS HAVE *STUDIED* THAT UNIT YOU BROUGHT BACK... A *PLAN* WAS DEVELOPED FOR USING IT.

MAYBE IF *I'D* HAD A PLAN BEFORE JUST JUMPING IN THAT Y-WING AND TAKING OFF--

--ARTOO WOULDN'T BE A CANDIDATE FOR THE *SPARE PARTS RESERVE!*

THE *STUPID* THING IS I THINK I WAS JUST TRYING TO MAKE UP FOR NOT COMPLETING MY *ORIGINAL* MISSION, PRINCESS. *

OTHER PILOTS WERE ALSO SENT TO LOOK FOR A SAFER BASE LOCATION, LUKE... NONE OF THEM EVEN MADE IT BACK!

EVERY MISSION *CAN'T* BE A SUCCESS... *WAR* JUST ISN'T THAT SIMPLE.

*SW#8.--AG.

NOR is it *FAIR*. THERE ARE MISSIONS FROM WHICH MEN CANNOT *POSSIBLY* RETURN... AND YET, WE STILL *SEND* THEM.

OFTEN... WE SEND OUR *BEST*.

GENERAL DODONNA...! *NO!* I THOUGHT LUKE WOULDN'T *HAVE* TO--

ANYONE ELSE IN SKYWALKER'S CLASS IS ALSO A *FLIGHT COMMANDER*, PRINCESS... OUR LESS EXPERIENCED PILOTS *NEED* SUCH LEADERSHIP.

BUT YOU'LL *THROW AWAY* THE LIFE OF THE MAN WHO DESTROYED THE *DEATH STAR!*

IF IT CAN PROLONG THE LIFE OF THE *ALLIANCE*, YOUR HIGHNESS... *YES!*

IT'S THE KIND OF DECISION YOUR *FATHER* WOULD HAVE MADE. AND, GIVEN THE TIME TO REFLECT... SO WOULD *YOU*.

NOBODY SEEMS TO BE *ASKING* ME, BUT IF YOU NEED A *VOLUNTEER*, GENERAL... I GUESS YOU'VE *GOT* HIM.

HOW ABOUT *SHOWING* ME WHAT I'M *IN* FOR?

SOON... IN THE VAST STONE CHAMBER THAT HOUSES THE REBEL FIGHTERS... A SHIP IS READIED.

WE'VE HAD THIS OLD *HULK* FOR YEARS... USED IT TO *FAMILIARIZE* OUR PILOTS WITH ENEMY CRAFT.

NOW IT'S OUTFITTED WITH THAT TAGGE *SIGNAL DEVICE*... AND ENOUGH *PROTON CHARGES* TO DESTROY A CITY. UNFORTUNATELY--

WHEN I DESTROY MY *TARGET*, I DESTROY WHATEVER CREATES THAT *STORM CORRIDOR*... THE ONLY WAY *OUT* OF YAVIN'S GAS ATMOSPHERE.

I *UNDERSTAND*, GENERAL. AND SINCE WAITING WON'T MAKE IT ANY *EASIER*... I'M READY TO GO *NOW*.

LUKE CLIMBS INTO THE ONE-TIME IMPERIAL CRAFT AND IS TOWED OUTSIDE. MOMENTS LATER, HE ROARS INTO THE NIGHT SKY ABOVE THE FOURTH MOON...

...RACING TOWARD WHATEVER *DESTINY* WAITS ON THE FAR SIDE OF YAVIN.

MAY THE *FORCE* BE WITH YOU, BOY,... *NOW* MORE THAN *EVER!*

WITHIN THE ANCIENT RUINS, ANOTHER SILENTLY *THINKS* WHAT GENERAL DODONNA HAS PUT INTO WORDS.

SHE HAS NOT *TRUSTED* HERSELF TO WATCH THE ACTUAL LAUNCH.

WHAT KIND OF *EXAMPLE* WOULD SHE BE IF A PRINCESS, SENATOR, LEADER AND SYMBOL OF THE REBEL ALLIANCE...

...SHOWED THAT SHE *CRIES?*

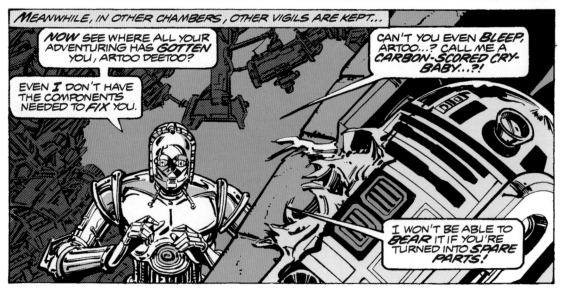

MEANWHILE, IN OTHER CHAMBERS, OTHER VIGILS ARE KEPT...

NOW SEE WHERE ALL YOUR ADVENTURING HAS *GOTTEN* YOU, ARTOO DEETOO?

EVEN *I* DON'T HAVE THE COMPONENTS NEEDED TO *FIX* YOU.

CAN'T YOU EVEN *BLEEP,* ARTOO...? CALL ME A *CARBON-SCORED CRY-BABY...?!*

I WON'T BE ABLE TO *BEAR* IT IF YOU'RE TURNED INTO *SPARE PARTS!*

SUCH IS THE MOOD AT THE *BASE*. ON THE MISSION...

THIS IS *IT*...! THE AREA WHERE LEIA AND I CAUGHT UP WITH THAT HOUSE OF TAGGE *MINING EXPLORER*--

--GENERAL DODONNA SENT A FLIGHT IN *PURSUIT* OF IT WHILE I WAS OUT AFTER THE SIGNAL DEVICE--

--BUT THE TAGGE SHIP HAD APPARENTLY ALREADY *FLED* THE AREA.

NO DOUBT IT'LL BE *BACK* WITH ANOTHER LOAD OF *TIE FIGHTERS!*

IT'S UP TO *ME* TO MAKE CERTAIN THAT WHEN THAT *HAPPENS*--

--THE *BASE* WHICH USES THEM IS *GONE!*

LUKE'S HAND FLICKS A SWITCH ON A CONTROL PANEL MODULE RECENTLY *ADDED* TO THE SALVAGED FIGHTER...

ACCORDING TO OUR *TECHNOS*... THIS SENDS OUT A *SIGNAL* AT HIGHER, MORE POWERFUL FREQUENCIES THAN ANYTHING *WE'VE* GOT.

SO IF IT *WORKS*--

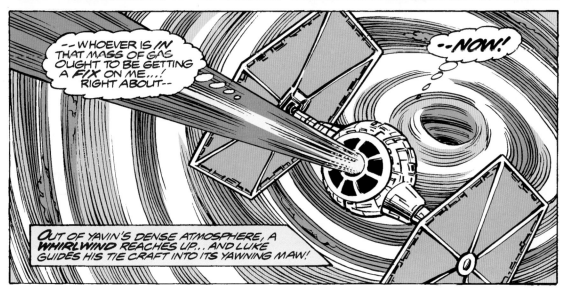

--WHOEVER IS *IN* THAT MASS OF GAS OUGHT TO BE GETTING A *FIX* ON ME...! RIGHT ABOUT--

--*NOW!*

OUT OF YAVIN'S DENSE ATMOSPHERE, A *WHIRLWIND* REACHES UP... AND LUKE GUIDES HIS TIE CRAFT INTO ITS YAWNING MAW!

DOWN AND **DOWN** HE PLUNGES, RIDING THE STORM CORRIDOR TOWARD THE UNKNOWN, UNTIL SUDDENLY, AWESOMELY... HIS **TARGET** LOOMS IN SIGHT!

AND *ABOARD* THE MINING EXPLORER...

BARON TAGGE! THE TURBINE STATION REPORTS A LONE *TIE FIGHTER* IS APPROACHING!

IT MUST BE ONE OF OUR *COOKOUT SHIPS!* WHEN THEY FAILED TO *RETURN* EARLIER--

--I FELT *CERTAIN* THE REBELS WERE *ON* TO US!

I-I... STILL WONDER IF WE SHOULD HAVE RETREATED DOWN INTO THIS *MURK*, SIR. IF ANYTHING EVER HAPPENED TO THE *STATION*--

MY STATION IS A *SUCCESS*, SHANKS, WE ARE SAFER HIDING FROM THE REBELS *HERE*--

--THAN DESPERATELY RACING TO MAKE SAFE *WARPING DISTANCE* WITH ALLIANCE FIGHTERS IN HOT *PURSUIT!*

WE'LL GO *OUT* WITH THE NEXT FLIGHT OFF TO RAID THE REBEL *STRONGHOLD.*

AND IT WON'T TAKE MANY *MORE* SUCH RAIDS BEFORE THAT STRONGHOLD *CRUMBLES!*

THEN, SHANKS, THE HOUSE OF *TAGGE* SHALL HOLD THE EMPEROR'S FAVOR INSTEAD OF THAT BLASTED *WIZARD*, DARTH VADER!

I'LL HAVE SWEET *VENGEANCE* ON THE DARK LORD WHO CURSED ME TO A *LIFETIME* OF CYBER-VISION AND--

BARON! WH-WHAT--?!

WHMMM!

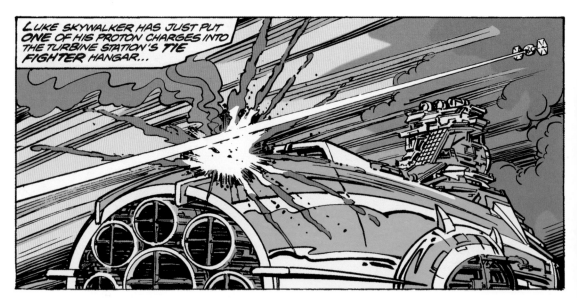

LUKE SKYWALKER HAS JUST PUT *ONE* OF HIS PROTON CHARGES INTO THE TURBINE STATION'S *TIE FIGHTER* HANGAR...

...AND KICKING THE SMALL CRAFT INTO AN ENGINE-STRAINING *FULL REVERSE*...

...HE SWIFTLY UNLEASHES HIS *SECOND CHARGE!*

THIS STATION DOESN'T HAVE THE ARMAMENT OF EVEN ONE *TRENCH* ON THE DEATH STAR... BUT IN THIS *SOUP,* IT DOESN'T NEED IT!

TRACKING INSTRUMENTS ARE *USELESS!* IF I LOSE *VISUAL CONTACT* WITH THE TARGET--

-- THERE'S ALMOST NO CHANCE OF *FINDING* IT AGAIN!

SO WHILE I'VE GOT THE TURBINE ENGINE IN *SIGHT*... I'M GIVING IT *ALL* I'VE GOT!

As General Dodonna said, the TIE carries enough proton charges to destroy a *city*. Baron Tagge's creation may be *bigger* than that...

...but it is, in its way, *more* vulnerable. Engines, reactors, weapon stores are in a more *concentrated* area, and once *some* start to blow...

...they *all* swiftly follow.

And *now*, Luke Skywalker's problems *truly* begin.

Within *instants*, the explosive flare that marked the successful accomplishment of his mission *fades*...

...and he is *alone*.

Alone. Fighting to trim and keep together a ship refitted in haste, pushed beyond capability in desperation.

Alone. Lost without instruments amid swirling, colliding gases that *are* the planet Yavin.

Alone. No way to mark up or down, the path of salvation... or destruction.

111

YOU KNEW IT WOULD BE THIS WAY WHEN YOU *VOLUNTEERED,* SKYWALKER--

IT'S ONE OF THE *REASONS* YOU VOLUNTEERED.

VERTIGO SWEEPS LUKE'S BODY. DISORIENTATION. HE LETS INSTINCT GUIDE HIM. THE SHIP SEEMS TO DIVE.

THANKS TO MY FATHER, TO BEN KENOBI... I HAVE A SPECIAL *GIFT.* NO ONE SHOULD HAVE TO *DIE* ON A MISSION LIKE THIS--

--WHEN I'VE GOT IT TO *USE.* ONLY... I HAVEN'T *MASTERED* IT.

WITHOUT A FIX ON UP OR DOWN, THE TIE SHIP COULD BE DOING ANYTHING...

I NEEDED BEN'S *VOICE* TO GUIDE ME ON THE DEATH STAR... I USED IT ALMOST *ACCIDENTALLY* AGAINST DARTH VADER ESCAPING THE WHEEL...

THE MIND DECEIVES THE BODY UNDER THESE CONDITIONS, PLAYS CRUEL TRICKS...

BUT I'VE BEEN *MEDITATING...* EXPANDING MY *FEELING.* I'VE USED THE ABILITY IN *SMALLER* TESTS... BUT THIS IS THE FIRST TIME I'VE CONSCIOUSLY *PLANNED* TO USE IT!

PULL *OUT,* YOU FOOL, EVERY CONSCIOUS THOUGHT SCREAMS. *PULL OUT OR DIE* IN THE HARD FROZEN *CENTER* OF YAVIN!

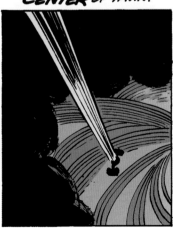

I *TRUST* IN WHAT BEN TAUGHT ME. I *BELIEVE* IN THE FORCE. AND *MORE*--

--I BELIEVE IN *MYSELF!*

AND LUKE'S *REWARD* FOR HIS FAITH IS THE STARRY SAFETY OF DEEP SPACE...

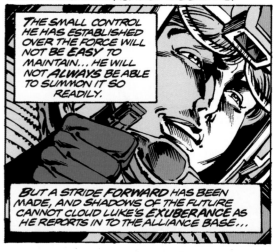

...AND THE KNOWLEDGE THAT HE IS *ALIVE,* ABLE TO USE THIS GROWING ABILITY *ANOTHER* DAY IN THE BATTLE AGAINST THE EMPIRE.

THE SMALL CONTROL HE HAS ESTABLISHED OVER THE FORCE WILL NOT BE *EASY* TO MAINTAIN... HE WILL NOT *ALWAYS* BE ABLE TO SUMMON IT SO READILY.

BUT A STRIDE *FORWARD* HAS BEEN MADE, AND SHADOWS OF THE FUTURE CANNOT CLOUD LUKE'S *EXUBERANCE* AS HE REPORTS IN TO THE ALLIANCE BASE...

A REPORT THAT IS *INTERCEPTED...* BY A SHIP THAT *SHOULDN'T* EXIST!

THE YOUNG REBEL HAS NO NOTION THAT WE *FOLLOWED* HIM OUT--

--YOU GAVE THE ORDER TO *CAST OFF* FROM THE TURBINE STATION JUST IN *TIME,* BARON TAGGE!

IRONIC... THIS SKYWALKER ACTUALLY *SAVED* US!

PARTICULARLY SO SINCE WE ONLY KEPT HIM IN *SIGHT* FOR THE SATISFACTION OF *DESTROYING* HIM BEFORE WE PERISHED IN THOSE GASES *OURSELVES!* BUT, *MIRACULOUSLY--*

HE DID THE *IMPOSSIBLE,* SHANKS! AND *RUINED* MY CHANCES OF SHOWING UP DARTH VADER IN THE PROCESS!

SOMEDAY, I'LL *LEARN* HIS SECRET. THEN DO TO *LUKE SKYWALKER--*

--WORSE THAN THE SITH LORD DID TO ME!

NEXT ISSUE: THE ATTEMPT TO RESTORE ARTOO DEETOO MAY BE DOOMED BY... THE *RETURN* OF THE *HUNTER!*

40¢ 27 SEPT 02817 CC

APPROVED BY THE COMICS CODE AUTHORITY

ADVENTURES *BEYOND* THE GREATEST SPACE-FANTASY FILM OF ALL!

STAR WARS ™

LUKE AND THREEPIO STALKED BY THE SINISTER CYBORG!

RETURN OF THE HUNTER!

Long ago in a galaxy far, far away. . .there exists a state of cosmic *civil war*. A brave alliance of *underground freedom fighters* has challenged the tyranny and oppression of the awesome *Galactic Empire*. This is their story!

LucasFilm PRESENTS: **STAR WARS**™ **THE GREATEST SPACE FANTASY OF ALL!**

CONTINUING THE SAGA BEGUN IN THE FILM *BY GEORGE LUCAS* RELEASED BY *TWENTIETH CENTURY-FOX*

ARCHIE GOODWIN, **CARMINE INFANTINO** **BOB WIACEK** J. COSTANZA, P. GOLDBERG, J. SHOOTER
WRITER/EDITOR   ARTISTS   *letters*   *colors*   *Ed.-in-chief*

RETURN OF THE HUNTER

*IN MOST OUTWORLD CANTINAS, SUDDEN **DEATH** IS NO GREAT NOVELTY. STILL, EVEN IN **THESE** ENVIRONS, WHEN DEALT WITH ENOUGH SWIFTNESS AND SAVAGERY...*

...SHOCK AND FRIGHT QUICKLY FOLLOW!

HE'S *MARKO TYNE.* *WANTED* IN NINE SYSTEMS FOR UNLICENSED SLAVING.

I'M *CLAIMING* HIM.

SINCE NO ONE'S TRIED TO SHOOT ME IN THE *BACK...* I TAKE IT HE DOESN'T HAVE ANY *FRIENDS* HERE.

IN WHICH CASE, *TWO* OF YOU WON'T MIND VOLUNTEERING TO CARRY HIS *BODY* FOR ME.

THAT'S *DROID* WORK, BOUNTY HUNTER. SO GO GET A--

YOU TAKE THE *HEAVY* END.

THE MAN *NEXT* TO YOU CAN GRAB THE *FEET.*

FIVE *WEEKS* HE'S BEEN AROUND..., AND AT LEAST *ONCE* A WEEK, HE DOES *THIS!*

IT'S BAD FOR *BUSINESS.*

IT WAS *WORSE* FOR MARKO TYNE! THAT BOUNTY HUNTER LOOKS HALF *CRAZY--*

--WHO *IS* HE?

HIS NAME IS *VALANCE*. ONCE HE WAS A SOLDIER OF PROMISE SERVING THE *EMPIRE*. THAT SERVICE WAS *ENDED* BY A REBEL AERIAL TORPEDO. * YET THANKS TO ADVANCED MEDICAL TECHNIQUES, HE *SURVIVES*... AND CURSES THE FACT THAT HE *DOES*. FOR VALANCE HAS BECOME SOMETHING *LESS* THAN HE WAS...

...AND SOMETHING FAR *MORE*!

SKINKER! IT'S PAYDAY!

* AS TOLD IN *STAR WARS* #16. --ARCHIE.

COLLECTED ANOTHER *REWARD*, DID YA? YOU'RE RIGHT *GOOD* AT YOUR WORK, VALANCE.

CAN'T RECALL ANY *OTHER* BOUNTY MAN EVEN *SURVIVIN'* THIS LONG ON JUNCTION.

NO SMALL TALK. YOU HAVE *DROIDS* FOR ME?

RIGHT *HERE*. SCAVENGER SHIPS HAD *SLIM PICKIN'S* THIS WEEK. NO *R-2* OR *3PO* MODELS... THIS IS THE *LOT*.

EXCUSE--MY *CONDITION*, SIR-- HOW MAY I *SERVE* YOU--?

VEEDOW! PA-KOOWW!

BY SAYING *GOOD-BYE*... JUNK!

SURE A *WASTE* OF GOOD CIRCUITRY! BUT LONG AS YOU'RE PAYIN' THE GOIN' RATE FOR *REBUILT DROIDS*--

-- I GOT NO *COMPLAINTS.* SAVES ME ALL THAT *TIME* TINKERIN' AROUND, TRYIN' TO FIX 'EM UP.

I'M PAYING YOU FOR *MORE* THAN THE MACHINES, SKINKER.

'COURSE YA ARE! AN' I GOT MY *EYE* OUT... YOU'RE AFTER A *REBEL LAD* WHO MOVES AROUND WITH A *3PO* AND *R-2* UNIT IN TOW.

MUST BE *SOME* REWARD ON 'IM!

ENOUGH. BUT EVEN IF THERE *WEREN'T*--

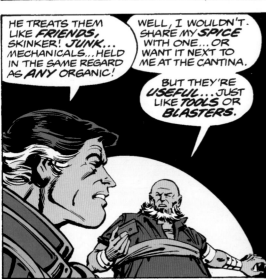

HE TREATS THEM LIKE *FRIENDS,* SKINKER! *JUNK*... MECHANICALS...HELD IN THE SAME REGARD AS *ANY* ORGANIC!

WELL, I WOULDN'T. SHARE *MY* SPICE WITH ONE... OR WANT IT NEXT TO ME AT THE CANTINA.

BUT THEY'RE *USEFUL*...JUST LIKE *TOOLS* OR *BLASTERS.*

LONG AS THEY KEEP THEIR *PLACE*... I CAN'T SEE *HATING* 'EM, NOT LIKE *YOU* DO, VALANCE. THAT'S--

SOMETHING YOU'LL *NEVER* UNDER- STAND, OLD MAN--

NOT IF YOU WANT TO GO ON *LIVING!*

THE MAN CALLED VALANCE HAS A SECRET. A TERRIBLE SECRET FOR ONE WITH HIS BELIEFS.

I'M *CLOSE.* I FEEL IT... *HUNTER'S* INSTINCT.

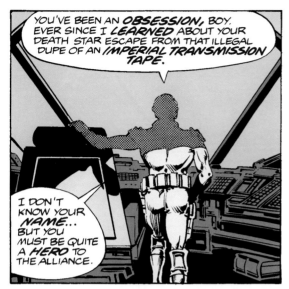

YOU'VE BEEN AN *OBSESSION,* BOY. EVER SINCE I *LEARNED* ABOUT YOUR DEATH STAR ESCAPE FROM THAT ILLEGAL DUPE OF AN *IMPERIAL TRANSMISSION TAPE.*

I DON'T KNOW YOUR *NAME...* BUT YOU MUST BE QUITE A *HERO* TO THE ALLIANCE.

I'VE WASTED A LOT OF TIME ROAMING THE GALAXY IN *SEARCH* OF YOU. STILL... I GAINED SOME IDEA OF REBEL *SUPPLY* METHODS.

AND WITH THIS NEW *IMPERIAL BLOCKADE* PUTTING ON PRESSURE* ...THE ODDS ARE *PERFECT* FOR A HOTSHOT LIKE YOU SHOWING UP *HERE.*

*IT BEGAN IN *SW#25.* --ARCH.

AND *THAT'S* WHEN I'LL *DESTROY* YOU, DROID-LOVER!

THIS THEN IS THE HUNTER'S *SECRET...* HIS TORMENT AND HIS SHAME.

THE PRICE OF *SURVIVING* THE AERIAL TORPEDO EXPLOSION WAS THAT *HALF* HIS BODY BE REPLACED BY *CYBERNETIC PARTS.* VALANCE, THE MAN WHO *HATES* ROBOTS.... IS A *CYBORG.*

DEEP SPACE! A LONE VESSEL PLIES ITS WAY THROUGH THE SELDOM-TRAVELLED STAR SECTOR KNOWN AS THE GORDIAN REACH...

MASTER LUKE, THIS DROPPING IN AND OUT OF *WARP* IS PLAYING *HAVOC* WITH MY INTERIOR DIRECTIONAL COMPENSATORS!

PART OF OUR *MISSION* IS TO PROBE THE *EXTENT* OF THE EMPIRE'S BLOCKADE, THREEPIO.

I FEAR YOU CAN DEFINITELY INCLUDE *THIS* SYSTEM, SIR! BECAUSE ACCORDING TO OUR *SCANNERS--*

-- THE IMPERIAL PRESENCE IS *WELL* REPRESENTED HERE!

A *BATTLE CRUISER...* USING THAT PLANETOID AS COVER!

THAT'S WHY OUR INSTRUMENTS DIDN'T PICK THEM UP *SOONER*--

DOES THIS MEAN WE'RE *DOOMED,* SIR?

NOT IF THIS LITTLE BABY *MANEUVERS* AS WELL AS THE ALLIANCE TECHNOS BACK ON YAVIN *PROMISED* IT WOULD!

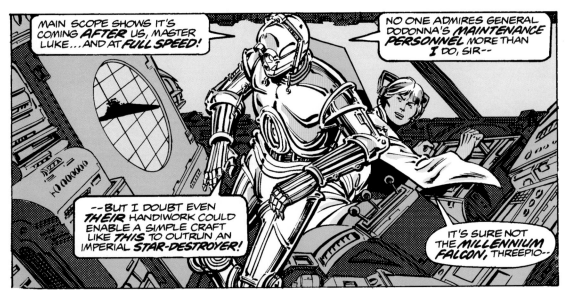

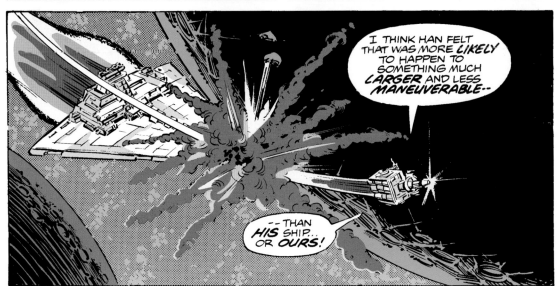

THAT SHOULD SLOW 'EM DOWN ENOUGH FOR US TO MAKE THE JUMP INTO HYPER-SPACE!

GET THE NAVIGATIONAL COMPUTER PERKING, THREEPIO--

-- WE'RE GOING INTO PHASE TWO OF OUR MISSION!

AND WITH SWIFTNESS AND EFFICIENCY, COORDINATES ARE SOON CALCULATED WHICH WILL BRING THE TRAVELERS TO A WORLD CALLED...

...JUNCTION! THERE ARE MANY PLANETS OF A SIMILAR NATURE SCATTERED ACROSS THE ENDLESS SPECTRUM OF THE OUTWORLDS.

ESSENTIALLY, THEY ARE TRADING POSTS... GATHERING PLACES AND WATERING HOLES FOR THOSE THAT ROAM BEYOND THE CIVILIZED SYSTEMS.

ANYONE SEEKING SUPPLIES, PARTICULARLY THOSE WHO FIND IMPERIAL REGULATION DISTASTEFUL...

... MUST SOONER OR LATER COME TO SUCH A PLANET.

WILL YOU LOOK AT THIS PLACE, THREEPIO? IT'S EVEN BIGGER THAN MOS EISLEY!

AND I BET YOU COULD STICK ALL OF ANCHOR-HEAD INTO THE GROUND FLOOR OF SOME OF THESE BUILDINGS!

THIS'LL BE THE FIRST REAL CITY I'VE HAD A CHANCE TO SEE. THAT TIME WE STOPPED ON CENTARES...* WE WERE TOO BUSY FLEEING DARTH VADER TO PLAY TOURIST!

FRANKLY, MASTER LUKE, IT APPEARS WILD, DIRTY, AND DANGEROUS TO ME--

*STAR WARS #25.--ARCHIE.

--ONLY THE PROSPECT OF GETTING THE *PARTS* WE NEED TO REPAIR *ARTOO DEETOO** WOULD MAKE ME COME HERE *VOLUNTARILY!*

THOUGH I HOPE YOU NEVER *TELL* THE LITTLE FELLOW THAT, SIR,... HE'S QUITE *SELF-CENTERED* AS IT IS!

YOUR SECRET'S *SAFE,* THREEPIO. AND DON'T *WORRY...* I'M NOT SO IMPRESSED WITH JUNCTION THAT I'LL FORGET TO TAKE CARE OF *BUSINESS!*

* FROM INJURIES SUSTAINED IN *ISSUE 26.*--ARCH AGAIN.

AS A MATTER OF *FACT,* THERE'S JUST WHAT WE'RE *LOOKING* FOR,... A *SALVAGE YARD!*

SHOULD WE JUST SETTLE FOR THE *FIRST* ONE, MASTER LUKE,...OR SHOP AROUND?

SINCE THE BLOCKADE, THE ALLIANCE NEEDS ALL *KINDS* OF SUPPLIES, THREEPIO. I'LL SPREAD OUR TRADE AMONG *DIFFERENT* SPOTS TO AVOID UNDUE *CURIOSITY*--

--BUT WE'VE GOT TO START *SOME-WHERE.* WHY *NOT* HERE?

WELL, WELL,...!

POLYP! GO GET *VALANCE!* TELL 'IM OL' SKINKER HAS COME ACROSS A LIKELY LOOKIN' *PROSPECT--*

VERY LIKELY!

THIS IS *SILLY*--

AND IT'S *WRONG,* GENERAL *DODONNA!* I SPENT TOO MANY YEARS AS AN ACTIVE *SENATOR*--

--TO GO THROUGH THE REST OF THE REBELLION *WAITING* WHILE EVERYONE *ELSE* RUNS AROUND BEING *BRAVE!*

BUT, YOUR *HIGHNESS*--

--WE'VE HAD THIS ARGUMENT *BEFORE.* YOU'RE MUCH TOO IMPORTANT A *SYMBOL* OF THE REVOLUTION TO--

THEN I SHOULD BE *SEEN*... AND IN *ACTION!* OTHERWISE I'M NO BETTER THAN THE *EMPEROR*...SKULKING IN HIS PALACE!

I WENT AGAINST YOUR THINKING ONCE *BEFORE,* GENERAL,* BUT FOR THE WRONG REASON... *PERSONAL* CONCERN OVER LUKE SKYWALKER.

I REALIZE NOW A *LEADER* CAN'T AFFORD TO *GIVE IN* TO SUCH FEELINGS--

YOU SHOULD REALIZE THE *SAME THING!*

* WAY BACK IN *STAR WARS* #9.--ANCIENT ARCHIE.

YOU'RE TRYING TO PROTECT *ME* THE WAY I'VE TRIED TO PROTECT *LUKE.* I *APPRE-CIATE* IT, BUT WE BOTH DESERVE *BETTER* THAN THAT--

--AND SO DOES THE *ALLIANCE!*

NOW LET'S GO INSIDE... THIS NIGHT AIR MAKES ME *TALK* TOO MUCH.

AND IF THAT TALK SHOULD DWELL TOO MUCH ON LUKE SKYWALKER AND HIS *MISSION*, OR THE UNKNOWN FATE OF *HAN SOLO*, SOME OF THIS RESOLVE NOT TO GIVE IN TO PERSONAL CONCERN MIGHT *SLIP*...

... HE SLIPS INTO A HUMBLE-SEEMING ROOM THAT BOASTS A CONCEALED LONG-RANGE *TRANSMITTER* AMONG ITS FURNISHINGS. BUT...

YOU CAN'T REPORT TO *DARTH VADER*, SPY... NOT ON *THAT* SET. I *FUSED* THE CIRCUITRY WHILE I WAS *WAITING* FOR YOU.

...SO LEIA ORGANA RETREATS INTO THE MASSASI RUINS. EVEN AS ON *JUNCTION*...

...A DARK *FIGURE* RETREATS DOWN A TWISTING ALLEYWAY.

UNTIL, CERTAIN HE HAS NOT BEEN *FOLLOWED*...

SPOTTED YOU SLIPPING AWAY FROM *SKINKER'S* AS I *APPROACHED* HIS PLACE.

MY FIRST WEEK IN A NEW PORT, I MAKE IT A HABIT TO LEARN *ALL* ABOUT SPIES-- IMPERIAL, REBEL, OR OTHERWISE. KNOWING YOUR *HIDEAWAY*--

--IT WAS NO PROBLEM *BEATING* YOU HERE.

GO DOWN FIGHTING... *SMART*.

AN EASIER DEATH THAN YOUR SITH LORD *MASTER* WOULD PERMIT--

--WHEN HE LEARNED *I'VE* FOUND THE BOY WITH THE DROIDS *AHEAD* OF HIM!

VA-KOW!

AND...

WHAT A *RELIEF*, MASTER LUKE...! FINALLY WE HAVE *ALL* THE COMPONENTS NEEDED TO *MEND* ARTOO DEETOO.

EXCEPT THIS *SKINKER* CHARACTER IS SURE TAKING HIS TIME *PACKING* THEM--

DOUBLE *BLAST* YA, POLYP! WHERE'S *VALANCE?* YA *SAID* YOU DELIVERED THE *MESSAGE!*

THE LAD SEEMS MORE *FARMER* THAN REBEL.... BUT EVEN *HE* COULD GET SUSPICIOUS.

STARTING RIGHT *NOW*, SCRAP-RUNNER!

EASY, YOUNG FELLA...! I DON'T THINK YA QUITE *UNDERSTAND* THE SITUATION--

TRY ME. I'M OPEN-MINDED... FOR A *FARMER*.

HE'S IN *MY* PAY, DROID-LOVER! NOW STEP *BACK*... BEFORE KILLING *YOU*, I MEAN TO MELT YOUR PET *JUNK* INTO SLAG!

M-MASTER LUKE! HE'S LOWERED THE GATE AND *LOCKED* IT! WE'RE--

INSIDE, THREEPIO--

--FAST!

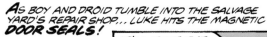

AS BOY AND DROID TUMBLE INTO THE SALVAGE YARD'S REPAIR SHOP... LUKE HITS THE MAGNETIC *DOOR SEALS!*

IT'LL TAKE THE MADMAN A *FEW* MINUTES TO BURN THROUGH WITH HIS BLASTER--

SHOW US THE *OTHER* WAY OUT, SKINKER!

DON'T SAY THERE *ISN'T*... I KNOW YOUR MESSENGER NEVER CAME PAST *US.*

H-HERE, BOY...! BUT YA CAN'T ESCAPE *VALANCE.* ONCE THAT BOUNTY HUNTER HAS YOUR *SCENT,* HE--

SO FAR THAT'S *ALL* HE'S GOT! THREEPIO, TAKE THOSE COMPONENT PACKS WE NEED AND HEAD FOR THE *SHIP*--

I'LL FOLLOW AFTER *SLOWING* MR. VALANCE DOW--

KA-BWOM!

I'VE *MORE* THAN *BLASTERS* AT MY COMMAND, REBEL--

AFTER WEEKS OF *WAITING...* I'M SORRY TO HAVE IT *OVER* SO QUICKLY.

--AS YOU AND THE OTHERS HAVE NOW *LEARNED* ...JUST A BIT *TOO LATE!*

STILL... THERE'S THE FAITHFUL *ROBOT!* SNEAKING AWAY DOWN POLYP'S *SCURRY-HOLE*... CAN'T HAVE *THAT.*

GUESS *AGAIN,* BOUNTY KILLER!

NOW STAY *PUT!* YOU'RE NOT THE *ONLY* ONE WHO USES MORE THAN A *BLASTER!*

A *LIGHT SABER*...! IN *THIS* DAY AND AGE... I DON'T BELIEVE IT!

MAYBE *THIS* WILL MAKE IT *EASIER!*

WOOMP

SSSSSST!

ZZAK!

NO! IT MERELY *FORCES* ME TO USE... *THIS!*

YOU TELL *ME,* BOY... WHICH IS *BETTER?*

VALANCE, *WHATEVER* YOU'VE GOT UP YOUR SLEEVE CAN'T EXPEND *THAT* MUCH FORCE--

--WITHOUT RUNNING OUT OF *POWER* SOON.

INTERESTING *THEORY,* DROID-LOVER! BUT ONCE OR TWICE *MORE* IS ALL I NE--

FRAK!

MY *BLAST*--! W-WHAT--?!

MOVING INSTINCTIVELY, WITHOUT CONSCIOUSLY THINKING--AS BEN KENOBI *TAUGHT*--LUKE HAS *BLOCKED* THE BLAST. BLOCKED IT, AND FURTHER...

...TURNED IT *BACK!*

N-NO! AAAAGH!

IT'S POWER IS GREATLY *DIMINISHED,* AND YET...

...NOT WITHOUT *EFFECT.*

VALANCE...! YOU... YOU'RE... A *BORG!*

IT *SHOCKS* YOU! EVEN THE REBEL WHO CALLS *ROBOTS* HIS FRIENDS--

I KNEW IT... I *KNEW* IT...! THE WHOLE TIME I WAS *SEARCHING* FOR YOU...!

THERE'LL BE NO *REWARD* FOR YOU, BOY...! NOT FROM THE *EMPIRE,* NOT SINCE I KILLED DARTH VADER'S IMPERIAL *SPY* HERE...!

BUT IT'S STILL *WORTH* IT--

--TO REMOVE A DROID-LOVING *HYPOCRITE* FROM THE GALAXY!

HROK!

LUKE BARELY HAS TIME TO DRAW BACK... TO MAKE A GLANCING BLOW OF ONE INTENDED TO KILL!

EVEN SO, HE IS SLAMMED VIOLENTLY, PAIN-FULLY INTO THE HARD GROUND OUTSIDE THE RUINED SHOP...

...OUT OF *REACH* OF HIS LIGHT SABER.

NOW IT'S *TOO LATE.* I'VE POWER ENOUGH FOR ONE LAST *SHOT...* YOU'VE GOT *NOTHING.*

YOU *HESITATED,* REBEL. YOU COULD HAVE SLICED *ME* EASILY AS YOU TURNED ASIDE THAT *BLAST--*

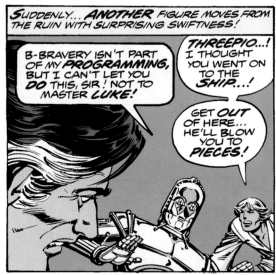

SUDDENLY... ANOTHER FIGURE MOVES FROM THE RUIN WITH SURPRISING SWIFTNESS!

B-BRAVERY ISN'T PART OF MY *PROGRAMMING,* BUT I CAN'T LET YOU *DO* THIS, SIR! NOT TO MASTER *LUKE!*

THREEPIO...! I THOUGHT YOU WENT ON TO THE *SHIP...!*

GET *OUT* OF HERE... HE'LL BLOW YOU TO *PIECES!*

THEN HIS *ADVANTAGE* WILL BE GONE, MASTER LUKE... AND YOU'LL BE RECOVERED ENOUGH TO *FIGHT.*

THIS TIME YOU WON'T HAVE TO HAVE YOUR *COM-PASSION* MISTAKEN FOR *WEAKNESS* BY HESITATING...!

THREEPIO, DO I HAVE TO GIVE YOU A *DIRECT COMMAND...?* GET--

MADNESS! DROIDS AND HUMANS DON'T *BEHAVE* LIKE THIS....!

THEY DON'T *SACRIFICE* THEMSELVES FOR ONE ANOTHER!

PERHAPS NOT IN *YOUR* EXPERIENCE, SIR. CERTAINLY IT'S NOT WIDELY *ACCEPTED.* BUT PERHAPS IF IT *WERE--*

--EVEN BEING A *CYBORG* MIGHT BE EASIER TO BEAR.

ENOUGH, ROBOT, TAKE YOUNG MASTER...MASTER...

SKYWALKER, SIR.

TAKE YOUNG MASTER SKYWALKER... PICK UP HIS LIGHT SABER...

--AND GET THE *TWO* OF YOU FAR, *FAR* FROM MY *SIGHT!*

ZZAKOW!!

HE SOUNDS LIKE A MAN WHO MIGHT CHANGE HIS *MIND* AT ANY MOMENT, MASTER LUKE!

HE SOUNDS LIKE A MAN WHO HASN'T MADE IT *UP* YET, THREEPIO. AND, BEFORE HE *DOES*--

--WE'LL BE ON OUR WAY BACK TO *YAVIN* WITH SUPPLIES FOR THE ALLIANCE AND THE PARTS TO *SAVE* ARTOO-DEETOO.

STILL, *WHATEVER* HIS DECISION... I DON'T THINK WE'VE HEARD THE *LAST* OF MISTER VALANCE!

NEXT ISSUE: A FEW *ANSWERS* CONCERNING *HAN SOLO*, HIS PARTNER, *CHEWBACCA*, AND...

WHAT EVER HAPPENED TO JABBA THE HUT!

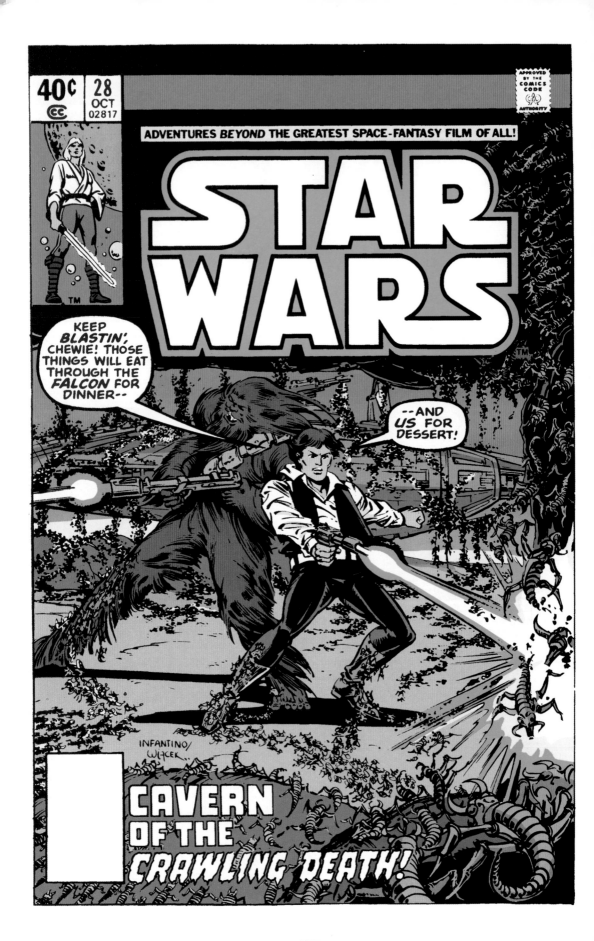

132

WHAT EVER HAPPENED TO JABBA THE HUT?

ANSWER: HE IS ALIVE AND WELL AND TRYING TO KILL *HAN SOLO* ON AN OBSCURE PLANET CALLED *ORLEON*.

I TAKE IT YOU AND YOUR HIRED CLOWNS ARE *REJECTING* OUR LATEST OFFER, JABBA--

134

--HERE'S THE *COMPANY* WE EXPECTED!

FTOM!

BA-ZOOM

HOW MANY DID WE LOSE *THIS* TIME?

ONLY *SKUD*, JABBA. BUT IF YOU'D JUST LET US ATTACK *FULL FORCE* WITH *PROTON GRENADES*, WE COULD--

DESTROY THE *MILLENNIUM FALCON* ALONG WITH HAN SOLO AND CHEWBACCA!

CAN'T ANY OF YOU *THUGS* UNDERSTAND THAT I'M A *BUSINESS MAN*...?

HAN HAS FAILED TO REPAY A VERY *LARGE DEBT* RUN UP WHILE SMUGGLING *SPICE* IN MY SERVICE--*

THAT JUSTIFIES HIS *DEATH*, BUT THERE'S NO *PROFIT* IN DESTROYING THE BEST *SPICE FREIGHTER*--

-- TO EVER MAKE THE *KESSEL RUN!* NOT WHEN TIME-- AND THE *ODDS*-- ARE ON *OUR* SIDE!

* A BIT OF ANCIENT HISTORY FROM *STAR WARS* #2. -- ARCHIVIST ARCHIE.

NUTRIENT PASTE--! FOR A MAN USED TO PRIME SAND LIZARD STEAK AND FIVE YEAR OLD SPICE WINE!

IF WE'RE DOWN TO *THIS* STUFF... OUR SITUATION'S *WORSE* THAN I THOUGHT!

BLAST IT! A FEW MORE ROTATIONS OF THIS *MUD BALL* AND WE'LL BE BEGGING JABBA TO BLAST US SO WE DON'T HAVE TO *STARVE!*

HOW'D I MANAGE TO GET US *INTO* SUCH A *DUMB SPOT...?!*

IT BEGAN WITH AN ESCAPE... FROM THE GREAT GALACTIC GAMBLING CENTER KNOWN AS THE WHEEL, AND FROM THE DARK LORD OF THE SITH, DARTH VADER!

THAT MONSTER'S GOT US DEAD IN ITS *SIGHTS*... BUT IT'S NOT *FIRIN'!* *

I NEVER LOOK A GIFT MIRACLE IN THE *MOUTH*, CHEWIE--

--WE'RE MAKIN' THE JUMP TO *HYPER-SPACE* BEFORE SOMEONE COMES TO THEIR *SENSES!*

* DUE TO LORD VADER SUDDENLY EXPERIENCING *FEEDBACK* OF THE FORCE. SEE *STAR WARS #23* FOR THE FULL STORY. --ARCHIE.

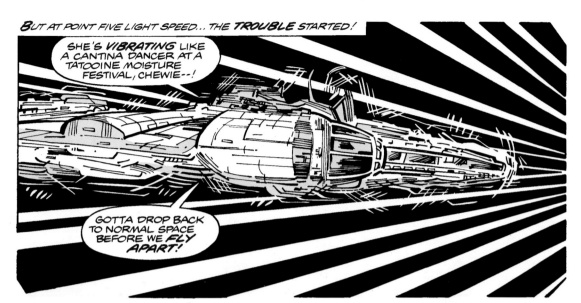

BUT AT POINT FIVE LIGHT SPEED... THE ***TROUBLE*** *STARTED!*

SHE'S ***VIBRATING*** LIKE A CANTINA DANCER AT A TATOOINE MOISTURE FESTIVAL, CHEWIE--!

GOTTA DROP BACK TO NORMAL SPACE BEFORE WE ***FLY APART!***

HRONK!

YEAH, I WAS THINKIN' THE ***SAME*** THING.

WHEN THOSE WHEEL TECHNOS THREW THE FALCON BACK TOGETHER AFTER ***STRIPPING*** AND ***SEARCHING*** IT--*

* SHOWN IN ***SW*** *#19.--ARCH.*

--THEY MUST HAVE LEFT SOMETHING ***OUT!*** BUT NO PROBLEM, BIG BUDDY--

CHECK THE NAVIGATIONAL COMPUTER ***READ OUT--***

--WE'RE NOT ***THAT*** FAR FROM ***ORLEON!***

AND BY A CAREFULLY ORCHESTRATED SERIES OF SHORT HOPS IN AND OUT OF ***WARP,*** *THE AILING SPICE FREIGHTER IS COAXED TO ITS* ***DESTINATION...***

AH! JUST AS MISERABLE AND ***UNINVITING*** AS EVER! ONE OF THE FEW PLACES IN THE MID-SYSTEMS ***NO ONE*** CAN STAND--

-- WHICH MAKES IT THE ***PERFECT PLACE*** FOR A COUPLE OF SHREWD SPICE SMUGGLERS TO HAVE AN ***EMERGENCY STATION,*** EH, CHEWIE?

BUT AS THE FALCON TOUCHED DOWN AND TAXIED INTO THE MOUNTAIN CAVERN THAT WAS THEIR OLD HIDEAWAY...

...NEITHER OF THE 'SHREWD SPICE SMUGGLERS' NOTICED AN ADDITION TO THE EQUIPMENT STORED INSIDE.

UNTIL...

VISITORS ARRIVING ON THE MUD PLAIN, CHEWIE! WHY WOULD ANYBODY--

WARRK!

BLAST IT... YOU'RE RIGHT! THAT'S THE VOIDRAKER... JABBA THE HUT'S PERSONAL FREIGHTER!

WELL, HAN, MY BOY...! THIS MOMENT HAS BEEN DREADFULLY LONG COMING.

I DIDN'T TRULY EXPECT YOU'D DARE VISIT THIS OLD HAUNT... BUT I INSTALLED A BUG TO ALERT ME JUST IN CASE!

SINCE THIS SAVES ME THE PRICE OF THE BOUNTY I'VE POSTED... I'VE ORDERED MY LADS TO GIVE YOU A SWIFT, DIGNIFIED DEATH.

THE CORELLIAN SKIPPER AND HIS MATE COUNTERED WITH A LONG, DESPERATE SIEGE!

YEAH, YEAH! WE'VE HELD OUT LONG ENOUGH TO HAVE THE FALCON BACK IN SOMETHING LIKE FLYING SHAPE.

BUT THE VOIDRAKER'S GUNS CAN NAIL US BEFORE WE EVEN--

CHEWIE--! BACK HERE... FAST!

VORRP!

FTOOM! FTOOM! VOW!

WURGUH!

NO, I HAVEN'T GONE *CAVE HAPPY.*

BUT IT'D BE *BETTER* IF I *WERE* IMAGINING THINGS!

I SPOTTED *THIS* CRAWLING ON THAT *FOOD TIN* I THREW AWAY EARLIER, PAL--

--IT'S A *STONE MITE!* THEY'RE THE *ULTIMATE SCAVENGERS!*

AN OLD TIMER TOLD ME ABOUT 'EM... THEY'RE A *BIOLOGICAL WEAPON* DEVELOPED DURING THE CLONE WARS.

THEIR BODIES MANUFACTURE AN *ACID* THAT ENABLES 'EM TO EAT THROUGH *ANYTHING!*

LOOK WHAT THIS *ONE* DID TO THAT TIN--

--AND THEY USUALLY MOVE IN *SWARMS!* THOUSANDS...MAYBE *MILLIONS*... SPECIALLY CREATED TO DEVOUR A PLANET'S *MINERAL RESOURCES.*

THEY MOSTLY TRAVEL THROUGH *SHEER ROCK*...FEEDING ON ANY VEINS OF *ORE!*

HARRU!!

RIGHT! THAT SCARES *ME,* TOO! IF OUR OLD HIDEOUT HAS SUDDENLY SPRUNG SOME *LEAKS*... IT MIGHT JUST BE *INFESTED* WITH THOSE LITTLE MONSTERS!

GET TO THE *FALCON...!* BEFORE IT BECOMES A *MAIN COURSE...* AND YOU AN' ME THE *DESSERT!*

BUT, AS THE PAIR *NEAR* THEIR SHIP....!

JABBA'S *GOONS* ARE HITTING THE *ENTRANCE* AGAIN--!

PA-VOOM! BA-DOW!

AND THEY'RE NOT *SPARING* THE PROTON GRENADES!

ROORP!

I *SEE* IT, CHEWIE....! THE *FORCE* OF THOSE BLASTS HAS STARTED A *CRACK* IN THE CAVERN CEILING--

IT'S TRAVELING *BACK*... TOWARD THE *FALCON!*

MOVE! BEFORE THE WHOLE *WORKS* COLLAPSES!

MEANWHILE...

LOOKS LIKE WE WERE *RIGHT* TO DISOBEY JABBA AND USE THOSE *GRENADES*. THE CAVE'S STILL STANDING--

--AND CHEWBACCA AND SOLO WOULDN'T LET US GET THIS *CLOSE* UNLESS THEY WERE *DEAD!*

NO! THERE'D BE *SOME* TRACES OF THEIR BODIES.

THEY'VE *RETREATED* BACK INTO THE *CAVERN*--

STAY CLOSE TO THE *WALLS* AND MOVE *IN* ON THEM!

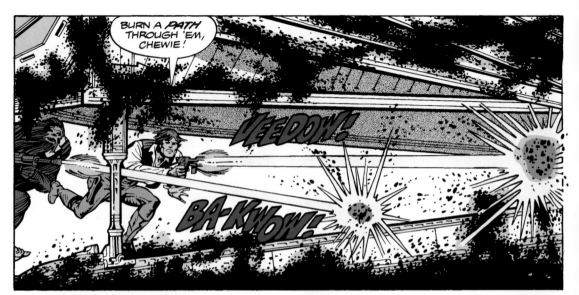

WHILE ON *ORLEON'S* RAIN-LASHED MUD PLAIN ...THE *VOIDRAKER* PREPARES TO DEPART. WHEN...

JABBA, I'M *GETTING* SOMETHING ON THE SCANNER...THE *FALCON'S* ENGINES, I BELIEVE.

THEN SOLO STILL *SURVIVES* WITHIN THAT GREAT STONE RUBBLE--

--THOSE FOOLS ONLY BURIED *THEMSELVES,* NOT HIM AND THE WOOKIEE! WHAT'S *WRONG* WITH THIS GALAXY THAT A SMUGGLING LORD CAN'T BUY COM-PETENT *HELP?!*

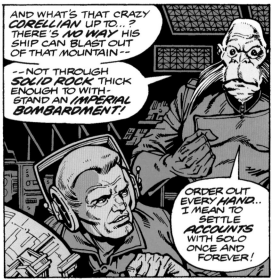

AND WHAT'S THAT CRAZY *CORELLIAN* UP TO...? THERE'S *NO WAY* HIS SHIP CAN BLAST OUT OF THAT MOUNTAIN--

--NOT THROUGH *SOLID ROCK* THICK ENOUGH TO WITH-STAND AN *IMPERIAL BOMBARDMENT!*

ORDER OUT EVERY *HAND...* I MEAN TO SETTLE *ACCOUNTS* WITH SOLO ONCE AND FOREVER!

AND SOON...

MOSTLY *LOOSE ROCK* BLOCKING THE ENTRANCE, JABBA...THE *LASER-BORER* WILL BE THROUGH IT IN SECONDS!

THERE'S SOMETHING ON THE *SCOPE* ALREADY...!

I-IT'S...ONE OF *OURS....!* BUT *WHAT...?*

STONE MITES! BACK TO THE SHIP... BACK!

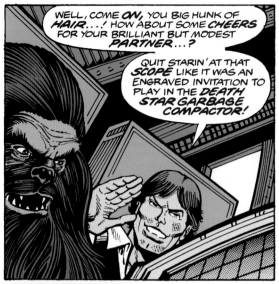

FIRE 'ER *UP* AGAIN, CHEWIE...! ONLY *THIS* TIME WE WON'T USE THE *DE-ICING* SYSTEM.

AND IN THE *SHATTERING* EXPLOSION OF FLYING *STONE...* THE *MILLENNIUM FALCON* BURSTS *FREE* OF ITS SEEMINGLY *INES-CAPABLE* MOUNTAIN PRISON!

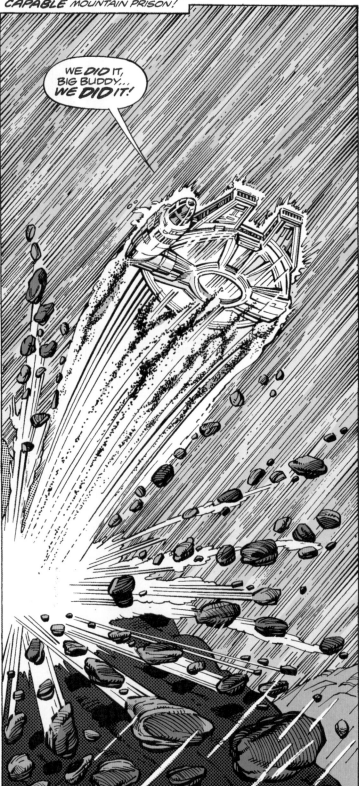

WE *DID* IT, BIG BUDDY... WE *DID* IT!

OKAY! I'M AT THE MAIN GUNS, PAL. WHEN I START *SHOOTING*--

ARRK!

--*TAKE OFF!*

PTOM! PTOM! BVOM!

147

RIGHT, JABBA. CHEWIE AN' ME DON'T *BELIEVE* IN GETTING EVEN--

ROART!

-- WE LIKE TO COME OUT *AHEAD!*

SO ALONG *WITH* THE GENEROUS OFFER YOU NO DOUBT PLAN TO MAKE CANCELING MY *DEBT* AND THE *PRICE* ON OUR HEADS--

--I'M SURE YOU'LL INCLUDE A *BONUS* FOR OUR *TIME* AND *TROUBLE.* YOU KNOW...LIKE OPENING *AIRLOCKS* AN' THE LIKE.

BUT NO NEED TO *RUSH,* JABBA...YOU MUST HAVE AT *LEAST* TWO HOURS BREATHING TIME IN THAT ARMOR.

UNLESS A FEW *STONE MITES* GOT TO IT BEFORE YOU ABANDONED SHIP!

JABBA THE HUT STARTS TO *CURSE...* THEN SHRUGS AND RELUC-TANTLY *SMILES.*

MENTALLY HE CALCULATES A LIKELY *OFFER,* AUTOMATICALLY CUTS IT IN *HALF,* ELECTS TO WAIT AN HOUR TO MAKE IT LOOK *GOOD...*

...AND BEGINS PLANNING FOR *ANOTHER* DAY, WHEN *HE'LL* HAVE THE UPPER-HAND.

BUT MEANTIME, *DARTH VADER* IS ALSO PLANNING, AS WILL BE SHOWN *NEXT ISSUE* IN...

DARK ENCOUNTER

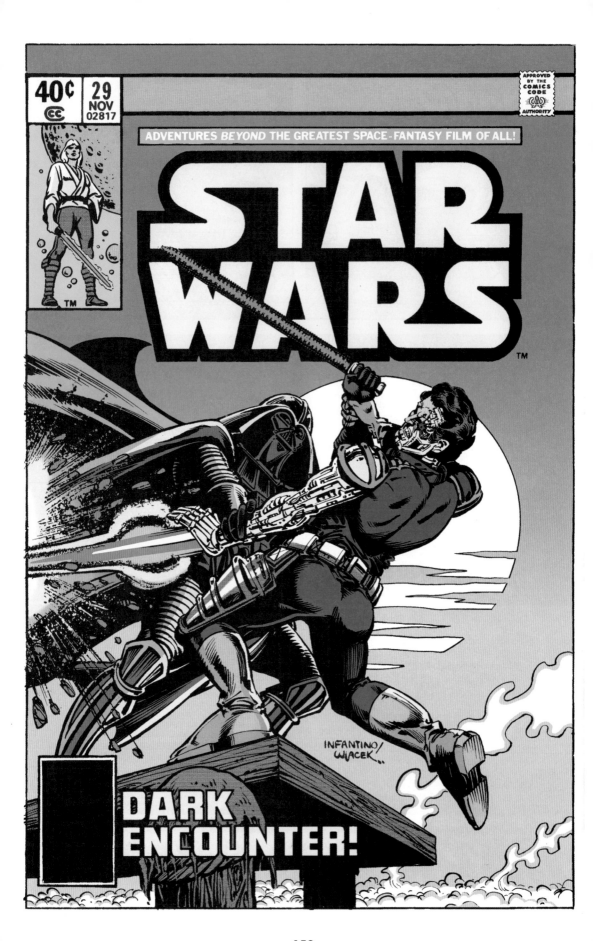

Long ago in a galaxy far, far away. . .there exists a state of cosmic *civil war*. A brave alliance of *underground freedom fighters* has challenged the tyranny and oppression of the awesome *Galactic Empire*. This is their story!

LucasFilm PRESENTS: **STAR WARS** ™ **THE GREATEST SPACE FANTASY OF ALL!**

CONTINUING THE SAGA BEGUN IN THE FILM BY *GEORGE LUCAS* RELEASED BY *TWENTIETH CENTURY-FOX*

ARCHIE GOODWIN WRITER/EDITOR * *CARMINE INFANTINO* & *BOB WIACEK* ARTISTS * *JOHN COSTANZA* LETTERER * *GLYNIS WEIN* COLORIST * *JIM SHOOTER* CONSULTING ED.

DARK ENCOUNTER

YES, I WOULD HAVE THAT *SEEN* TO, WERMIS. MOST PEOPLE GET INDIGESTION *AFTER* A MEAL... NOT *BEFORE*.

JUST BE CERTAIN WE CAN MOVE WITHOUT *DELAY* THE INSTANT I HAVE WHAT I SEEK.

THE *NAME,* REBEL. START WITH THE *NAME...*

TYLER LUCIAN...?

THIS IS ONE CANTINA IN A FAIR-SIZE CITY IN A WHOPPING BIG *GALAXY,* STRANGER. WHAT MAKES YOU THINK ANYONE *HERE* WOULD KNOW YOUR MAN?

ZA-DAAP!

BWOW!

NOW, MERL, YOU WERE ABOUT TO *TELL* ME SOMETHING.

WEREN'T YOU?

YOU... YOU'RE NOTHING *SENTIENT...!* YOU...*CAN'T...* BE...*EEEEEEEEE!*

Swiftly, the cantina owner begins to talk. A short time later, the cloaked figure DEPARTS, stepping out onto the main thoroughfare of Centares space port's infamous OLD TOWN section. But as he starts anxiously AWAY...

ONE *MOMENT,* CITIZEN.

WE'VE HAD REPORTS OF A *DISTURBANCE* AT MERL'S,... WHICH YOU SEEM IN A *HURRY* TO LEAVE.

TURN AROUND AND TELL US *WHY*... BUT BE *SLOW* AND *CAREFUL* ABOUT IT.

NATURALLY. THE *LAST* THING I WANT IS TROUBLE WITH *IMPERIAL TROOPERS.*

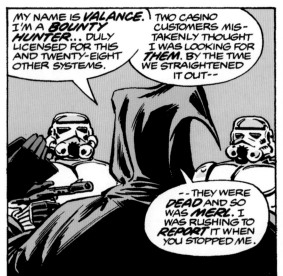

MY NAME IS *VALANCE.* I'M A *BOUNTY HUNTER*... DULY LICENSED FOR THIS AND TWENTY-EIGHT OTHER SYSTEMS.

TWO CASINO CUSTOMERS MISTAKENLY THOUGHT I WAS LOOKING FOR *THEM.* BY THE TIME WE STRAIGHTENED IT OUT--

--THEY WERE *DEAD* AND SO WAS *MERL.* I WAS RUSHING TO *REPORT* IT WHEN YOU STOPPED ME.

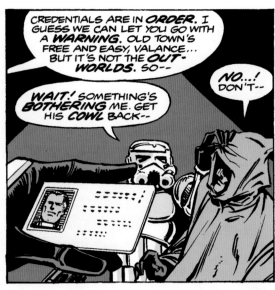

CREDENTIALS ARE IN *ORDER.* I GUESS WE CAN LET YOU GO WITH A *WARNING.* OLD TOWN'S FREE AND EASY, VALANCE... BUT IT'S NOT THE *OUT-WORLDS.* SO--

WAIT! SOMETHING'S *BOTHERING* ME. GET HIS *COWL* BACK--

NO...! DON'T--

I *THOUGHT* I SAW A GLINT OF *METAL!* HE'S--

A *BORG!* MISERABLE CYBORGS... TRYING TO *PASS!*

WE CAN'T LET SOMETHING LIKE *HIM* GET AWAY WITH KILLING *NORMAL ORGANICS!*

THANK YOU, TROOPER! UNTIL *NOW* I DON'T THINK I WAS *CERTAIN* ABOUT MY COURSE OF ACTION--

FRAZAK!

NOW I'M *COMMITTED.* I'M IN A RACE AGAINST *DARTH VADER*--

--AND *TYLER LUCIAN* IS THE PRIZE!

IN THE DAYS OF THE OLD REPUBLIC, RUBYFLAME LAKE WAS A SPLENDID, POPULAR **RESORT**, ATTRACTING VISITORS BY THE THOUSANDS TO CENTARES FROM THROUGHOUT THE MID-SYSTEMS.

UNDER THE HAND OF THE **EMPIRE**, DEEPLY BURIED LAVA BEDS WHICH WARMED THE LAKE WERE TAPPED FOR INTENSE **INDUSTRIAL PURPOSE**...

WITHIN A DECADE, THE LAVA BEDS WERE **EXHAUSTED**. THE ONCE SPARKLING, GEM-LIKE WATERS WERE OPAQUE, CLOUDED FOREVER BY **WASTE**...

...AND ONCE ELEGANT **GUEST TOWERS** WERE FALLEN INTO RUIN AND DISUSE.

YET...THE AREA STILL ATTRACTS **SOME**. IF THEY ARE **DESPERATE**...OR WITHOUT **HOPE**.

TYLER LUCIAN IS **BOTH**... AND NO MORE SO THAN DURING THE LONG MELANCHOLY MOMENTS OF **SUNSET**.

THE POLLUTANTS IN THERE CAN DISSOLVE **METAL** IN HOURS... **FLESH** WOULD SURELY ONLY TAKE MINUTES.

ONE MORE **STEP** IS ALL IT WOULD TAKE... AN EASY **PLUNGE** INTO THOSE BLOOD RED WATERS.

BUT IF I HAD *THAT* KIND OF NERVE... I WOULDN'T HAVE FLED *YAVIN BASE* AS THE *DEATH STAR* WAS APPROACHING!

ANNIHILATION SEEMED SO *CERTAIN.* IF THERE'D BEEN A *SHRED* OF HOPE... I MIGHT HAVE HELD ON.

ONLY *AFTER* I'D STOLEN THE SUPPLY SHIP... RACED AWAY... *THEN* I HEARD ON THE TRANSCEIVER... ABOUT *HIM!*

THE T-65 PILOT WHO SHUT DOWN HIS *COMPUTER...* AND PUT A TORPEDO INTO THE DEATH STAR EXHAUST PORT *UNASSISTED!*

A MERE *FARM BOY* FROM TATOOINE... *LUKE SKYWALKER!*

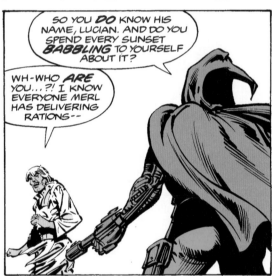

SO YOU *DO* KNOW HIS NAME, LUCIAN. AND DO YOU SPEND EVERY SUNSET *BABBLING* TO YOURSELF ABOUT IT?

WH-WHO *ARE* YOU...?! I KNOW EVERYONE MERL HAS DELIVERING RATIONS--

MERL WON'T BE *PROVIDING* ANYMORE SERVICES, LUCIAN.

AND YOU WON'T BE *NEEDING* ANY.

M-MERL *SAID* ALLIANCE SPIES WERE SEARCHING FOR ME. ARE *YOU*--?

UP 'TIL NOW, IF I FAVORED ANYONE... IT WAS THE *EMPIRE.* AFTER ALL, I USE TO *SERVE* THEM--

--UNTIL A REBEL BOMBARDMENT TURNED ME INTO SOMETHING I HATED... A *MACHINE!*

THEN... WHY ARE YOU *DOING* THIS...?!

I'VE... *VALUE* TO THE EMPIRE... WITH WHAT I *KNOW.* I'D HOPED TO JUST BE LEFT *ALONE*... BUT IF IT WILL SAVE MY *LIFE*...

YOU'RE *PITIFUL,* TYLER LUCIAN.

UNFORTUNATELY,... I'M NOT *KNOWN* FOR MY PITY.

THE *TIE* FIGHTER APPEARS SUDDENLY, SCREAMING LOW OVER THE LAKE OUT OF THE SETTING SUN.

AND ITS BENT-WING SILHOUETTE, ITS SLEEK STRUCTURE, MAKE IT PLAIN IT IS NOT JUST *ANY* TIE SHIP.

DARTH VADER!

IT IS ONLY A *MOMENT'S* DISTRACTION...

HERE *THIS* SOON...!

BUT A MOMENT IS FAR MORE THAN TYLER LUCIAN *THOUGHT* HE HAD...

HE GRASPS IT DESPERATELY, USING IT TO *RACE* FOR SANCTUARY!

V-DOW!

TOO *LATE*... HE'S INSIDE THE TOWER! YOU'RE A *FOOL*, VALANCE.

AND NOW YOU'RE GOING TO *DIE* FOR IT.

BUT THEN YOU'VE SUSPECTED *THAT* FOR SOME TIME... EVER SINCE YOU LET *LUKE SKYWALKER* AND *C-3PO* GET AWAY *ALIVE* BACK ON THE JUNCTION. *

THE HUNTER TURNS HIS BACK ON HIS PREY. AND FLINGING OFF HIS CLOAK, HE CHARGES TOWARD THE WALKWAY LEADING TO SHORE...

...THE WAY *DARTH VADER* WILL COME.

*STAR WARS #27. --ARCHIE.

HERE, WITHIN THE GREAT STONE WALLS OF THE MASSASI RUINS... A *VIGIL* IS IN PROGRESS.

THIS IS UNFAIR... TOTALLY *UNFAIR!* A PROTOCOL DROID ISN'T EQUIPPED TO SUFFER AN EXPERIENCE LIKE THIS *ONCE*... MUCH LESS *TWICE!*

WHAT CAN BE TAKING SO *LONG*...? MASTER LUKE AND I BROUGHT BACK ALL THE *MATERIALS* THEY NEEDED.

SUPPOSE SOME OF THE PARTS WE GOT ON JUNCTION ARE *FAULTY?*

WITH THE IMPERIAL BLOCKADE... THEY CAN'T BE EASILY *REPLACED!* MAYBE ARTOO DEETOO *CAN'T* BE REPAIRED* AS HE WAS AFTER THE BATTLE OF THE *DEATH STAR!*

*HE WAS ALMOST *FATALLY* DISABLED IN *STAR WARS* #26.--ARCH.

NO, *NO*...! I MUSTN'T *THINK* THAT! WHY, IF THEY CAN MAKE THAT LITTLE DROID *FUNCTIONAL* ONCE MORE...I'LL *NEVER* SAY A HARSH WORD TO HIM! I'LL--

BEEP-A-DEEP!

SURPRISE...?! WHY YOU UNREASONING LITTLE MOUND OF MISPLACED CIRCUITRY!

DO YOU SUPPOSE I HAVE NOTHING *BETTER* TO DO THAN IDLE ABOUT WAITING FOR *YOU* TO PLAY PRACTICAL JOKES?!

FWEE-BOOP!

JUST LIKE *OLD* TIMES AGAIN...? WHAT DO YOU *MEAN*, TWERP...?

AND AS A PERPETUAL ARGUMENT IS RESUMED OUTSIDE THE SUPPLY AND MAINTENANCE AREA...

...*OTHERS* ARE HAVING WORDS AS WELL.

HOW COULD YOU *DO* IT, GENERAL DODONNA...LET THE PRINCESS RUN OFF ON A MISSION *ALONE?!*

BECAUSE SHE CONVINCED ME *I* MIGHT BE LETTING *PERSONAL* CONSIDERATIONS KEEP HER AT THE BASE, SKYWALKER... MUCH AS *YOU* MIGHT BE.

Y-YOU COULD BE *RIGHT*, SIR. I'M SORRY. BUT... DIDN'T YOU ALWAYS SAY SHE WAS *NEEDED* HERE...AS A *SYMBOL* OF THE ALLIANCE?

LEIA ORGANA HAS ABILITIES FAR *BEYOND* THAT... AS WE BOTH KNOW. YET IN THE PLACE WHERE SHE HAS GONE... A SYMBOL IS *DESPERATELY* REQUIRED.

AND PERHAPS RATHER THAN WAIT AND WORRY *HERE*...

..., YOU *TOO* NEED A MISSION, LUKE.

HERE, AN *INTERLUDE* ENDS...

...AS LIGHT YEARS AWAY, ABOVE THE POISONED WATERS OF RUBYFLAME LAKE ON CENTARES...

...A *CONFRONTATION* BEGINS.

THE MAN IN THE TOWER HAS A *NAME* I REQUIRE, BOUNTY CHASER--

--THE ONLY PROFIT FOR *YOU* WILL BE IN LETTING ME PASS TO *GET* IT.

TODAY, LORD OF THE SITH... I'M NOT *AFTER* PROFIT.

YOU MAY HAVE WRUNG *TYLER LUCIAN'S* NAME FROM SOME REBEL SPY--

--BUT I'M READY TO *FIGHT* TO SEE YOU DON'T GET THE DEATH STAR DESTROYER'S NAME FROM *HIM.*

I *BELIEVE* YOU, VALANCE--

-- BUT THE *WHY* OF IT INTRIGUES ME. WHEN I FIRST *HEARD* OF YOU... ＊ WE SEEMED *RIVALS* FOR THE SAME PREY.

DON'T *TALK*, VADER... *DEFEND* YOURSELF.

SURELY YOU'VE NOTICED... I ALREADY *AM.*

＊ SW #21.--AG

WHY *ELSE* HAVEN'T YOU BEEN ABLE TO *FIRE* YET--?

WHY ELSE HAS YOUR WEAPON BECOME SO *HEAVY*--

--IT IS *IMPOSSIBLE* FOR YOU TO HOLD?

HOW CAN YOU *FIGHT*... AGAINST THE POWER OF THE *FORCE?*

LIKE... *THIS....!*

FRA-KOW!

IT'S NO *SMALL THING* TO BRING DARTH VADER TO HIS KNEE. ON SOME WORLDS, IT MIGHT BE THE STUFF OF *LEGEND*...

BUT IT'S *NOT ENOUGH*.

SLAYING YOU WILL BE A *WASTE*. A BOUNTY HUNTER... WITH YOUR PARTICULAR *ABILITIES*... COULD SERVE ME *WELL*.

A USEFUL *FREAK*--

--NOT UNLIKE YOUR *OWN* POSITION WITH THE EMPIRE.

VRAMM!

HIGH IN THE DECAYING TOWER BEYOND THE WALKWAY, TYLER LUCIAN WATCHES WITH HORRIBLE FASCINATION...AND LISTENS.

THAT *BOY* YOU'RE SEEKING... AND HIS *DROID*... HELD OUT HOPE OF SOMETHING *BETTER*, VADER.

A TIME, A LIFE, WHEN EVEN SOMEONE LIKE ME MIGHT NOT *BE* A FREAK.

A FOOLISH *DREAM*, NO DOUBT... BUT SO WAS DESTROYING THE *DEATH STAR!*

FRRAK!

THE CHASM TORN BY THE BLAST IS *WIDE*... WIDER THAN MOST MEN MIGHT LEAP.

BUT THE LORD OF THE SITH IS *NOT* MOST MEN!

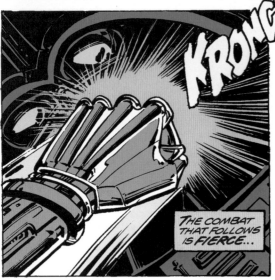

KRONG!

THE COMBAT THAT FOLLOWS IS *FIERCE*...

...AND *BRIEF.*

SHRAAAK!

AND DARTH VADER TURNS TO THE BUSINESS THAT *BROUGHT* HIM...

TYLER LUCIAN!

N-NO...!

THE CYBERNETIC HAND CLAMPS LIKE A *VISE*...

...SQUEEZING, TIGHTENING.

STILL *ALIVE*...! STILL FIGHTING...! I COULD ALMOST *ADMIRE* YOU, VALANCE.

GIVE THIS UP, *JOIN* ME... THE MEDICS ON MY CRUISER CAN PROBABLY STILL *SAVE* YOU.

N-NO.'

DARTH VADER SHRUGS, KICKS. THE BOUNTY HUNTER IS LIKE A GREAT SHACKLE, A WEIGHT THAT WILL NOT SHAKE FREE.

LUNACY.' EVEN IF I *QUIT* NOW... LEFT YOU AND THE CRINGING COWARD IN THE TOWER... NOTHING WOULD *CHANGE.*

OTHERS IN THIS GALAXY WILL HAVE THE SAME INFORMATION. IF I DON'T ACQUIRE IT TODAY... I WILL *TOMORROW.*

AND FOR *WHAT* WILL YOU HAVE *SACRIFICED* YOURSELF...?

TIME, FORCE MASTER. THE BOY YOU SEEK... THE ONE WITH THE DROIDS... IS *GOOD.* AND HE'S GROWING...

SOMEDAY HE'LL BE YOUR *EQUAL...* OR YOUR *BETTER.*

ANY *DELAY* WORKS IN HIS *FAVOR...* INCREASES HIS *CHANCES.*

ANY...

DELAY...

THEN, VALANCE... THERE CAN *BE* NO MORE!

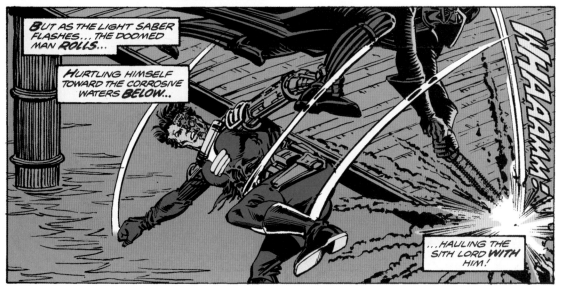

BUT AS THE LIGHT SABER FLASHES... THE DOOMED MAN ROLLS...

HURTLING HIMSELF TOWARD THE CORROSIVE WATERS BELOW...

WHAAMM

...HAULING THE SITH LORD *WITH* HIM!

AND DARTH VADER BEGINS TO FEEL JUST HOW HEAVY...

...A DYING MAN, HALF-HUMAN, HALF-*MACHINE*, CAN BE.

THE MOMENTS THAT FOLLOW ARE *LONG*...

BUT...

SKRAAK!

...THEY END.

ENDING WITH THEM...

...VALANCE, THE HUNTER.

BUT HIS LAST *WORDS* STILL ECHO IN THE MIND OF TYLER LUCIAN.

AND THE MAN WHO COULD NOT FACE THE *DEATH STAR*...

...*FINDS* THE COURAGE THAT HAS SO LONG DESERTED HIM.

FOR A TIME, THE ONLY SOUND ON RUBYFLAME LAKE IS THE STEADY, LABORED RASP OF THE DARK LORD'S BREATH MASK.

THEN, HE *TURNS*...

...*AND* MAKES HIS WAY BACK TO THE ORBITING CRUISER.

FINALLY OFF-DUTY. I *HATE* THESE DOUBLE-SHIFTS.

RIGHT! CAN'T WAIT TO SHED THIS *ARMOR*. BEEN IN IT SO LONG I FEEL LIKE A BLASTED *BORG*--

--OR *WORSE*.

GET UNDER WAY AT *ONCE*, WERMIS. I'LL SUPPLY YOU WITH COORDINATES.

AND UNTIL I DECREE *OTHERWISE*--

--WE ARE ON *ALERT STATUS.* EVEN OFF-DUTY PERSONNEL WILL REMAIN IN *FULL ARMOR!*

AND A LONG SEARCH...

...*BEGINS AGAIN.*

NEXT ISSUE: *A PRINCESS ALONE!*

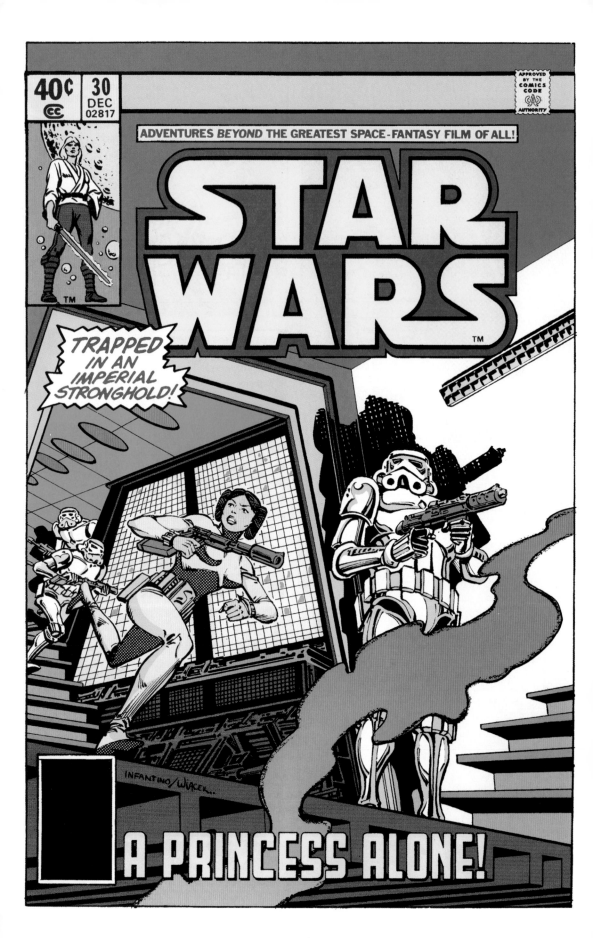

169

170

172

MEANWHILE, IN ONE OF THE *HIGHEST* OF THE UNDERGROUND CITY'S MONOLITHIC TOWERS...

BARON TAGGE! THE HEAD OF THE GALAXY'S MOST *RENOWNED* INDUSTRIAL CONCERN VISITING *MY* HUMBLE FACTORY WORLD... WHAT AN UNEXPECTED *PLEASURE!*

PLEASURE DOESN'T ENTER INTO IT, GOVERNOR CORWYTH--

MY PRESENCE ON METALORN AMOUNTS TO *PENANCE.*

THE FAILURE OF *ONE* TAGGE PROJECT AGAINST THE REBEL ALLIANCE* LEFT THE EMPEROR DOUBTING *ALL* OF THEM. TO *REASSURE* HIM... I'M FORCED TO *PERSONALLY* CHECK EACH ONE.

YOU'LL GAIN AN EASY ENDORSEMENT *HERE,* DEAR FELLOW.

*SCUTTLED BY *LUKE* IN SW 25&26. --ACCOUNTABLE ARCH.

THANKS TO YOUR TAGGE *WEAPONS DETECTION SYSTEM,* AND MY OWN *INFORMATION CONTROL PROGRAM*--

-- THE REBELLION DOESN'T *EXIST* ON METALORN. NOT EVEN AS A *RUMOR.*

MY SYSTEM CAN DETECT UNAUTHORIZED *ARMS* OR *EXPLOSIVES* BROUGHT ONTO YOUR PLANET, GOVERNOR--

--THAT DOESN'T PRECLUDE *UNARMED SPIES* SLIPPING PAST NORMAL SECURITY.

AND SO AN OCCASIONAL ONE *MIGHT,* MY DEAR BARON! BUT *THEN* WHAT...? *SABOTAGE...?*

TO DO ANY *REAL* DAMAGE... THEY'D HAVE TO *STEAL* A STORM-TROOPER'S WEAPON. *DIFFICULT,* AT BEST--

-- SINCE YOUR EXCELLENT SYSTEM *ALSO* MONITORS THOSE! SO, IN OUR REGIMENTED SOCIETY, IT IS ALMOST *IMPOSSIBLE* TO --

SIR! WE'VE A *CONDITION RED* AT POST 994-203!

PULSE BEAT SENSORS INDICATE MONITORED WEAPON IS *NO LONGER* IN AUTHORIZED HANDS!

SOMEONE SEEMS TO HAVE *DONE* THE DIFFICULT, CORWYTH... THE *IMPOSSIBLE* MAY NOT BE FAR BEHIND.

POST 994-203...

WE'VE **FOUND** THE TROOPER, MONITOR CONTROL.

PLAYBACK OF HIS **RECORDING UNIT** INDICATES HE STOPPED A LONE **FEMALE** COMING FROM THE DOCKING AREA FOR **ROUTINE** QUESTIONING.

HE WAS ABOUT TO CHECK AN **IRREGULARITY** ON HER PAPERS... WHEN SHE **ATTACKED!**

THE ASSAILANT WAS **CLEVER**...USED **ADHESIVE SPRAY** FROM A FIRST AID PACK TO CLOG THE **VENTILATION SYSTEM** OF OUR MAN'S ARMOR.

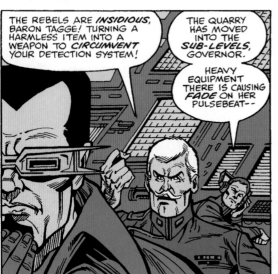

THE REBELS ARE **INSIDIOUS**, BARON TAGGE! TURNING A HARMLESS ITEM INTO A WEAPON TO **CIRCUMVENT** YOUR DETECTION SYSTEM!

THE QUARRY HAS MOVED INTO THE **SUB-LEVELS**, GOVERNOR.

HEAVY EQUIPMENT THERE IS CAUSING **FADE** ON HER PULSEBEAT--

--BUT WE STILL HAVE A STRONG **MONITOR FIX** ON THE BLASTER ITSELF, SIR!

ALERT ALL THE MEN IT **TAKES**... **FOLLOW** THAT SIGNAL! INSTEAD OF **ARMING** HERSELF, OUR LITTLE SPY WILL FIND SHE'S TIED A **NOOSE** TO HER NECK!

"AND THE FURTHER AND FASTER SHE **RUNS**...

"...THE **TIGHTER** IT'S GOING TO GET!"

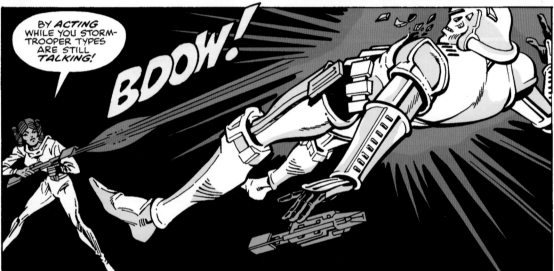

THE REBEL SPY HAS ELUDED THE *PURSUIT SQUADS*, GOVERNOR CORWYTH... SHALL I HAVE THE CONVEYER *HALTED*?

AND CUT OFF THE *ORE FLOW* TO THE PLANET'S *FURNACES*...? CAUSE A TEMPORARY *SHUT DOWN*?!

THAT WOULD BE DOING THE ALLIANCE'S WORK *FOR* THEM, YOU FOOL! EVEN *MY* INFORMATION CONTROL COULDN'T HIDE SOMETHING LIKE *THAT*!

AS LONG AS WE'RE MONITORING THE *WEAPON*... SHE CAN'T *ESCAPE*! ORDER OUT *MORE UNITS*... HAVE THEM *CONVERGE* ON THE SIGNAL!

"NATURALLY, ALL THIS ACTIVITY WON'T GO *UNNOTICED* BY OUR WORKER-CITIZENS, SEE THAT THEY HAVE A REASONABLE-- AND *FALSE*-- EXPLANATION."

DO NOT BE *ALARMED*, THIS IS MERELY A *SECURITY TEST* FOR YOUR PROTECTION.

MAINTAIN YOUR *WORK STATIONS*. THIS IS--I REPEAT-- A *TEST*.

MONITOR INDICATES SHE'S STAYING *WITH* THE ORE CONVEYER, SIR.

SHE MUST INTEND *SABOTAGE* TO ONE OF THE FURNACES.

BUT WE'LL HAVE EVERY AVAILABLE UNIT WAITING TO *CUT HER OFF* AT SMELTER BAY FIVE!

EXCELLENT! YOU HEAR THAT, TAGGE--

--THIS WHOLE NASTY EPISODE IS JUST GOING TO WIND UP *PROVING* THAT THE SYSTEM STILL *WORKS*!

UH... *BARON*...?

HE RUSHED OUT *EARLIER*, GOVERNOR--

--WHEN THE *TROUBLE* STARTED.

ODD! HE NEVER HAD THE *REPUTATION* OF A MAN WHO SHIED AWAY FROM TROUBLE.

PERHAPS THAT WAS *BEFORE* HIS RUN-IN WITH *DARTH VADER!*

BEING BLINDED BY A *LIGHT SABER*... FORCED TO RELY ON *CYBER-VISION*... WOULD MAKE *ANYONE*...UH... CAUTIOUS.

* A TALE YET TO BE *CHRONICLED.* --ARCHIE.

AH WELL....!

WE HAVE BETTER THINGS TO DO THAN PONDER THE ARISTOCRATIC *PSYCHE*... HOW DOES THE *HUNT* PROGRESS?

THE *LAST UNIT* IS NOW IN POSITION IN SMELTER BAY FIVE, GOVERNOR CORWYTH. AND THE *MONITOR* SHOWS...

"...THE ORE CONVEYER IS SPEEDING THE REBEL SPY STRAIGHT *INTO* THEIR WAITING GUNS!"

5

THE NEXT CAR WILL BE THE *ONE!* SET ALL BLASTERS AT LOW LEVEL INTENSITY--

--WE WANT TO DESTROY THE *WOMAN,* NOT THE CONVEYER! AT MY *COMMAND*--

--FIRE!

SHTUM! BA-KOW! VDOW!

THE *REBEL'S* NOT IN THE CAR... ONLY THE STOLEN *WEAPON!*

NOW IT'S CLEAR WHY THE GOOD BARON FLED! HE MUST HAVE *KNOWN* HIS WEAPON DETECTION SYSTEM WOULD *FAIL* US!

IN ALL *FAIRNESS,* GOVERNOR... THE SYSTEM *WORKED.*

WHO COULD ANTICIPATE THE ALLIANCE AGENT *USING* IT TO DECOY US AFTER THE BLASTER INSTEAD OF *HER?*

IS THAT SUPPOSED TO *COMFORT* ME? THE WOMAN'S *DEADLY...* AND THERE ARE *MILES* OF ENDLESS CORRIDORS AND BYWAYS SHE COULD HAVE *VANISHED* INTO WHILE *WE* CHASED THE SIGNAL FROM THAT GUN!

FIND HER! IF IT TAKES EVERY *STORM- TROOPER* ON METALORN... *FIND THAT REBEL WITCH!*

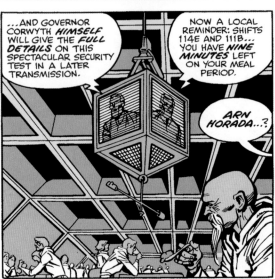

...AND GOVERNOR CORWYTH *HIMSELF* WILL GIVE THE *FULL DETAILS* ON THIS SPECTACULAR SECURITY TEST IN A LATER TRANSMISSION.

NOW A LOCAL REMINDER: SHIFTS 114E AND 111B... YOU HAVE *NINE MINUTES* LEFT ON YOUR MEAL PERIOD.

ARN HORADA...?

DO... DO I *KNOW* YOU, YOUNG WOMAN? YOU'RE NOT ON MY SHIFT...

NO, I'M FROM YOUR *PAST.* WHEN YOU TRAVELED FROM HERE TO *ALDERAAN* TO INSTRUCT A LITTLE GIRL IN GALACTIC HISTORY--

--*LEIA,* PROFESSOR HORADA. PRINCESS LEIA ORGANA.

N-NO...! ARE YOU TRYING TO GET ME IN *TROUBLE...?* ALDERAAN IS *DESTROYED...* OBLITERATED BY A *METEOR STORM...!*

CENTRAL INFORMATION TOLD US THAT *LONG AGO...!* NONE OF THE ROYAL HOUSE SURVIVED... *NONE!*

THEY *LIED* TO YOU, PROFESSOR... I'M HERE TO TELL YOU THE *TRUTH.*

AND TO *ENLIST* HIM IN BRINGING THE *REBELLION* TO METALORN, PRINCESS...?

YOU'RE... BARON TAGGE.

YES! SINCE YOU HAVE MOST OF THE AREA'S TROOPERS ON A WILD GOOSE CHASE IN THE SUB-LEVELS--

--I THOUGHT SOMEONE SHOULD BE WAITING WHEN YOU CONTACTED YOUR OLD INSTRUCTOR!

HOW COULD YOU KNOW...?

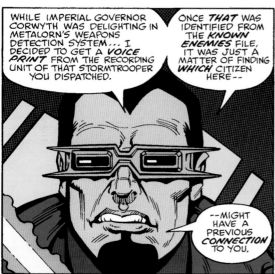

WHILE IMPERIAL GOVERNOR CORWYTH WAS DELIGHTING IN METALORN'S WEAPONS DETECTION SYSTEM... I DECIDED TO GET A VOICE PRINT FROM THE RECORDING UNIT OF THAT STORMTROOPER YOU DISPATCHED.

ONCE THAT WAS IDENTIFIED FROM THE KNOWN ENEMIES FILE, IT WAS JUST A MATTER OF FINDING WHICH CITIZEN HERE--

--MIGHT HAVE A PREVIOUS CONNECTION TO YOU.

WHY THE ALLIANCE WOULD LET ITS MOST RENOWNED LEADER RISK HER LIFE ATTEMPTING TO RECRUIT SOME BROKEN, USELESS FORMER HISTORIAN ELUDES ME...

I'LL LET YOU EXPLAIN THAT TO THE EMPEROR... WHEN I DELIVER YOU PERSONALLY!

SINCE HE WOULDN'T UNDERSTAND ANY MORE THAN YOU DO--

--LET'S NOT BOTHER WITH THE TRIP!

181

BLAST YOU, WOMAN! FOR THAT--

SHRAAAAK!

--YOU'LL VISIT THE EMPEROR AS A *CORPSE!*

BUT WITH HIS CYBER-VISION *BLOCKED,* THE THREAT IS EASIER MADE THAN CARRIED OUT...

AND EVEN AS TAGGE STRUGGLES TO CLEAR HIS LENSES OF FOOD PASTE... UNSEEN *OBSTACLES* APPEAR!

PROFESSOR *HORADA* KICKED THE CHAIR INTO HIS PATH...!

GIVEN THE OPPORTUNITY, THE PRINCESS MOVES SWIFTLY TO *CAPITALIZE* ON IT...

...USING THE *ENERGY SHACKLES* MEANT FOR HER!

KLIK!

DON'T STAND LIKE UNPROGRAMMED *DROIDS!* AN ENEMY OF THE *EMPEROR* IS ESCAPING!

B-BUT... THE EMPEROR *HAS* NO ENEMIES...! THE DAILY *INFORMATION BROAD-CASTS* ASSURE US OF THIS...!

AND MATTERS OF *DIS-OBEDIENCE* ARE ONLY TO BE SETTLED BY *IMPERIAL TROOPERS...!*

ALREADY *CHASING* THAT WITCH.... DOWN A *FALSE TRAIL!*

YES! WHERE *ARE* THE STORM-TROOPERS...?!

VRAM!

MOVE, YOU MISINFORMED DOLTS! CLEAR MY WAY TO THE NEAREST *EXIT...* THAT'S WHERE SHE WAS *HEADED!*

THE BARON PLUNGES *ON...* THE EXCITEMENT FADES... THE CROWD DISPERSES...

THANKS FOR THE *COVER,* YOUNG LADY. YOU'RE VERY *BRAVE* TO HELP ME.

IT WAS *FUN!* I UNDER-STAND 'CAUSE SOME-TIMES *I* GET IN TROUBLE, TOO!

ONLY...AREN'T YOU *SCARED* WITH STORMTROOPERS AND EVERYBODY *CHASING* YOU?

VERY. BUT SOMETIMES-- WHEN YOU *BELIEVE* IN SOMETHING ENOUGH-- YOU DO IT ANYWAY.

E-EVEN IF EVERYONE ELSE SAYS YOU *CAN'T...?* THAT IT'S *IMPOSSIBLE...?*

MAYBE *ESPECIALLY* THEN.

NOW I CAN'T *STAY* ANY LONGER, SWEETHEART.

MAY THE *FORCE* BE WITH YOU.

THE F-FORCE...?

AND AS THE REST OF SHIFT 114 AND INSTRUCTION UNIT 51 RUSH THROUGH WHAT'S LEFT OF THEIR MEAL PERIOD, LEIA ORGANA VANISHES INTO THE LABYRINTH CORRIDORS OF METALORN...

...WATCHED ONLY BY A GIRL NAMED *TAMMI.*

183

PRINCESS *LEIA ORGANA* RIGHT HERE ON *MY* PLANET... AND SHE SLIPS THROUGH OUR *FINGERS!*

I BLAME *YOU* FOR THIS, TAGGE! KEEPING HER PRESENCE *SECRET*... SO YOU COULD REGAIN THE EMPEROR'S *FAVOR* BY CAPTURING HER *YOURSELF!*

AND *I* BLAME YOUR *GOVERNING POLICIES* AND STUPID *HANDLING* OF THE WHOLE AFFAIR.

NEITHER STANCE WILL *UNDO* WHAT'S HAPPENED.

I CAN AT LEAST REASSURE THE EMPEROR BY *EXECUTING* THAT OLD MAN... *ARN HORADA!*

ANY RETALIATION TO HIM IS LIKE AN *ADMISSION* THAT YOU'VE *LIED* ABOUT THE REBELLION... AND THAT THE EMPIRE QUAKES IN *FEAR* OF IT.

BUT I'M THE *GOVERNOR*...! THERE MUST BE *SOMETHING* I CAN DO!

YES, YOU CAN KEEP *QUIET*... NOT TROUBLE THE EMPEROR OR METALORN'S CITIZENS ANY MORE THAN THEY ALREADY *ARE.*

THAT'S *MY* ADVICE. AND EVEN IF IT'S WRONG, THE NICE THING ABOUT IT IS--

-- YOU WON'T BE ANY *WORSE* OFF THAN YOU ARE *NOW.*

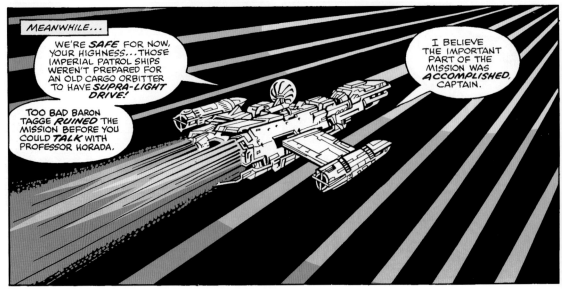

MEANWHILE...

WE'RE *SAFE* FOR NOW, YOUR HIGHNESS...THOSE IMPERIAL PATROL SHIPS WEREN'T PREPARED FOR AN OLD CARGO ORBITTER TO HAVE *SUPRA-LIGHT DRIVE!*

TOO BAD BARON TAGGE *RUINED* THE MISSION BEFORE YOU COULD *TALK* WITH PROFESSOR HORADA.

I BELIEVE THE IMPORTANT PART OF THE MISSION WAS *ACCOMPLISHED,* CAPTAIN.

WITH ALL RESPECT, PRINCESS LEIA...*HOW?* NOTHING WAS SABOTAGED... NO RESISTANCE FORCE ESTABLISHED.

WHAT'S DIFFERENT ABOUT METALORN *NOW* THAN *BEFORE* WE ARRIVED?

YOU'RE MAKING THE SAME MISTAKE THE *EMPIRE* DOES, CAPTAIN. THERE'S *MORE* TO THE REBELLION THAN GUERILLA WARFARE.

A TEACHER, A HISTORIAN, LIKE *ARN HORADA* CAN EVENTUALLY LEAD A RESISTANCE WHEN IT'S SAFE, NOT TO *FIGHT*... BUT TO POUR *SAND* IN THE IMPERIAL WAR MACHINE.

BUT *FIRST*... HE AND OTHERS THERE NEEDED TO BE SHOWN THERE *WAS* A REBELLION... TO SEE THAT ITS LEADERS *SURVIVE* AND CONTINUE THE *FIGHT*...

TO *GIVE* METALORN WHAT IT'S BEEN LACKING BEFORE--

A *BLASTER* ISN'T CONSTRUCTED RIGHT...*TRANSCEIVER SETS* GET FAULTY PARTS.

--HOPE.

AND ON THE IMPERIAL CONTROLLED FACTORY PLANET LEFT BEHIND.... A YOUNG *GIRL* SNEAKS AWAY FROM HER INSTRUCTION UNIT DURING PLAY PERIOD.

A YOUNG GIRL NAMED *TAMMI*...

TASK ACCOMPLISHED, SHE SITS DOWN AND WAITS. WAITS FOR HER *SEEDS* TO GROW...

PATIENTLY. HOPEFULLY.

NEXT: *RETURN TO TATOOINE!*

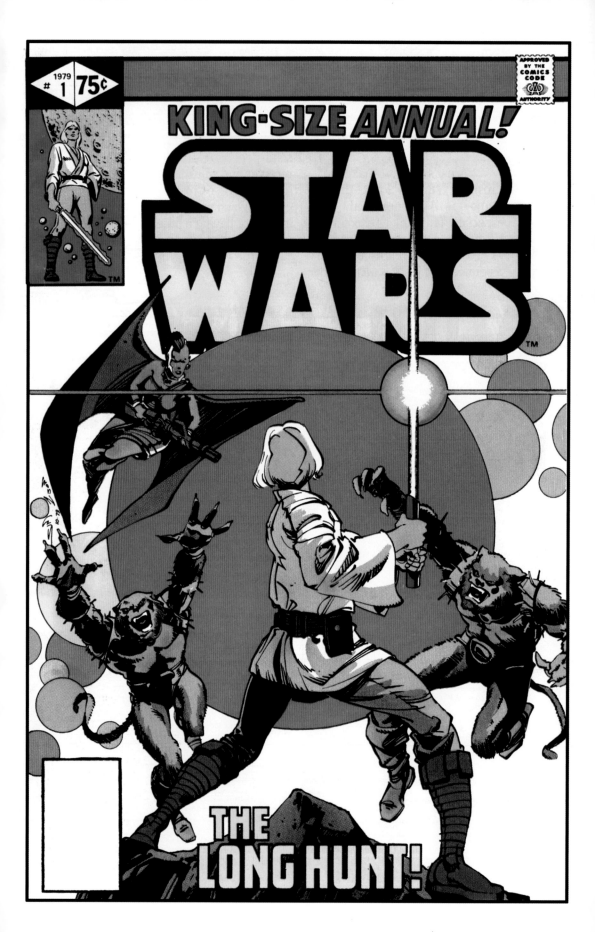

Long ago in a galaxy far, far away. . .there exists a state of cosmic *civil war*. A brave alliance of *underground freedom fighters* has challenged the tyranny and oppression of the awesome *Galactic Empire*. This is their story!

LucasFilm PRESENTS: **STAR WARS** THE GREATEST SPACE FANTASY OF ALL!

CONTINUING THE SAGA BEGUN IN THE FILM BY GEORGE LUCAS RELEASED BY TWENTIETH CENTURY-FOX

| CHRIS CLAREMONT *guest writer* | MIKE VOSBURG & *guest artists* | STEVE LEIALOHA | JOHN COSTANZA *letterer* | BOB SHAREN *colorist* | ARCHIE GOODWIN *editor* | JIM SHOOTER *consulting ed.* |

THE LONG HUNT

AS THE SAYING GOES, IT'S A **BIG** EMPIRE-- STRETCHING FROM ONE SPIRAL ARM OF THE GALAXY TO THE OTHER, ENCOMPASSING MILLIONS OF STAR SYSTEMS, THOUSANDS OF INHABITED WORLDS.

IN ALL THAT VAST AMOUNT OF SPACE, AMONG ALL THOSE COUNTLESS BILLIONS OF SAPIENT BEINGS, IT'S EASY TO UNDER-STAND HOW A MERE **FOUR** MIGHT OCCASIONALLY GO UNNOTICED.

Y'KNOW, PRINCESS, I'M GLAD HAN HAD TO PUT THE **MILLENNIUM FALCON** IN HERE FOR SUPPLIES. I'VE BEEN COOPED UP TOO LONG ON STARSHIPS. I WAS STARTING TO GO BATTY!

EVEN WHEN TWO OF THOSE FOUR ARE **PRINCESS LEIA ORGANA**-- FORMER IMPERIAL SENATOR FROM ALDERAAN, NOW A LEADER OF THE REBEL ALLIANCE--

--AND **LUKE SKYWALKER**, TATOOINE MOISTURE FARMER TURNED STAR-FIGHTER PILOT.

187

THEY'RE RUNNING A CALCULATED RISK BY VISITING TIRAHNN THAT-- AMONG THE CROWDS THRONGING THIS ANCIENT, LEGENDARY BAZAAR.. *NO ONE* WILL RECOGNIZE THEM. THE ODDS ARE IN THEIR FAVOR.

BUT SOMETIMES, EVEN WHEN YOU PLAY THE ODDS, YOU *LOSE.*

BY THE SEVEN MOONS OF SKÄRTIS-- IT'S *THEM!*

"TWO OF THOSE THE TYRANT SEEKS,! AND IF THE FEMALE AND THE YOUTH ARE HERE--

"--HAN SOLO CANNOT BE FAR AWAY.' I MUST NOTIFY THE TYRANT-- AT ONCE!"

UNAWARE THAT THEY'VE BEEN SPOTTED...

...LUKE AND LEIA CONTINUE THEIR STROLL THROUGH THE BAZAAR.

ALL MY LIFE, I'VE HEARD TALES OF THE GREAT TIRAHNN FAIR, BUT I NEVER THOUGHT I'D GET TO VISIT IT.

LIKE WHAT YOU SEE?

WELLL-- THAT OUTFIT LOOKS A LITTLE DARING TO ME. ON TATOOINE, SHE'D BE ASKING FOR A BAD CASE OF SUNBURN OR WIND SCAR.

BUT THIS ISN'T TATOOINE, LUKE. ACTUALLY, THE GOWN'S A LITTLE... DEMURE FOR MY TASTES.

WHAAAT--???

PRINCESS...

...YOU'RE... JOKING, AREN'T YOU?

I WAS WONDERING HOW LONG IT WOULD TAKE YOU TO NOTICE.

FOR THE FIRST TIME IN QUITE A WHILE...

TWO YOUNG PEOPLE WHO'VE SEEN MORE THAN THEIR SHARE OF TRAGEDY REVEL IN THE JOY OF SIMPLY BEING ALIVE.

THE MOOD DOESN'T LAST LONG.

HUH--?! PRINCESS, THE CROWD--!

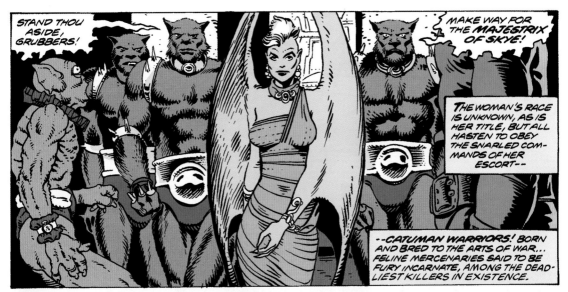

STAND THOU ASIDE, GRUBBERS!

MAKE WAY FOR THE *MAJESTRIX* OF *SKYE!*

THE WOMAN'S RACE IS UNKNOWN, AS IS HER TITLE, BUT ALL HASTEN TO OBEY THE SNARLED COMMANDS OF HER ESCORT--

--CATUMAN WARRIORS! BORN AND BRED TO THE ARTS OF WAR... FELINE MERCENARIES SAID TO BE FURY INCARNATE, AMONG THE DEADLIEST KILLERS IN EXISTENCE.

LIKE EVERYONE ELSE, LEIA MOVES ASIDE-- BUT NOT QUITE FAST ENOUGH.

:OH!!:

THAT WINGED WOMAN SLAMMED INTO YOU *DELIBERATELY!* WHO THE HECK DOES SHE THINK SHE IS--?!

HUSH, LUKE. I'M ALL RIGHT.

LET IT PASS.

THE LAST THING WE NEED IS TO MAKE TROUBLE AND DRAW ATTENTION TO OURSELVES.

I SUPPOSE. I'LL ADMIT THOSE CATUMEN SURE LOOKED DANGEROUS.

IT'S SAID EVEN WOOKIEES GIVE THEM A WIDE BERTH, WHAT'S THAT?

A MONEY POUCH-- ISN'T IT YOURS?

THIEF!!

YOU DARE PRACTICE YOUR *PICK-POCKET'S* TRADE ON ME?!

THAT'S CRAZY. YOU MUST HAVE DROPPED THIS...

LIAR!

THESE HUMANS HAVE OFFENDED ME, MY PETS--

--SLAY THEM!!

189

LUKE'S REACTION IS INSTINCTIVE...

...AND FAR FASTER THAN HE WOULD HAVE BELIEVED POSSIBLE NOT SO LONG AGO. IN ONE SMOOTH, FLUID MOTION, HIS *LIGHTSABER* IS IN HIS HAND, ITS SEARING ENERGY BLADE SENDING THE LEAD CATUMAN TO A WELL-DESERVED REWARD.

AARRRGH!!

THE OTHER WARRIORS PAUSE, SUDDENLY RESPECTFUL OF THEIR FOE'S WEAPON AND HIS OBVIOUS ABILITY.

FOR THE MOMENT, THE ADVANTAGE IS LUKE'S. HE DOESN'T INTEND TO THROW IT AWAY.

PRINCESS--*RUN!* HEAD FOR THE FALCON. I'LL BE RIGHT BEHIND YOU!

BUT, LUKE-- WHAT ABOUT THE CATUMEN?!

"DON'T WORRY. I THINK I'VE GOT A WAY TO SLOW 'EM DOWN."

LUKE FEINTS LEFT, THEN SLASHES RIGHT WITH HIS LIGHTSABER, CUTTING THROUGH A THICK TANGLE OF HALYARDS...

...AND TOPPLING A LINE OF AWNINGS ON TOP OF THE TWO STARTLED WARRIORS. THEN, HE, TOO, IS ON HIS WAY.

EXCELLENT, YOUNG ONE. YOU'RE EVEN MORE IMPRESSIVE THAN I'D HOPED.

THOUGH YOU DO NOT YET KNOW IT, THE *LONG HUNT* HAS BEGUN. YOU AND PRINCESS LEIA WILL LEAD ME STRAIGHT TO *HAN SOLO*-- AND THIS TIME, HE WILL NOT ESCAPE.

AND WHEN THE HUNT IS DONE, YOU WILL ALL DIE, SLOWLY, BY MY HANDS.

TIRAHNN-- TRADING NEXUS OF AN ENTIRE STELLAR CLUSTER, A CITY LARGER THAN SOME COUNTRIES, ITS ARCHITECTURE RANGING FROM THE STREET LEVEL HURLY-BURLY OF THE BAZAAR TO MILE-HIGH CORPORATE SKYSCRAPERS AND LUXURY PALACES.

IT'S AN EASY PLACE TO LOSE SOMEONE IN. SOMETIMES, ALL YOU HAVE TO DO IS TURN A CORNER, OR LOOK THE WRONG WAY AT THE WRONG MOMENT.

BUT, TRY AS THEY MIGHT, LUKE AND LEIA CAN'T SHAKE THE TWO CATUMEN RELENTLESSLY DOGGING THEIR TRAIL.

LUKE TRIES EVERY TRICK HE'D EVER LEARNED ON TATOOINE-- HE EVEN INVENTS SOME BRAND NEW ONES ON THE SPOT-- TO NO AVAIL. EVERY TIME HE SPARES A QUICK GLANCE OVER HIS SHOULDER, THE CATUMEN ARE THERE.

SEEMS LIKE WE'VE BEEN RUNNING FOR-EVER. DON'T KNOW ABOUT THE PRINCESS, BUT I'M ALMOST *WINDED.* WE CAN'T KEEP UP THIS PACE MUCH LONGER.

SUDDENLY...

LUKE!

OH, *NO!* ONE OF THEM CUT AHEAD OF US! WE'RE TRAPPED IN THIS ALLEY!

NO CHOICE-- WE HAVE TO MAKE A STAND.

HE DOES HIS BEST, BUT HE'S TIRED, SLOW, AND THIS TIME THE CATUMAN IS READY FOR HIM.

BEFORE LUKE QUITE KNOWS WHAT HAPPENED, THE WARRIOR'S FIST RAKES HIS CHEST, KNUCKLE-SPIKES DRAWING *BLOOD.*

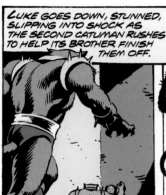

LUKE GOES DOWN, STUNNED, SLIPPING INTO SHOCK AS THE SECOND CATUMAN RUSHES TO HELP ITS BROTHER FINISH THEM OFF.

KRAK

THE WARRIOR'S HASTE MAKES HIM CARELESS. THE CATUMAN NEVER SEES THE MASSIVE ARM THAT BRINGS HIM DOWN.

NOR DOES HIS BROTHER SEE THE BLASTER BOLT THAT STOPS HIM IN HIS TRACKS.

THE FORCE BE PRAISED...!

VDOW

HAN SOLO! CHEWBACCA!

HRONNK!

YEAH, CHEWIE, I CAN SEE THE KID'S HURT. AFTER GOING ONE ON ONE WITH A "CAT," HE'S LUCKY TO BE ALIVE.

C'MON, YOUR WORSHIP, LET'S GET OUTTA'HERE BEFORE THE LOCAL PREFECTS WORK UP ENOUGH COURAGE TO COME SEE WHO'S STILL BREATHING.

LATER, ABOARD THE STARSHIP MILLENNIUM FALCON, DOCKED AT TIRAHNN'S CENTRAL STARPORT...

HOW DID YOU FIND US, HAN? HOW DID YOU KNOW WE WERE EVEN IN TROUBLE?

I WISH I COULD TAKE THE BOWS, PRINCESS...

...BUT THE CREDIT BELONGS TO YOUR DROID BUDDIES. ARTOO HEARD THE ORIGINAL RADIO ALARM TO SECURITY HEADQUARTERS, THEN PATCHED INTO ONE OF SECURITY'S AIRBORNE "SPY-EYES" TO TRACK YOU DOWN.

PRINCESS--WILL MASTER LUKE RECOVER?

BOIP BDIP... BOEEP?

THANKS TO YOU TWO, THREEPIO, I THINK HE'LL BE JUST FINE.

KID, IF YOU FEEL UP TO TALKING... WHAT EXACTLY HAPPENED IN THE BAZAAR? THE REPORTS ARTOO PICKED UP WERE PRETTY CON-FUSED.

UH-OH... I HEAR SOMEONE OUTSIDE THE MAIN HATCH. I'D BETTER ANSWER-- COULD BE PREFECTS.

COVER ME, CHEWIE, IN CASE IT'S BROOD MATES OF THOSE CATMEN WE ZAPPED--

SAME OLD SOLO-- SAYIN' "HI" TO AN OLD FRIEND BY STICKING A BLASTER IN HER FACE.

WHA--?! MOONS OF YAVIN-- KATYA!!

IT'S BEEN YEARS, WOMAN! HOW'VE YOU BEEN?!

LIVIN', SOLO. WORKIN'. LAUGHIN'. NOTHIN' SPECTACULAR-- BUT NO COM-PLAINTS, EITHER.

LUKE, PRINCESS-- MEET KATYA M'BUELE.

WE CREWED TOGETHER ON A CORELLIAN RIM-RUNNER-- YOU NAME IT, WE'D SMUGGLE IT. THEY WERE GOOD TIMES, MOSTLY.

WELL, WELL, WELL-- THIS IS A SIDE TO CAPTAIN SOLO WE'VE NEVER SEEN BEFORE.

SHE'S A NICE-LOOKING LADY, PRINCESS, ARE YOU JEALOUS?

LEIA DOESN'T REPLY, AND FOR THE UMPTEENTH TIME, LUKE SKYWALKER THINKS OF HIS ATTRACTION TO SHE, AND WONDERS HOW SHE TRULY FEELS ABOUT HIM.

BACK TO BUSINESS, KID. I STILL WANT TO HEAR YOUR STORY.

THERE ISN'T MUCH TO TELL. WE WERE IN THE BAZAAR, WHEN THIS WINGED WOMAN ACCUSED US OF...

WINGED WOMAN?! DESCRIBE HER, LUKE!

UH, TALLER THAN YOU, REAL SLIM, BEAUTIFUL. HER BODY AND WINGS WERE GREEN, SHE WAS BALD, TOO, EXCEPT FOR A SILVER CREST...

HAN-- IT'S HER!

HAN-- WHAT IS IT?! DO YOU KNOW THE WOMAN?!?

IT'S OLD BUSINESS, KID, NOTHIN' FOR YOU TO WORRY ABOUT. AN' NOTHIN' YOU CAN HELP WITH.

HAN, WHAT ARE YOU GOING TO DO?

SEE A MAN, ASK SOME QUESTIONS. CALL IN SOME OLD DEBTS.

I'M COMING WITH YOU.

YOU'RE STAYING.

I KNOW YOU'RE SCARED, KATYA; I'M SCARED, TOO. BUT WHAT I HAVE TO DO, I CAN DO BEST ALONE. YOU'LL BE SAFER HERE, ANYWAY.

IF I'M NOT BACK BY DAWN, TAKE THE FALCON AND RUN. WHEN YOU'RE SPACEBORNE, TELL CHEWIE AND THE OTHERS WHO THE TYRANT IS, WHY SHE'S AFTER US, DO WHAT I ASK, KATYA--PLEASE?

YOU KNOW I COULD NEVER REFUSE YOU ANYTHING, YOU HAND-SOME LUG.

TAKE CARE, SOLO. I'LL BE HERE WAITING FOR YOU.

THE HEIGHTS.

THESE ARE HOMES OF TIRAHNN'S ELITE-- THE MERCHANT PRINCES WHO RULE THIS WORLD--HUGE, FANTASTIC PALACES SPRAWLING ACROSS MILES OF GROUND, OR REACHING IM- POSSIBLY HIGH INTO THE EMERALD SKY.

IN ONE SUCH TOWER LIVES A MAN ONCE KNOWN AS LASKAR. HE USED TO BE A SNEAK THIEF AND SMALL-TIME FENCE, BUT OVER THE YEARS HE'S AMASSED A CONSIDERABLE FORTUNE...

...UNTIL NOW, HE RANKS AS ONE OF THE MOST POWERFUL MEN ON TIRAHNN. HE THINKS HE BURIED HIS PAST LONG AGO, THAT HE HAS NOTHING--AND NO ONE-- TO FEAR FROM THE OLD DAYS.

HE'S IN FOR A SURPRISE.

EVENIN', LASKAR.

WHA--?! WHO--?!? HOW DARE YOU-- BY THE STARS!

HAN SOLO!

THE ONE AND ONLY, LASKAR.

SOLO, DON'T GET HASTY, MAN! I CAN PAY--I ALWAYS MEANT TO PAY!

GLAD TO HEAR IT, OL' BUDDY. BUT FIRST, LET'S TALK ABOUT A MUTUAL ACQUAINTANCE--

--THE GREAT TYRANT OF SKYE.

TIME PASSES.

THE MILLENNIUM FALCON'S CARGO HOLD. AN UNUSUALLY DISGRUNTLED WOOKIEE DOES A LATE GUARD TOUR. CHEWBACCA AND SOLO ARE AS CLOSE AS TWO BEINGS CAN GET. THEY'VE SAVED EACH OTHER'S LIVES MORE TIMES THAN EITHER CARES TO COUNT.

YET, THIS EVENING, FOR THE FIRST TIME, HAN REFUSED TO CONFIDE IN HIS FIRST MATE. AND, THOUGH CHEWBACCA WOULD DIE BEFORE ADMITTING IT, HAN'S ACTIONS *HURT*.

THE WOOKIEE IS SO WRAPPED UP IN HIS OWN TROUBLED THOUGHTS THAT HE FAILS TO NOTICE A SPARKLING SPIRAL OF SMOKE...

...MATERIALIZING IN THE MAIN AREA BEHIND HIM.

SILENT AS DEATH, THE SHIFTING CLOUD SLITHERS ACROSS THE DECK, ITS SHAPE BECOMING MORE DEFINITE, MORE OMINOUS...

...AS IT PAUSES BEFORE EACH OF THE TEMPORARY CABINS HAN HAD PARTITIONED OFF FOR THIS TRIP...

...UNTIL IT FINDS THE ONE IT WANTS.

INSIDE, KATYA M'BUELE LIES ASLEEP...

...SECURE IN THE KNOWLEDGE THAT THE SLIGHTEST SOUND, THE MEREST HINT OF DANGER, WILL WAKE HER.

...A RIFLE BLASTER CRADLED IN HER ARMS...

BUT THIS TIME, HER SENSES FAIL HER. SHE AWAKENS TO THE SMOKE DEMON'S TOUCH.

TOO LATE. WITH SOME WARNING HER MIND, HER NERVES, MIGHT HAVE RESISTED. BUT NOW...

EH--?!?

NO--OH, *NO!!*

ITS TOUCH PARALYZES HER COMPLETELY...

...LEAVING HER CONSCIOUS, BUT HELP-LESS.

THEN, THE DEMON'S SMOKY SUBSTANCE FLOWS INTO HER BODY, ENTERING THROUGH HER VERY PORES.

KATYA'S SKIN TURNS TRANS-LUCENT, TRANSPARENT, AND FINALLY FADES AWAY...

...AS HER ENTIRE BODY IS TURNED TO SMOKE AND ABSORBED BY THE DEMON.

IN A FEW SECONDS, IT'S ALL OVER. THERE ARE MANY SLOWER WAYS TO DIE, BUT FEW MORE *TERRIBLE. IT* DOES NOT GO *UNNOTICED.*

I HEARD--FELT--A DISRUPTION IN THE FORCE--LIKE A SCREAM OF *ANGUISH* INSIDE MY MIND!

KATYA--!?!

THE DEMON REACTS WITH THE SPEED OF THOUGHT, AND THE RAW, IRRESISTABLE POWER OF AN ENRAGED BANTHA.

WH-WHAT *IS* THIS THING?! HOW DID IT GET ABOARD WITHOUT TRIGGERING THE *ALARMS?!*

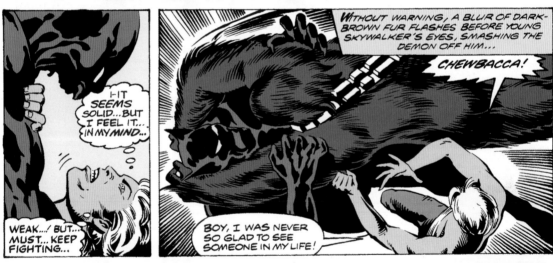

I-IT *SEEMS* SOLID...BUT I FEEL IT... IN MY *MIND...*

WEAK...! BUT... MUST... KEEP FIGHTING...

WITHOUT WARNING, A BLUR OF DARK-BROWN FUR FLASHES BEFORE YOUNG SKYWALKER'S EYES, SMASHING THE DEMON OFF HIM...

CHEWBACCA!

BOY, I WAS NEVER SO GLAD TO SEE SOMEONE IN MY LIFE!

LUKE'S JOY IS SHORT-LIVED, HOWEVER, AS THE DEMON SHRUGS OFF THE GIANT WOOKIEE'S ATTACK WITH *CONTEMPT-UOUS* EASE.

LUKE, CHEWBACCA, GET AWAY FROM THERE! I'LL COVER YOU!

LEIA'S INTENTIONS ARE ADMIRABLE, HER AIM PERFECT...

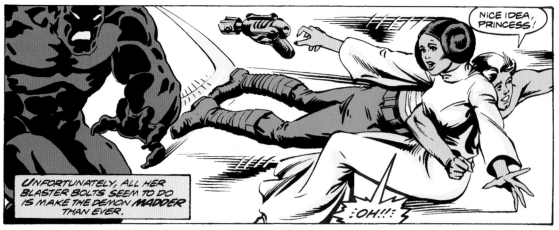

NICE IDEA, PRINCESS!

:OH!!:

UNFORTUNATELY, ALL HER BLASTER BOLTS SEEM TO DO IS MAKE THE DEMON *MADDER* THAN EVER.

TOO BAD IT DIDN'T WORK.

BUT WHAT NOW?! OUR WEAPONS WON'T STOP THE CREATURE--

--AND I'VE A NASTY FEELING THESE WALLS WON'T KEEP IT OUT. *UH-OH!*

LUKE!

AS THE DEMON TOUCHES LUKE, ITS SMOKY ESSENSE BEGINS...

...TO PENETRATE HIS BODY AS IT DID KATYA'S.

LUKE FEELS HIS LIMBS STIFFEN-- HIS MIND AND SOUL BEGIN TO COLLAPSE UNDER THE HELLISH PSYCHIC AND PHYSICAL ONSLAUGHT. HE GROPES DESPERATELY FOR *SALVATION...*

...AND FINDS IT!

WITH A CRACK OF THUNDER, HIS LIGHT-SABER KEYS TO LIFE IN HIS HAND, THE PURE LIGHT OF ITS *ENERGY BLADE...*

...SWEEPING UP IN A CLASSIC KILLING STROKE THAT IMPALES THE SMOKE DEMON! THE CREATURE DIES WITHOUT AUDIBLE SOUND, YET THE PSYCHIC SCREAM THAT ECHOS AND RE-ECHOS IN LUKE'S MIND WILL STAY WITH HIM TILL HE DIES.

AS THE SMOKE CLEARS, LUKE ISN'T ALL THAT SURPRISED TO FIND HIMSELF *SHAKING*, TO FIND HIS FACE STAINED WITH UNACCUSTOMED *TEARS*.

IS--IS IT...*DEAD*?

IT'S *DEAD*.

AND ALL THE *SOULS* OF ITS VICTIMS--TRAPPED WITHIN THAT MONSTER --ARE FINALLY *FREE*.

I'VE BEEN *SCARED* BEFORE--I'VE FACED DEATH BEFORE, *LOTS* OF TIMES--BUT I'VE NEVER FELT ANYTHING LIKE THIS.

THAT DEMON WAS...A CREATION OF THE *FORCE*-- GIVEN LIFE BY SOMEONE WHOSE POWER RIVALS *DARTH VADER'S*.

CHEWBACCA--MEDICINE AND HOT SOUP, QUICKLY! AND BLANKETS, TOO! LUKE'S SLIPPING INTO SHOCK!

I DON'T LIKE IT, HE'S SO PALE. HE LOOKS ALMOST AS BAD AS HE DID THAT TIME HIS MIND ACCIDENTALLY TOUCHED DARTH VADER'S.*

THAT SOUND-- IT'S THE ENTRY ALARM!

BREEP BREEP BREEP

* WAAAAY BACK IN *STAR WARS* #18--ARCHIE.

CAUTIOUSLY, CHEWBACCA ADMITS THE VISITOR, AND...

WHAT THE BLAZES IS GOIN' ON HERE?! I'VE BEEN POUNDIN' ON THAT BLASTED HATCH FOR FIVE MINUTES!

HAN! THANK THE FORCE IT'S YOU.

LEIA QUICKLY TELLS THE CORRELLIAN STAR-PILOT WHAT'S HAPPENED...

KATYA--LAUGHIN' KATYA... DEAD...?

I'M SORRY, HAN, I KNOW SHE WAS YOUR FRIEND.

SHE WAS THAT, PRINCESS-- AND A LOT MORE.

SHOW ME.

IT'S *MY* FAULT. I SHOULDN'T HAVE LEFT HER. I THOUGHT SHE'D BE *SAFE* HERE--THAT *I'D* BE TAKING ALL THE RISKS.

YOU DID ALL YOU COULD, HAN.

YEAH? I COULD HAVE *RUN*, LADY. I SURE WANTED TO.

SOMEHOW, THAT DOESN'T SEEM YOUR STYLE.

YOUR ROYALNESS, WHAT YOU DON'T KNOW ABOUT ME--OR MY 'STYLE'--WOULD FILL THE *IMPERIAL LIBRARY!*

STRAP LUKE IN, CHEWIE--AN' THE PRINCESS AS WELL--

--WE'RE GETTIN' OUTTA HERE.

AND, A FEW MINUTES LATER...

WHAT IN THE NINE MOONS--?!?

HAN LIFTS THE MILLENNIUM FALCON OUT OF THE PLANETARY ATMOSPHERE AT *FULL THROTTLE*--

UNIDENTIFIED FREIGHTER, FROM TIRAHNN PORT CONTROL--ABORT LIFT-OFF AT ONCE! *ABORT--!*

OH, WHAT'S THE USE?

--BARELY MISSING A HOUSE OF TAGGE STARLINER ON FINAL APPROACH--

--AND HE MAKES THE JUMP INTO *HYPERSPACE* AS SOON AS IT'S *FEASIBLE,* SHAVING THE TOLERANCES AS *CLOSE* AS ANYONE HAS EVER DARED AND LIVED TO TELL THE TALE.

HE'S A DRIVEN MAN THIS NIGHT...

...AND HE REMAINS ONE FOR THE NEXT FEW DAYS, AS THE FALCON 'JUMPS' TOWARD THE *RIM.*

THEN...

WELL, WE'RE ALMOST THERE.

THAT'S NICE, WHERE'S 'THERE'?

"NOT MANY PEOPLE IN THE EMPIRE HAVE HEARD OF IT; IT'S A *RESTRICTED* WORLD.

MARAT V--KNOWN TO ITS INHABITANTS AS *SKYE.*

"KATYA AND I WERE PART OF A *SMUGGLING* CREW THAT SNEAKED IN THERE YEARS AGO, ON THE PROD FOR SOME FAST, EASY TAKINGS. WE WERE CAPTURED BY *KHARYS,* THE MAJESTRIX--THE WINGED FEMALE YOU AND LUKE RAN INTO IN THE BAZAAR.

"SHE AND HER PEOPLE...*HUNTED* US. TWENTY MEN AND WOMEN--*CORELLIANS* ALL, AS TOUGH AND DANGEROUS A CREW AS EVER RAISED SHIP TOGETHER. ONLY KATYA AND I *ESCAPED.*

IN A WAY, I GUESS I'VE BEEN RUNNING EVER SINCE, I DON'T THINK A *DAY* HAS PASSED WHEN I HAVEN'T LOOKED OVER MY SHOULDER, EXPECTING KHARYS, TO BE THERE.

WELL, I'VE *HAD IT* WITH RUNNING, WITH PLAYING THIS GAME BY *HER* RULES. WE'RE HEADING FOR SKYE, PRINCESS. I'M GONNA DO WHAT THE LADY LEAST EXPECTS, CONFRONT HER ON HER OWN TURF-- *HUH?!?*

HRRRAK!

OH, SOLO, MY POOR SOLO-- YOUR BIGGEST PROBLEM...

A HOLOGRAM IMAGE-- OH!!

BLASTER FIRE!

YOU AND YOUR FRIENDS ARE VERY RESOURCEFUL, SOLO, VERY *LUCKY*...

...BUT I'M AFRAID YOUR STRING HAS JUST ABOUT *RUN OUT.*

"FAREWELL. FOR NOW. WE WILL MEET AGAIN. "

NOT IF *I* CAN HELP IT.

HAN-- WHAT ARE WE UP AGAINST?!

OH, BROTHER!

TIE FIGHTERS-- A WHOLE SQUADRON...

...WAITING TO HIT US THE INSTANT WE DROPPED OUT OF HYPERSPACE.

...IS THAT YOU'RE SO TOTALLY *PREDICTABLE.* FAR FROM OUTSMARTING ME, YOU'VE PLAYED RIGHT INTO MY HANDS.

TAKE THE TOP TURRET, PRINCESS...

...WHILE I TRY TO LOSE 'EM!

HOLD THE FALCON STEADY FOR A MOMENT LONGER, HAN. I'M LOCKED ON SOME TARGETS.

THREE SHOTS. THREE DIRECT HITS. THREE *LESS* TIE FIGHTERS TO WORRY ABOUT

THREE DEAD IMPERIALS TO WEIGH IN THE BALANCE AGAINST THE *MILLIONS* SLAUGHTERED WITHOUT MERCY WHEN THE EMPEROR'S *DEATH STAR* DESTROYED LEIA'S HOMEWORLD, *ALDERAAN.* ✻

NICE SHOOTING, PRINCESS!

I DO MY HUMBLE BEST.

✻*STAR WARS #3* --ARCHIE.

TROUBLE IS...

...THERE'S A LOT *MORE* WHERE THOSE CAME FROM. THEY'RE HITTING US FROM *ALL* SIDES!

AS A STAR-PILOT, HAN SOLO IS IN A CLASS BY HIMSELF--

--AND SO IS HIS SHIP--

--BUT THERE ARE TIMES WHEN ALL THE SKILL AND DARING IN CREATION WON'T DO YOU A BIT OF GOOD.

THIS IS *ONE* OF THEM.

STOP BLEEP-ING, ARTOO!

YOU RUST-CHOKED GEAR-BOX-- I CAN *SEE* WE'RE FLOATING!

THE ARTIFICIAL GRAVITY'S GONE!

VRP-BEEP!

CHEWIE-- AUXILIARY SYSTEMS! *FAST!*

I'M SORRY, SIR, BUT THOSE ARE ALSO COM-PLETELY *DIS-FUNCTIONAL.*

IN ADDITION, WE SEEM TO HAVE LOST MOST OF OUR SHIELDS.

FOR ALL INTENTS AND PURPOSES, SIR, WE ARE *DEFENSELESS.*

TUMBLING END OVER END...

...AND TRAILING A TAIL OF FIRE *KILOMETERS* LONG, THE MILLEN-IUM FALCON PLUNGES INTO SKYE'S ATMOSPHERE.

A TIE FIGHTER FOLLOWS HER DOWN, UNTIL SHE FINALLY *DISAPPEARS* INTO THE MASSIVE CLOUD FORMATIONS THAT SHROUD SKYE'S MAJESTIC MOUNTAIN PEAKS.

IN SECONDS, THE IMPERIAL WARCRAFT IS ONCE MORE IN SPACE, AND REPORTING TO ITS BASE...

...ATMOSPHERIC TURBULENCE PRECLUDED CONTINUED CLOSE PURSUIT. WILL CONTINUE TRACKING WITH SURFACE-SCANNING RADAR.

...HE'S OURS!

SOLO CAN'T STAY DOWN THERE FOREVER, AND WHEN HE RISES...

MEANWHILE...

INTO THE LIFEPOD, YOU TWO.

HAN--N-NO....! WE CAN....HELP YOU.

MISTRESS, MASTER LUKE'S LIFE-READINGS...!

I KNOW, THREEPIO. LUKE...

PRINCESS--! HE'S PASSED OUT. HE'S RUNNING A FEVER.

HELP ME WITH HIM, THREEPIO.

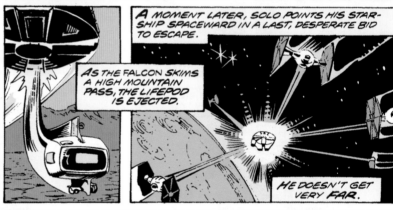

A MOMENT LATER, SOLO POINTS HIS STAR-SHIP SPACEWARD IN A LAST, DESPERATE BID TO ESCAPE.

AS THE FALCON SKIMS A HIGH MOUNTAIN PASS, THE LIFEPOD IS EJECTED.

HE DOESN'T GET VERY FAR.

MISTRESS, WHY DID MASTER SOLO ABANDON US? ARE YOU AND MASTER LUKE NOT HIS FRIENDS?

HE DID IT TO SAVE US, THREEPIO. HE KNEW THE FALCON HAD NO CHANCE--IT'S TOO BIG A TARGET TO MISS.

BUT THE IMPERIALS MIGHT OVERLOOK A LIFEPOD.

"THERE HAS TO BE A STARPORT ON SKYE--OTHERWISE, HOW COULD THE MAJESTRIX TRAVEL TO TIRAHNN? WE MIGHT BE ABLE TO BUY OR STEAL A SHIP. IT'S A SLIM HOPE, BUT IT'S STILL A HOPE. THAT'S A LOT MORE THAN HAN OR CHEWBACCA HAVE."

BOLD WORDS. THEY HAUNT LEIA NOW...

...AS SHE SITS IN THE DARK, SHIVERING--DESPITE THE THICK FUR CLOAK GATHERED TIGHT AROUND HER SHOULDERS.

WHERE...AM I? WHY...SO COLD...?

OOOOOHHH...

LUKE! YOU'RE ALL RIGHT!!

I'M... *ALIVE.* BEYOND THAT, I WOULDN'T TAKE ANY BETS. WHAT... *HAP-PENED?* WHERE'S HAN AND THE *FALCON?!* WHERE ARE *WE?!?*

SLOW DOWN! IT FEELS LIKE YOUR FEVER'S BROKEN, BUT YOU'RE STILL *WEAK* AS A BABY. SAVE YOUR STRENGTH; YOU'LL *NEED* IT.

HAN, CHEWBACCA-- THE *FALCON* --ARE *GONE.* THEY SACRIFICED THEMSELVES TO GIVE US A CHANCE FOR FREEDOM. AND THEY DIED FOR *NOTHING.* WE WERE CAPTURED THE MINUTE OUR LIFE-POD LANDED. YOU AND I HAVE BEEN IN THIS *CELL* EVER SINCE.

HAN...CHEWIE-- *DEAD?!* I DON'T BELIEVE IT-- *LEIA!*

OH!!

OUTWORLDERS, I AM *ARAGH,* LORD OF THE HIGHLANDS, *PA-TRIARCH* OF THE S'KYTRI-- THE WINDBORN.

IN THE NAME OF THE *COUNCIL,* I GREET YOU, AND SUMMON YOU TO *TRIAL!*

LUKE, THIS IS WHAT I STARTED TO TELL YOU. THESE BEINGS WHO CAPTURED US ARE THE *SAME RACE* AS THE MAJESTRIX WHO WANTED US DEAD!

TRIAL?! ON WHAT CHARGE?!

WE'RE *STRANGERS* TO YOUR WORLD, PATRIARCH. WE CAME IN PEACE. WE'VE COMMITTED NO CRIME.

YOU ARE *WALKERS.* THAT IS CRIME ENOUGH. YOUR PRESENCE HAS PROFANED OUR SACRED AERIES. THAT, TOO, IS A CRIME.

ARISE AND FOLLOW ME--AT ONCE! AND SPEAK NO MORE TO ME. IT IS FOR THE COUNCIL TO DECIDE YOUR FATE--

--LIFE... OR *DEATH!*

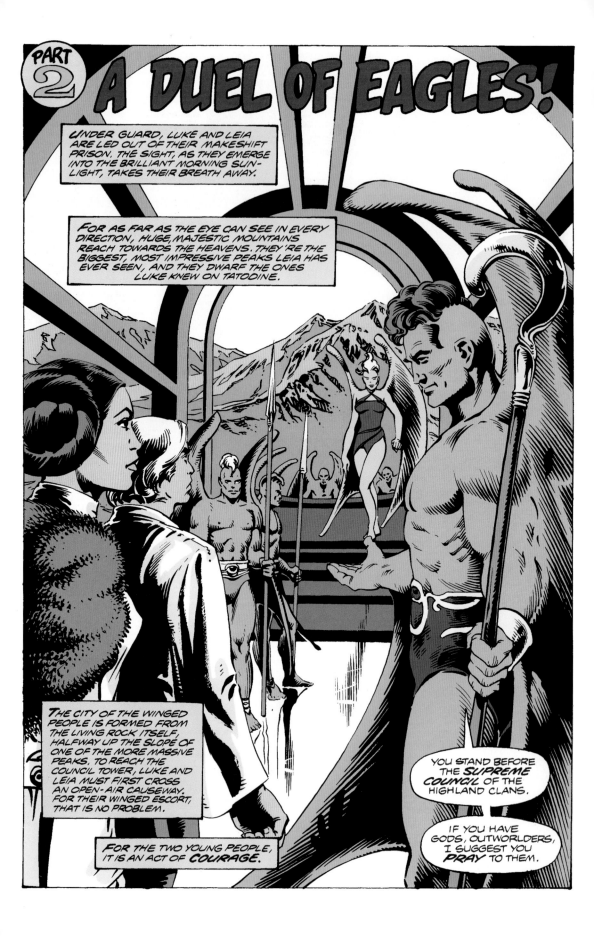

PART 2 # A DUEL OF EAGLES!

UNDER GUARD, LUKE AND LEIA ARE LED OUT OF THEIR MAKESHIFT PRISON. THE SIGHT, AS THEY EMERGE INTO THE BRILLIANT MORNING SUNLIGHT, TAKES THEIR BREATH AWAY.

FOR AS FAR AS THE EYE CAN SEE IN EVERY DIRECTION, HUGE, MAJESTIC MOUNTAINS REACH TOWARDS THE HEAVENS. THEY'RE THE BIGGEST, MOST IMPRESSIVE PEAKS LEIA HAS EVER SEEN, AND THEY DWARF THE ONES LUKE KNEW ON TATOOINE.

THE CITY OF THE WINGED PEOPLE IS FORMED FROM THE LIVING ROCK ITSELF, HALFWAY UP THE SLOPE OF ONE OF THE MORE MASSIVE PEAKS, TO REACH THE COUNCIL TOWER, LUKE AND LEIA MUST FIRST CROSS AN OPEN-AIR CAUSEWAY. FOR THEIR WINGED ESCORT, THAT IS NO PROBLEM.

FOR THE TWO YOUNG PEOPLE, IT IS AN ACT OF COURAGE.

YOU STAND BEFORE THE *SUPREME COUNCIL* OF THE HIGHLAND CLANS.

IF YOU HAVE GODS, OUTWORLDERS, I SUGGEST YOU *PRAY* TO THEM.

I AM DEVERÉN.

I SPEAK FOR THE COUNCIL.

YOU HAVE VIOLATED S'KYTRI SPACE, YOU COME TO OUR WORLD UNINVITED, BEARING *WEAPONS,* AND WITH THE STENCH OF BATTLE ABOUT YOU.

WE ALSO CAME WITH *FRIENDS!* WHERE ARE THEY? WHAT HAVE YOU DONE WITH OUR *DROIDS?!*

DO NOT RAISE YOUR VOICE TO ME, YOUNG MALE. YOUR LIVES HANG BY A *THIN* ENOUGH THREAD AS IT IS.

YOUR..."*FRIENDS*"... ARE HERE--AND, LIKE YOU, THEY ARE UN-HARMED, FOR THE MOMENT.

MASTER LUKE! OH, THANK THE MAKER-- IT'S SO *GOOD* TO SEE YOU AGAIN!

SEE-THREEPIO! ARTOO-DETOO!

LUKE, WHAT ARE YOU *DOING?!*

THEY'RE BEING HELD IN SOME KIND OF *STASIS LOCK.* I'M GOING TO SEE IF THEY'RE ALL RIGHT!

WHREET! DEEDLE-BOOP!

ON SECOND THOUGHT, MAYBE I'LL JUST STAY RIGHT WHERE I AM.

AS HE BACKS AWAY FROM THE DROIDS, LUKE THINKS OF HAN SOLO...

WE SHOULD HAVE STAYED WITH YOU, HAN. WE'D BE NO WORSE OFF THAN WE ARE NOW.

...AND OF THE *SACRIFICE* THE DASHING SMUGGLER MADE TO SEE HIS FRIENDS SAFELY AWAY IN THE LIFEBOAT...

EVEN IF I GOT MY LIGHTSABER -- AND LEIA HER BLASTER -- WE COULDN'T ESCAPE FROM THIS CITY WITHOUT A SHIP, OR ANTI-GRAVITY BELTS, OR *WINGS*.

PATRIARCH, COUNCILLORS, WE KNOW YOUR WORLD IS RESTRICTED. BUT BEFORE WE COULD MAKE PROPER DIPLO-MATIC APPROACH...OUR SPACE-CRAFT WAS ATTACKED. OUR VIOLATIONS ARE UNINTENTIONAL.

ALL WE ASK IS SAFE TRANSPORT TO YOUR PLANETARY STARPORT. WE'LL BE OFF-PLANET AS SOON AS WE CAN BOOK PASS-AGE.

AN ELOQUENT APPEAL -- *PRINCESS LEIA ORGANA OF ALDERAAN!*

BUT THIS IMPERIAL WARRANT SPEAKS JUST AS *ELOQUENTLY,* DOES IT NOT?

LEIA ORGANA, PRINCESS-SENATOR OF ALDERRAN **WANTED:**

...OR TREASON AGAIN THE EMPIRE

YOU ARE A LEADER OF THE *REBEL ALLIANCE.* YOU CRASHED BECAUSE IMPERIAL FORCES STATIONED IN THIS SYS-TEM ATTACKED IN PERFOR-MANCE OF THEIR DUTY.

I SEE. WHAT WILL YOU DO WITH US, THEN?

YOU ARE ENEMIES OF THE IMPERIUM THE WINDBORN ARE SWORN TO *SERVE. OUR* DUTY REQUIRES THAT WE *SURRENDER* YOU IMMEDIATELY TO THE IMPERIAL LEGATE HERE.

THAT'S IT, THEN. WE'RE AS GOOD AS *DEAD*.

YOUNG MALE, THIS WEAPON IS *YOURS?*

IT IS.

I WOULD KNOW YOUR NAME.

LUKE SKYWALKER.

206

‹BY THE DAWN WIND, I THOUGHT THAT WEAPON LOOKED *FAMILIAR*.›

‹IS HE THE *ONE*?›

‹HIS NAME IS THE *SAME* AS OUR *WINGLESS BLOOD BROTHER'S*.›

‹BUT HE IS SO YOUNG --AND VIRTUALLY *ALONE*! THE *MAJESTRIX* IS POWERFUL, WITH AN *ARMY* AT HER BACK!›

‹YET, IF HE IS THE ONE, WE OWE HIM A DEBT THAT CAN NEVER BE REPAID. I WILL PUT FORWARD ONE FINAL TEST -- ONE OF *HONOR*.›

WHAT ARE THEY SAYING, LUKE?

‹THEN WE WILL *DECIDE*.›

I WISH I KNEW. I DON'T LIKE IT, THOUGH.

YOUR STARSHIP WAS ATTACKED AS IT NEARED OUR WORLD.

AND DESTROYED. AFTER WE... ABANDONED HER.

NOT SO. THE VESSEL WAS *CAPTURED* AND TAKEN INTACT TO THE MAJESTRIX' FORTRESS.

"*INTACT?!*" THEN-- THAT MEANS HAN AND CHEWBACCA COULD STILL BE *ALIVE*!

WE DON'T KNOW THAT FOR SURE.

I DON'T CARE. IF THERE'S THE *SLIGHTEST* CHANCE THEY'RE ALIVE, WE'VE GOT TO TRY TO *RESCUE* THEM.

LUKE-- YOU'RE *CRAZY*! YOU'RE GOING TO BREAK INTO AN IMPERIAL STRONGHOLD, TAKE ON LORD KNOWS *HOW* MANY STORMTROOPERS, TO SAVE TWO PEOPLE WHO ARE PROBABLY ALREADY DEAD?!

YES.

THEN *I* MUST BE CRAZY, TOO--

--BECAUSE I'M GOING WITH YOU.

‹PRAISE THE SACRED WINDS-- HE *IS* THE ONE!›

‹AS THE PROPHECY FORETOLD-- WITH HIS HELP, THE S'KYTRI MAY ONCE MORE FLY *FREE*!›

HEAR AND HEED THE WORDS OF THE COUNCIL! WE PROCLAIM LUKE SKYWALKER AND LEIA ORGANA-- *FRIENDS* OF THE S'KYTRI.

WHAT AID WE CAN GIVE IS THEIRS FOR THE ASKING.

ELSEWHERE...

...ATOP THE HIGHEST PEAK IN THIS MOST AWESOME OF MOUNTAIN RANGES...

...STANDS THE FORTRESS-KEEP OF KHARYS, MATRIARCH OF THE S'KYTRI--SELF-PROCLAIMED MAJESTRIX OF SKYE.

UNDER HER DIRECT COMMAND IS A FORCE OF STARSHIPS AND STORM-TROOPERS THAT MANY SECTOR GOVERNORS WOULD ENVY. EVEN SO, SHE CARES NOT A WHIT FOR THE EMPIRE SHE IS PLEDGED TO SERVE; SHE IS BOUND BY AN OLDER, DEEPER OBLIGATION, TO A MAN THAT MOST OF THE GALAXY HAS REASON TO FEAR-- *DARTH VADER.*

THAT FURRY MISANTHROPE MAKES TOO MUCH NOISE, CAPTAIN. IT DISTURBS ME. *SILENCE* THE BEAST-- WITHOUT HARMING IT-- OR YOU WILL TAKE ITS PLACE.

UH...YES, MAJESTRIX.

HRRAWR!

CHEWIE, SHUT UP! YOU BOTHER THE NICE LADY!

AND, AS EVER, YOUR MOUTH KEEPS GETTING YOU INTO *TROUBLE.*

WHAT'S THE POINT OF BEING NICE, KHARYS? YOU'RE GOING TO *KILL* ME ANYWAY, RIGHT?

OF COURSE. BUT THERE ARE *MYRIAD* WAYS TO DIE, SOLO.

SOME WOULD MAKE MY "SMOKE DEMON" SEEM QUITE *PLEASANT* BY COMPARISON.

AS *GALLANT* AS EVER, HAN SOLO.

IT'S BEEN A LONG TIME SINCE WE LAST PARTED.

NOT LONG ENOUGH--

UNNNGH!

YOU AND YOUR FELLOW CORRELLIANS PROVIDED ME A RARE, FINE HUNT, SOLO, BUT NOW THE HUNT IS *ENDED.*

BEFORE I TAKE YOUR LIFE, HOWEVER...

THERE ARE SOME THINGS I WOULD KNOW ABOUT YOUR TRAVELLING COMPANIONS, PRINCESS LEIA AND, MORE IMPORTANTLY, THE BOY WHO DESTROYED THE DEATH STAR, THE ONE YOU CALL *LUKE.*

WHAT ARE THEY TO YOU?

TO ME-- NOTHING. TO THE DARK LORD OF SITH, WHOM I SERVE, PERHAPS *EVERY-THING.*

NO ANSWER? WHAT A...PITY.

YOU FORCE ME TO RESORT TO THE TENDER MERCIES OF AN IMPERIAL *INTERROGATOR.*

HAN'S FACE PALES SLIGHTLY UNDER HIS SPACER'S TAN AS THE HUMMING, GLEAMING ORB MOVES TOWARDS HIM.

DARTH VADER USED A SIMILAR MACHINE ON LEIA WHEN SHE WAS HIS PRISONER ABOARD THE DEATH STAR.

SHE STILL REFUSES TO SPEAK OF WHAT HAPPENED, AND THE MEMORIES STILL GIVE HER *NIGHTMARES.*

MEANWHILE, UP ON THE FORTRESS' BATTLEMENTS...

CAPTAIN OF THE GUARD!

FLIERS, SIR-- SCORES OF 'EM! I'VE NEVER SEEN SO MANY!

HM-- THEY'RE HIGHLAND CLANS, BY THEIR MARKINGS. LED BY *ARAGH* HIMSELF, TOO. PROBABLY TAKING SOME HATCHLINGS OUT FOR THEIR INITIATION HUNT.

BUT ALERT THE GARRISON-- AND THE *MAJESTRIX*-- JUST IN CASE.

YOU KNOW, LUKE, IF I WEREN'T SO SCARED, I'D BE HAVING THE TIME OF MY LIFE RIGHT NOW.

I KNOW WHAT YOU MEAN.

OUR *ANTI-GRAV* BELT PACKS KEEP US ALOFT, BUT THESE WINGS GET US WHERE WE WANT TO GO. JUST LIKE THE S'KYTRI, WE HAVE TO FOLLOW THE WINDS, RIDE THE AIR CURRENTS AND THERMALS, WATCH OUT FOR DOWNDRAFTS.

THE DIFFERENCE IS, THEY'VE HAD A WHOLE *LIFETIME* TO PRACTICE. WE'VE ONLY HAD A *DAY*.

THESE BODY-SUITS SHOULD *DISGUISE* US UNTIL WE'RE RIGHT ON TOP OF THE CASTLE.

THE CLANS HAVE COME AS FAR AS WE CAN, GIVEN WHAT ASSISTANCE WE CAN. I AM SORRY, SKYWALKER, BUT YOU TWO MUST WIN OR LOSE YOUR FIGHT... *ALONE.*

GREAT.

READY, LEIA?

NOT REALLY --BUT DO I HAVE A CHOICE?

MAY THE *FORCE* BE WITH YOU.

SHE SCREAMS, HER WINGS FOLDING IN ON THEM-SELVES...

...AND THEN, SHE *FALLS.*

WHAT IS IT, CAPTAIN?

ONE OF 'EM'S HIT A DOWN-DRAFT. HER MATE'S TRYING TO SAVE HER.

A KILOBUCK SAYS HE DOESN'T MAKE IT.

YOU'RE ON. ANYONE ELSE WANT TO *BET*?

BY THE ETERNAL-- SHE'S NO FLIER!

SHE'S *HUMAN!*

CORRECT, BUTCHER-- AND A *PRINCESS OF ALDERAAN!*

VORP!

VOOW

SOUND THE ALARM! IT'S AN *AMB-- AARRRGH!!*

THEIR INITIAL STRAFING RUN CUTS DOWN EVERY STORMTROOPER IN SIGHT, AND, AS THEY WHEEL FOR A SECOND PASS...

...LEIA *DISENGAGES* FROM HER WINGS AND DROPS *LIGHTLY* TO THE PARAPET.

I'M *DOWN*-- AND STILL IN ONE PIECE!

UH-OH! MORE TROOPERS!

BLAST! I'M PINNED DOWN!

IF LUKE DOESN'T GET THESE KILLERS OFF MY BACK, OUR GREAT ESCAPE WILL BE *OVER* BEFORE IT'S EVEN BEGUN!

AND, ALMOST ON CUE...

WHA--?! BLASTER FIRE!

YEAAGKH!

TAKE COVER, MEN! WE'RE *SITTING DUCKS* OUT HERE IN THE OPEN!

I DIDN'T WANT LEIA GOING INTO THE CASTLE BY HERSELF, BUT I COULDN'T THINK OF ANY OTHER VIABLE PLAN.

I FLEW *GLIDERS* ON TATOOINE LONG BEFORE I BUILT MY T-16. I'M A LOT *BETTER* WITH THESE WINGS THAN SHE IS-- IT'S UP TO ME TO KEEP THE STORM-TROOPERS OCCUPIED...

...WHILE SHE LOOKS FOR HAN AND CHEWBACCA.

SOUNDS LIKE LUKE'S GIVING KHARYS' STORMTROOPERS A RUN FOR THEIR MONEY-- GOOD. I'LL BET HE'S MORE WORRIED ABOUT ME THAN THEM!

I CAN TAKE CARE OF MYSELF, MR. SKYWALKER, THANK YOU VERY MUCH.

STILL, IT'S NICE TO KNOW HE CARES.

I WONDER HOW DEEP INSIDE THE MOUNTAIN I AM?

WAIT-- THAT MUFFLED CRY!

THESE CATACOMBS SEEM TO GO ON FOREVER.

HER ENTRANCE IS DRAMATIC-- AND VERY EFFECTIVE-- SHE KICKS THE DOOR IN.

EVERYONE-- FREEZE!!

HAN! HE'S HOOKED UP TO AN IMPERIAL INTERROGATOR...

...JUST AS I WAS.

THE MAJESTRIX IS TRYING TO PSYCHO-PROBE HIM!

WHO DARES--?!

...UNLESS YOU WANT TO TEST WHETHER THOSE WINGS CAN OUT-FLY MY BLASTER FIRE!

I DARE! LEIA ORGANA!

RELEASE HAN SOLO AND CHEWBACCA-- NOW! AND NO FALSE MOVES...

YOU SEEM TO HAVE ME AT A *DISADVAN-TAGE*, PRINCESS, BUT SURELY YOU KNOW YOU HAVEN'T A PRAYER OF LEAVING HERE ALIVE.

WE'LL TAKE OUR CHANCES.

BEHIND ME--A *NOISE!?*

SEIZE HER!

CATUMAN WARRIORS!

AAYIIII--!!

TWO OF THEM! LOST MY RIFLE! CAN'T TRY FOR IT-- OUT OF REACH!

GOT TO KEEP MOVING, STAY AWAY FROM THEM--BUT THEY'RE SO *FAST!*

MY *SHOULDER!*

SPIKES BIT DEEP--HOPE THEY WEREN'T *POISONED.* THEY EXPECT ME TO KEEP RUNNING. INSTEAD, I'LL MAKE A STAND...

...AND HOPE MY *HAND BLASTER* IS ENOUGH TO STOP THEM!

WITH BLINDING, UNEXPECTED SPEED, LEIA DRAWS HER SIDEARM...

...BUT QUICK AS SHE IS, THE CATUMAN IS EVEN *QUICKER.*

NO!!

THE WARRIOR'S ARM HITS LEIA'S LIKE A STEEL BAR, AND HER LIMB GOES *NUMB* FROM HAND TO SHOULDER...

THE STUNNING IMPACT SENDS THE HAND-GUN FLYING. AGAIN, LEIA DOES THE *UNEXPECTED*, RAKING HER NAILS DOWN THE CATUMAN'S FACE...

BOK!

...BEFORE KICKING *AWAY* FROM HIM WITH ALL HER STRENGTH.

THE "CATS" ARE *OFF-BALANCE*. THEY UNDERESTIMATED ME, THOUGHT I'D BE AN EASY KILL.

NOT A *BIG* ADVANTAGE. BUT IN COMBAT... EVEN A *SMALL* ONE CAN MAKE THE DIFFERENCE. SHE FIRES AS SHE ROLLS...

...THE THIN, SCARLET BEAM CUTTING A DEADLY SWATHE ACROSS THE VAST CHAMBER. ONE CATUMAN DUCKS HER SHOT. HIS BROODMATE ISN'T SO LUCKY.

YAHURRR

HRRR

ZRAKT

AS HE DIES, HE TWIST-FALLS BACKWARDS INTO THE *FORCE FIELD* HOLDING CHEWBACCA--A COMPLEMENT TO THE *MANACLES* CLAMPED TIGHT AROUND THE WOOKIEE'S WRISTS. THE FIELD SHORTS OUT.

THE SUPPOSEDLY "*UNBREAKABLE*" MANACLES RESTRAIN CHEWIE FOR ALL OF A SECOND LONGER.

AS THE SURVIVING CATUMAN LUNGES TOWARDS LEIA, THE *MILLENNIUM FALCON'S* FIRST MATE DIVES FOR HIM.

THE FIGHT IS *NO CONTEST.*

SHOULDER SLASH IS MESSY, BUT I DON'T THINK IT'S SERIOUS. I CAN STILL MOVE MY ARM FAIRLY EASILY.

NO SIGN OF KHARYS-- TOO BAD. WE HAVEN'T TIME TO *SEARCH* FOR HER, EITHER.

HEY, BEAUTIFUL... REMEMBER ME...?

HAN!

ARE YOU ALL RIGHT?!

NEVER FELT... BETTER... YOUR REGALNESS.

CAN YOU *WALK*?

SHOW ME SOME *PROFIT* IN IT AND I'LL RUN A *MARATHON.*

SURE YOU WILL.

CHEWBACCA, CARRY HIM. AND FOLLOW ME.

FUNNY, DON'T UNDER-STAND... WHY... LEGS FOLDED UP LIKE THAT.

THEY WORKED... FINE... THIS MORNING.

HEAR THOSE EXPLOSIONS, OL' BUDDY? SOUNDS LIKE THIS PLACE IS COMING APART AT THE SEAMS.

MY COMPLIMENTS, PRINCESS, THIS ESCAPE PLAN'S GOING SO WELL, YOU'D THINK IT WAS ONE OF *MINE.*

OH? ALL OF A SUDDEN, I'M *WORRIED.*

KHARYS!

STAND YOU BACK, STORM-TROOPERS!

THE BOY'S LIFE IS *MINE!*

SHE'S CARRYING A *LIGHT-SABER!* AND I HAVE A NASTY FEELING...

...SHE *KNOWS* HOW TO USE IT!

SO, THE HATCHLING HAS *FANGS* OF HIS OWN.

THAT LIGHTSABER WILL NOT *SAVE* YOU, BOY.

YOU COULD BE THE FINEST WARRIOR IN CREATION-- ON THE *GROUND*--

--BUT NOW, YOU ARE IN *MY* ELEMENT!

SHE'S-- GOOD!

AND, WORSE, I'VE GOT TO WORRY ABOUT HER WING AND FOOT CLAWS, AS WELL AS THAT SABER.

ARAGH AND THE CLAN ELDERS-- THEY'RE WATCHING! THEN THEY, TOO, MUST BELIEVE HE IS-- THE *ONE*.

THE ONE WHOSE COMING TO SKYE WILL MEAN *MY* DEATH, AND MY PEOPLES' *LIBERATION*.

BEN KENOBI HARDLY HAD ANY TIME TO TRAIN ME HOW TO USE THIS THING...

...BEFORE DARTH VADER KILLED HIM.

BUT IT'S OBVIOUS KHARYS HAS BEEN USING LIGHTSABERS ALL HER LIFE!

I NEED... BREATHING SPACE...

HIT *FULL-RISE* ON MY ANTI-GRAV BELT, IT'LL TAKE ME OUT OF HER REACH, BUY ME SOME TIME.

BUT, WHAT NOW?! I'M ONLY DELAYING THE INEVITABLE. KHARYS IS *TOO GOOD* FOR ME. I CAN'T--CAN'T... BEAT HER.

NO! WHAT...AM I THINKING?! SO... *HARD* TO THINK-- WHY?!

"*IT'S THE FORCE!*

"SHE'S USING IT TO DULL MY WITS, MAKE ME AN EASY, *HELPLESS* TARGET, AND HERE SHE COMES TO *FINISH THE JOB!*

NO MORE FANCY MOVES--MY HEAD'S STILL PRETTY *MUDDLED.*

I CAN'T AFFORD TO SPLIT MY CONCENTRATION.

GRIMLY, ALMOST DESPERATELY-- LUKE SKYWALKER FOCUSES ALL THE POWER OF HIS WILL.

BY THE DARK LORD!

HE'S TRYING TO SHAKE OFF MY PSYCHIC ATTACK!

HE WANTS ONLY ONE THING-- TO MOVE. HE TRIES. HE *FAILS.*

WITH THE BATTLE CRY OF HER ANCIENT, AVIAN RACE...

...KHARYS DIVES FOR THE KILL.

BUT AT THE LAST INSTANT-- IMPOSSIBLY-- THAT ATTACK IS *CHECKED!*

HER SABER GLANCES OFF LUKE'S AND BEFORE HER STARTLED MIND IS EVEN AWARE OF WHAT'S HAPPENING, THE MATRIARCH IS *DEAD.*

IT TOOK *EVERY-THING* I HAD TO PRETEND I WAS STILL FROZEN-- BUT I HAD TO *DECOY* HER IN CLOSE.

I HAD TO BE *SURE* I WOULDN'T *MISS*.

FUNNY-- I THOUGHT I'D FEEL GOOD ABOUT WINNING THIS FIGHT. BUT I DON'T. I FEEL... *SOMEHOW* SAD.

LATER, AFTER THE WINGED CLANS OF S'KYTRI HAVE MADE SHORT WORK OF THE *AERIE'S* IMPERIAL GARRISON, AND THE *MILLENNIUM FALCON* IS ONCE MORE READIED FOR SPACE...

WE ARE NO LONGER BOUND BY OUR OATH-- THANKS TO SKYWALKER. IF ANY IMPERIALS COME SEEKING VENGEANCE FOR THEIR SLAIN COMRADES, THEY WILL FIND THE WINDBORN WAITING FOR THEM...

ARAGH, I'VE *HEARD* YOUR PEOPLE REFER TO LUKE AS *"THE ONE."* ONE WHAT? WHAT DO THEY *MEAN* BY THAT?

"*YEARS* AGO, MY FRIEND, DURING WHAT YOU HUMANS CALLED THE 'CLONE WARS,' THREE *JEDI KNIGHTS* SAVED SKYE FROM DESTRUCTION. ONE WAS *OBI-WAN KENOBI*; THE OTHERS, HIS PUPILS. IN GRATITUDE, WE SWORE ETERNAL FRIEND-SHIP AND FEALTY TO THEM.

"*MUCH LATER*, ONE OF THE PUPILS RETURNED. HE TOLD US THAT OBI-WAN AND THE JEDI WERE DESTROYED-- BY HIS HAND-- THEN, HE INVOKED OUR OATH AND MADE SKYE AN IMPERIAL SATRAPY, TO BE RULED IN HIS NAME BY KHARYS, TO WHOM HE GAVE A PORTION OF HIS KNOWLEDGE AND POWERS. THAT... MAN WAS *DARTH VADER*."

AND OBI-WAN'S *OTHER* PUPIL, WHO WAS HE?

YOUNG ONE...

YOU WEAR HIS *SABER*.

LUKE, IS ANYTHING THE *MATTER*?

I'M *FINE*, PRINCESS. HONEST. I'VE JUST GOT SOME THINGS TO THINK ABOUT...

...*SOME...* MEMORIES TO *CHERISH*.

YOU LOOK SO...*STRANGE*.

"I NEVER KNEW MY *FATHER*, BUT I KNOW NOW... THAT HE WAS A MAN TO BE *PROUD* OF.

"I HOPE I CAN BE *HALF* AS GOOD."

FIN.

Long ago in a galaxy far, far away. . . .there exists a state of cosmic *civil war*. A brave alliance of *underground freedom fighters* has challenged the tyranny and oppression of the awesome *Galactic Empire*. This is their story!

LucasFilm PRESENTS: **STAR WARS** THE GREATEST SPACE FANTASY OF ALL!

CONTINUING THE STORY BEGUN IN THE FILM BY **GEORGE LUCAS** RELEASED BY **TWENTIETH CENTURY FOX**

ARCHIE GOODWIN WRITER/EDITOR / **CARMINE INFANTINO & BOB WIACEK** ARTISTS / **JIM NOVAK** LETTERER / **CARL GAFFORD** COLORIST / **JIM SHOOTER** CONSULTING EDITOR

PROLOGUE:
DEEP SPACE! HERE, A MEETING IS IN PROGRESS. A *RENDEZVOUS* BETWEEN A HOUSE OF TAGGE MINING EXPLORER AND AN IMPERIAL BATTLE CRUISER...

LF619

...AND BETWEEN TWO *BROTHERS!*

...NOT *ANOTHER* PLAN, ORMAN! THE *LAST* WAS NEARLY AS GREAT A FIASCO AS THE *DEATH STAR!*

BECAUSE OF ONE YOUNG REBEL WHO DID THE IMPOSSIBLE... *LUKE SKYWALKER.*

*STAR WARS #26. --ARCHIE.

WELL, THE ALLIANCE HAS A WAY OF *ATTRACTING* THAT SORT, THEY WON'T BE DEFEATED EASILY... OR SWIFTLY.

PARTICULARLY NOT IF THE EMPIRE DEPENDS *SOLELY* ON YOUR STARFLEET'S *BLOCKADE,* LITTLE BROTHER.

SINCE THE DEATH STAR, IMPERIAL POLICY IS ONE OF *CAUTION.* BUT, WHEN THE MOMENT IS *RIGHT--*

--THE EMPIRE WILL *STRIKE BACK!*

LED NO DOUBT BY *DARTH VADER!* WHY SHOULD YOUR CAREER-- AND OUR FAMILY'S *PRESTIGE*--TAKE HIND POSITION IN THE EMPEROR'S FAVOR TO THAT BLASTED *WIZARD?!*

A SUCCESS *NOW* COULD *ECLIPSE* THE SITH LORD!

HE'S *DANGEROUS* TO OPPOSE OPENLY, ORMAN. BUT...YOU ALREADY *KNOW* THAT.

I'M MOVING IN *SECRET,* ULRIC,...USING THE HOUSE OF TAGGE'S GREAT SCIENTIFIC AND COMMERCIAL RESOURCES. WITH *YOU* TO ASSURE CONTINUED MILITARY COOPERATION--

WE'LL HAVE *REVENGE...* AND *MORE!*

IT'S ALL COMING TO *FRUITION,* LITTLE BROTHER--

--ON A QUIET, UNSUSPECTING BACKWATER WORLD CALLED *TATOOINE!*

222

"IF THERE'S A BRIGHT *CENTER* TO THIS UNIVERSE, YOU'RE ON THE WORLD *FARTHEST* FROM IT." TO LUKE SKYWALKER, IT SEEMS *AGES* AGO THAT HE SPOKE THOSE WORDS ABOUT HIS HOME PLANET. IT FEELS AS IF HE WERE A DIFFERENT *PERSON* THAN THAT RESTLESS, INEXPERIENCED FARM BOY. NOW HE IS A *HERO*... AND A WARRIOR'S MISSION HAS BROUGHT HIM *BACK*.

RETURN TO TATOOINE!

ARTOO AND I HAVE UNLOADED THE *LANDSPEEDER*, SIR.

GREAT, THREEPIO! GET THE CAMOUFLAGE COVER OVER THE *FREIGHTER*!

EVEN THE *SAND PEOPLE* DON'T SPEND MUCH TIME IN *THIS* PART OF THE DUNE SEA, BUT THERE'S NO POINT IN TAKING--

MOVE WITH THAT COVERING! *FAST!*

223

OH, DEAR! IT'S PROBABLY WILD *BANTHAS*...OR PERHAPS EVEN THOSE REPULSIVE LITTLE *JAWAS!*

I *KNEW* IT WAS A MISTAKE COMING BACK TO THIS FORSAKEN PLACE!

WHAT DO YOU *MEAN* IF I FEEL THAT WAY I SHOULDN'T HAVE *VOLUNTEERED...?!*

I COULDN'T TRUST A NON-LOGICAL *RUST-POT* LIKE *YOU* TO LOOK AFTER MASTER *LUKE!*

FREEPA BRIIIT!

THREEPIO! THE *COVER--!!*

"-- THERE'S AN *IMPERIAL PATROL* OUT ON THE FAR RIDGE!

"ONE OF THEM IS CARRYING A *SCANNER PACK!*"

KEEP YOUR MIND ON THE *JOB.* YOU DIDN'T SCAN THE SECTOR OFF ON OUR *LEFT.*

MY MIND IS ON THE FACT THAT ONE *TIE FIGHTER* COULD DO THE WORK OF *TEN* OF THESE PATROLS.

AND ATTRACTS TEN TIMES THE *ATTENTION.* ORDERS ARE TO *AVOID* THAT.

ARE THEY AFRAID WE'LL UPSET THE LOCAL *SAND LICE?* THAT'S ABOUT ALL WE EVER--

WAIT! I'VE *GOT* SOMETHING--!

RELAX--! IT'S ONLY A *LAND-SPEEDER*. SOME LOCAL FARMER OUT HUNTING *WOMP RATS*, NO DOUBT.

ATMOSPHERIC DISTORTION MADE IT SEEM *BIGGER* FOR AN INSTANT...NOTHING WORTH INVESTIGATING.

ALL RIGHT THEN. QUIT WASTING OUR TIME... WE'VE GOT A LOT OF *TERRITORY* TO COVER.

DON'T COMPLAIN ...*WE'RE* THE ONES WHO ARE *WALKING*. TOMORROW *I* GET THE *DEWBACK*.

ALL *CLEAR*, THREEPIO. YOU AND ARTOO GOT THE FREIGHTER COVERED JUST IN *TIME*.

THAT *ELECTRONICALLY-CHARGED FABRIC* WILL KEEP ANY SCANNER FROM PICKING UP WHAT'S *UNDER* IT.

BUT THAT *PATROL* WORRIES ME. EXCEPT FOR A SMALL GARRISON AT MOS EISLEY... YOU USED TO *NEVER* SEE A STORM-TROOPER ON TATOOINE.

NO *OFFENSE* TO A NATIVE, SIR... BUT IT DOESN'T *COMPUTE* THAT THIS GRITTY SAND PILE SUDDENLY HAS *STRATEGIC VALUE*.

WELL, OUR MISSION IS TO RECRUIT *BLOCKADE RUNNERS*.

SINCE SOME OF THE BEST *SMUGGLER PILOTS* IN THE GALAXY HANG OUT AT MOS EISLEY... *THAT'S* WHERE WE'RE HEADED.

AND IF ANYTHING *ELSE* IS GOING ON ...THERE'S SURE TO BE *GOSSIP* ABOUT IT!

BUT AS THE TRIO MOVE ALONG A CIRCUITOUS ROUTE TO THE DESERT WORLD'S SPACE-PORT...

THREEPIO! STOP THE SPEEDER!

MASTER LUKE! THIS SURELY CAN'T BE WISE. IF SOMETHING STRANGE IS GOING ON, WE SHOULDN'T--

BRR-KLIK VADOOT!

HOW DARE YOU SAY MY MEMORY CIRCUITS HAVE WARPED, ARTOO! I--OH! OF COURSE!

WHAT HAS DRAWN LUKE IS A RUIN...A RUIN ONCE THE MAIN BUILDING OF A MOISTURE FARM. AND FOR MOST OF HIS TWENTY YEARS... THAT FARM WAS LUKE SKYWALKER'S HOME.

AUNT BERU....! UNCLE OWEN...! MUCH AS I ALWAYS COMPLAINED ABOUT BEING STUCK HERE...

...MUCH AS I GLORY IN SOME OF THE THINGS I'VE DONE SINCE LEAVING... I STILL MISS YOU BOTH VERY MUCH!

THEN... A SOUND MAKES LUKE TURN HIS MISTY EYES BEYOND THE LONG-CHARRED RUBBLE.

THAT VAPORATOR....! IT'S WORKING... ACTIVE...!

B-BUT... THAT SHOULDN'T BE!

HOLD IT RIGHT THERE!

DO EXACTLY WHAT I SAY... OR START SPENDING THE REST OF YOUR LIFE DEAD!

EASE YOUR *BLASTER* FROM ITS HOLSTER... JUST USE TWO FINGERS... *THAT'S* IT...!

NOW TOSS IT *BACK* TO ME.

LUKE *OBEYS*, BUT HE MAKES THE TOSS TOO *HIGH*...

...SO HIS CAPTOR'S *EYES* INADVERTANTLY FOLLOW IT, ONLY FOR AN INSTANT...

...BUT *IN* THAT INSTANT, HE SWIFTLY *WHIRLS!*

HAN SOLO TAUGHT ME ABOUT *DISTRACTING* A FOE--

SHRAAAAK

--AND THE FAST *LIGHT SABER* WORK I LEARNED FROM *OBI-WAN KENOBI!* THAT'S TWO REASONS YOU'RE SUDDENLY ON THE *WRONG END* OF THIS FRACAS!

SUPPOSE *YOU* COME UP WITH ONE FOR *WHY* IT STARTED IN THE *FIRST PLACE!*

S-SKY-WALKER...?

FIXER! WHY AREN'T YOU AT TOSHI STATION REPAIRING EQUIPMENT INSTEAD OF OUT HERE *AMBUSHING* INNOCENT TRAVELLERS?!

I-I DON'T *WORK* AT THE STATION ANYMORE, LUKE. GOT A BETTER JOB... MORE FUTURE.

AT LEAST... THAT'S WHAT I *THOUGHT.*

E-EVERYONE ASSUMED YOU *DIED*, LUKE... ALONG WITH YOUR AUNT AND UNCLE WHEN THE *TUSKEN RAIDERS* HIT THIS PLACE.*

I'VE BEEN MAKING IT *OPERATIONAL* FOR THE NEW OWNER.

WHAT?!

*FIXER DOESN'T KNOW IT WAS *THE EMPIRE'S* DOING. SEE SW #2.--A.G.

THE HOUSE OF *TAGGE* HAS BOUGHT UP A LOT OF LOCAL MOISTURE FARMS... THOUGH *YOUR* SHOWING UP COULD FOUL THEIR *CLAIM.*

BUT THAT LEGAL STUFF CAN *WAIT.* COME OVER *HERE,* LUKE!

HOLD IT, FIXER! I WANT--

HEY, SWEETHEART! YOU CAN EASE UP GUARDING THE *SKY HOPPER!* INSTEAD OF A THIEVING *PARTS SCAVENGER* LIKE I EXPECTED TO CATCH--

--IT'S *SKYWALKER...* BACK FROM THE DEAD!

NOT LITTLE *WORMIE...?!*

HELLO, CAMIE...I HAVEN'T HEARD THAT NICKNAME FOR A *LONG* TIME.

NOT SINCE THAT DAY I CAME RACING INTO ANCHORHEAD TO TELL EVERYONE ABOUT THE BIG *SPACE BATTLE...*

AND IF THE LOVE OF MY LIFE HAD SEEN YOU IN *ACTION* A MINUTE AGO... SHE'D NEVER HAVE *DARED* TO USE IT.

*ANCIENT HISTORY FROM *STAR WARS #1.*-- A.G.

I DON'T KNOW WHAT LUKE BOY'S BEEN *DOING* ALL THIS TIME... BUT HE'S SURE *CHANGED.*

YES, I CAN *SEE* THAT NOW. HE LOOKS... *TALLER* SOMEHOW.

WE'VE CHANGED TOO. RIGHT, CAMIE...? MARRIED. THE TAGGE OUTFIT'S SET US UP IN THE OLD DARKLIGHTER PLACE.

THEIR PEOPLE ARE CONCENTRATING ON EXPANSION WORK OUT IN THE DUNE SEA AND JUNDLAND WASTES--

--SO THEY TOOK ME ON AS A SORT OF CARE-TAKER OF THEIR OTHER PROPERTIES. DOESN'T SOUND TOO EXCITING...

BUT YOU DON'T GET MANY BIG OPPORTUNITIES ON A PLACE LIKE TATOOINE.

AND ANY KIND OF TROUBLE COULD RUIN IT.

LIKE ME TRYING TO RECLAIM MY UNCLE'S PLACE, CAMIE? I'VE BEEN OFF WORLD TOO LONG TO GO BACK TO MOISTURE FARMING. MY ONLY BUSINESS IS IN MOS EISLEY.

I JUST DON'T LIKE THE TAGGE FAMILY GETTING IT... WITH THEIR CONNECTIONS, IT'S PRACTICALLY LIKE GIVING IT TO THE EMPIRE!

FIXER AND I DON'T HAVE MUCH TIME FOR POLITICS... WE'RE KEPT BUSY JUST TRYING TO MAKE OUR LIVES A LITTLE BIT BETTER!

I UNDERSTAND, CAMIE, IT'S ONLY THAT--

MASTER LUKE--!

"ARTOO'S SENSORS HAVE PICKED UP A VEHICLE IN THE AREA, SIR. LARGER THAN A LAND SPEEDER... SMALLER THAN A JAWA SAND-CRAWLER.

"THAT SOUNDS DISTRESSINGLY LIKE AN IMPERIAL TROOP CARRIER TO ME, SIR!"

THIS IS TAGGE COMMAND, UNIT THREE. ANY SUCCESS YET?

NEGATIVE, COMMAND. WE ARE STILL SEARCHING.

I'M SORRY TO HAVE RUSHED YOU AWAY FROM YOUR OLD *FRIENDS*, SIR. IT SEEMED *BEST* UNDER THE CIRCUMSTANCES.

IT'S *OKAY*, THREEPIO. WE DON'T SEEM TO HAVE MUCH IN *COMMON* NOW ANYWAY.

FUNNY. ONCE I WOULD'VE GIVEN *ANYTHING* TO BE IN FIXER'S PLACE...TO HAVE A GIRL LIKE *CAMIE*. BUT NOW I--

MASTER *LUKE!* LOOK *OUT--!*

HOLY--! HOLD *TIGHT!* IT'S GONNA BE *CLOSE!*

EVERYONE ALL *RIGHT...?* WE STOPPED SHY OF THE CANYON WALL BY AT LEAST AN *INCH!*

THREEPIO...? *THREEPIO?!*

W-WHAT...? OH... *EXCUSE* ME, SIR. I THINK I *SHUT DOWN* FOR A MOMENT.

IS THAT AWFUL *BEAST* STILL--

STANDING THERE LIKE A *STATUE!* I'VE NEVER HEARD OF A *BANTHA* BEHAVING LIKE THAT!

I'M GOING TO TAKE A *LOOK*, THREEPIO.

THIS CAN'T *BE...!* I-IT'S *DEAD*--

BUT...IT FEELS *COLD!* FROZEN *STIFF*--

--RIGHT HERE UNDER TATOOINE'S *TWIN SUNS!*

BLOM-DEEP!

MASTER LUKE! ARTOO'S AUDIO RECEPTORS HAVE CAUGHT THE *SOUND* OF THAT *TRANSPORT*--

IT'S COMING *THIS* WAY...WE'VE GOT TO *RUN* OR *HIDE!*

NO SOONER DO THE TRIO GET THE LANDSPEEDER TO COVER, THAN...

AT *LAST,* COMMANDER! STUPID CREATURE MUST HAVE WANDERED INTO THE CANYON BEFORE THE *EFFECT* TOOK!

THAT EXPLAINS WHY OUR *SCANNER* HAD TROUBLE PICKING IT UP!

NOW THAT WE'VE *FOUND* IT...YOU *KNOW* WHAT TO DO.

SUDDENLY, THE CANYON IS *ALIVE* WITH THE ECHOING THUNDER OF LASER BOLTS AND PROTON GRENADES...

FOLLOWED BY... *SILENCE.*

THEY'RE *GONE*... AND SO IS ANY *TRACE* OF THAT BANTHA.

THE SAME MIGHT BE TRUE OF *US*, SIR...IF WE HADN'T BACKED AROUND THIS *BEND* IN THE CANYON.

THE WHOLE *INCIDENT* SEEMS QUITE SINISTER AND IRRATIONAL... WHY *VAPORIZE* SOMETHING ALREADY DEAD?

MAYBE SO NO ONE CAN LEARN *HOW* IT DIED, THREEPIO.

WHATEVER THE TAGGE INTERESTS ARE DEVELOPING OUT IN THE WASTELANDS... IT SURE ISN'T NEW METHODS FOR *MOISTURE FARMING!*

OUR FIRST DUTY IS TO DIG UP SOME *BLOCKADE RUNNERS* LIKE GENERAL DODONNA ASSIGNED US TO DO.

BUT THAT TAGGE BUNCH IS OBVIOUSLY WORKING ON *SOMETHING* FOR THE *EMPIRE* --

-- AND I'M NOT LEAVING *TATOOINE* UNTIL I FIND OUT *WHAT!*

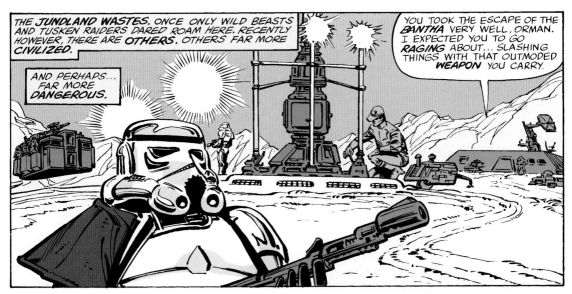

THE *JUNDLAND WASTES*. ONCE ONLY WILD BEASTS AND TUSKEN RAIDERS DARED ROAM HERE. RECENTLY HOWEVER, THERE ARE *OTHERS*. OTHERS FAR MORE *CIVILIZED*.

AND PERHAPS... FAR MORE *DANGEROUS*.

YOU TOOK THE ESCAPE OF THE *BANTHA* VERY WELL, ORMAN. I EXPECTED YOU TO GO *RAGING* ABOUT... SLASHING THINGS WITH THAT OUTMODED *WEAPON* YOU CARRY.

I HAD THIS LIGHT SABER CONSTRUCTED IN *IMITATION* OF THOSE CARRIED ONCE BY JEDI KNIGHTS.

I'M *SAVING* IT FOR THE DAY WHEN I CAN PAY DARTH VADER BACK IN *KIND* FOR WHAT HE DID TO ME.

AND *YOU'RE* CLOSE ENOUGH TO SUCCESS THAT A *SLIGHT* SECURITY BREACH-- SWIFTLY REPAIRED-- SHOULDN'T MATTER.

IN *FACT*, SILAS, ONE REASON I *PICKED* THIS ABOMINABLE LITTLE WORLD AS A SPOT FOR YOU TO CONDUCT YOUR *EXPERIMENTS*--

--WAS THE HOPE THAT *WORD* OF IT MIGHT REACH A CERTAIN PARTY. A YOUNG *REBEL*.

ANOTHER VENDETTA? DOESN'T BEING *BARON* AND RUNNING OUR *FAMILY* KEEP YOU *BUSY* ENOUGH?

GETTING *EVEN* IS ONE OF THE GREAT FOSSIL FUELS OF *LIFE*, BROTHER SILAS. AND THE HAND OF *FATE* IN THIS MATTER SEEMED TOO *STRONG* TO RESIST.

THERE WERE SEVERAL ARID PLANETS THAT FIT *YOUR* CONDITIONS... BUT A NAME IN THE IMPERIAL CENSUS RECORDS DREW ME TO *THIS* ONE. LUKE SKYWALKER.

PERHAPS HE'LL COME. PERHAPS HE WON'T. BUT IF HE *SHOULD*... I'LL BE READY.

EMOTIONAL, ORMAN. BUT TO BE EXPECTED FROM A MAN WHO STILL PREFERS *REAL MEAT*--

--WHEN SCIENCE PROVIDES SOMETHING AS EFFICIENT AS *FOOD PASTE*.

LIGHTS AHEAD, MASTER LUKE...WE'RE APPROACHING MOS EISLEY.

EVENING'S A GOOD TIME. COMING OUT OF THE DESERT LIKE THIS, I'LL SEEM LIKE ANY FARM BOY LOOKING FOR A WILD NIGHT IN THE WICKED CITY.

HOPEFULLY, THAT'S NOT WHAT WE'LL FIND, SIR.

Y'KNOW, THREEPIO, MAYBE AFTER THIS MISSION, YOU'LL FINALLY JUST START CALLING ME LUKE... INSTEAD OF 'SIR' AND 'MASTER' ALL THE TIME.

YOU, ARTOO, AND I HAVE BEEN THROUGH TOO MUCH TOGETHER FOR THAT.

OLD PROGRAMMING DIES HARD, BUT I'LL CERTAINLY TRY, SI-- ER...MAS--UH...LUKE!

NONE OF YOUR COMPLAINING, ARTOO DETOO! YOUR BALANCE INTENSIFIER IS PERFECTLY CAPABLE OF HANDLING YOUR BEING ON YOUR SIDE THIS LONG.

YOU BOTH CAN RELAX IN A MOMENT...THE CANTINA IS JUST AHEAD.

VREEEP-HTOOT

I DON'T REALLY HAVE FOND RECOLLECTIONS OF THAT PLACE. ARE YOU SURE YOU'LL BE ALL RIGHT?

WELL, NOTHING'S CERTAIN IN THIS GALAXY. BUT I KNOW MY WAY AROUND A BIT BETTER THAN MY FIRST VISIT THERE.

OF COURSE... I DON'T HAVE BEN KENOBI TO BAIL ME OUT OF TROUBLE.

PULL AROUND TO THE REAR...AND KEEP THE SPEEDER READY TO MOVE. JUST IN CASE.

OH, BROTHER...! THE PLACE HASN'T *CHANGED* A BIT!

GENERAL DODONNA GAVE ME THIS ASSIGNMENT SO I'D HAVE *SOMETHING* TO DO INSTEAD OF WORRYING ABOUT THE *PRINCESS*--*

WRAK!

* LEIA HAS HER *OWN* MISSION. SEE *LAST ISSUE*-- ARCH AGAIN.

TRYING TO SELECT A FEW REASONABLY TRUSTWORTHY *STAR HOPPERS* FROM THIS MOTLEY COLLECTION OUGHT TO *MORE* THAN DO THE TRICK!

I'D GIVE *ANYTHING* JUST TO SEE A *FRIENDLY FACE* RIGHT NO--

:UNGHHH!:

HAN!

HEY, KID! HAVEN'T YOU LEARNED TO *STAY OUT* OF LOW CLASS DIVES... YOU DON'T KNOW *WHO* YOU'LL BUMP INTO!

WRAP UP THE FIGHT, CHEWIE! WE'VE GOT SOME *SERIOUS* CELEBRATING TO DO!

THOK!

235

...SO AFTER RESOLVING OUR DIFFERENCES WITH *JABBA THE HUT,** CHEWIE AN' ME DELIVERED HIM BACK *HERE* AND DECIDED TO HANG OUT FOR A WHILE.

WANTED TO LET *YOU* ENJOY A FEW MOMENTS WITH HER ROYALNESS BEFORE *I* SHOWED UP TO SWEEP HER OFF HER FEET.

BESIDES...YOU NEEDED SOME TIME TO SPEND THAT EXTRA *BONUS* YOU FORCED OUT OF JABBA.

*CHRONICLED IN *STAR WARS #28.* --ARCHIE.

CAN YOU BEAT THAT, CHEWIE...? KID DOES A LITTLE STAR-ROVING AND HE BECOMES A *CYNIC!*

WELL, IF *YOU'RE* FEELING IDEALISTIC, HAN, I'M ON A MISSION THAT YOU TWO WOULD BE *PERFECT* FOR AND--

WAIT A SECOND!

FIXER! WHAT ARE *YOU* DOING IN THIS PLACE?

LUKE...? I-I'VE... BEEN TRYING TO *FIND* YOU!

CAMIE AN' ME... DID SOMETHING *BAD.* I...CAME TO *WARN* YOU.

TRY TO *UNDERSTAND,* SKYWALKER...YOU MADE IT *OFF* THIS SANDPILE. BUT CAMIE AN' ME ARE *STUCK* HERE...WE'VE GOT TO GET BY AS *BEST* WE CAN!

FROM STUFF SAID THIS AFTERNOON... IT SOUNDS LIKE YOU'RE A *REBEL,* LUKE! TO PROTECT MY *JOB* CAMIE AN' ME DECIDED THERE WAS NO *CHOICE* BUT TO--

YOU *REPORTED* ME, FIXER! I OUGHT TO--

FORGET ANY *THREATS*, KID...YOU GOT NO TIME TO CARRY 'EM *OUT!* YOU'RE *FINGERED*...AND CHEWIE AND ME ARE *GUILTY* BY ASSO-CIATION!

OUT THE *REAR!* WE GOT *IMPERIAL VISITORS* COMIN' IN THE FRONT DOOR!

YOU THREE... *HALT!*

SECONDS LATER...A MOS EISLEY ALLEYWAY BECOMES A **BATTLEGROUND**...

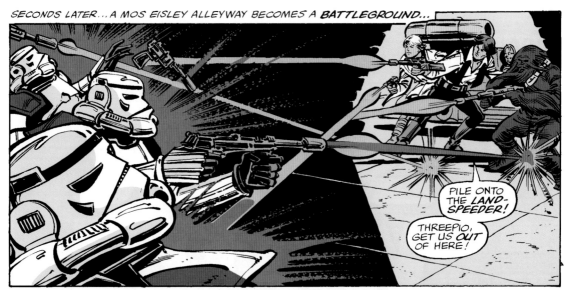

PILE ONTO THE *LAND-SPEEDER!*

THREEPIO, GET US *OUT* OF HERE!

STREETS ARE CRAWLING WITH *STORMTROOPERS!* NO CHANCE OF REACHING THE *FALCON*, KID!

HEAD FOR THE *OPEN DESERT*, THREEPIO!

SWERVING WILDLY BETWEEN TWO OUTLYING BUILDINGS... THE ONE-TIME PROTOCOL DROID DOES JUST *THAT!*

NOT *BAD*, BRONZE BRITCHES. WE'RE MOVING OUT OF THEIR *RANGE.*

IF THIS BABY DOESN'T COLLAPSE FROM THE *LOAD* IT'S CARRYING... I THINK WE'LL BE *OKAY!*

BUT BACK AT THE EDGE OF TOWN...

I'VE CALLED OUT A *TROOP CARRIER*... BUT THOSE REBELS HAVE A *BIG LEAD.*

NO MATTER! ONE OF OUR BLASTS *SCORED*. THAT SPEEDER IS LEAKING *COOLANT!*...IT'LL BE *BURNT OUT* BY MORNING!

IF ONE OF OUR *DESERT PATROLS* DOESN'T GET THEM OUT THERE...THE *TWIN SUNS* WILL!

NEXT ISSUE: **THE JAWA EXPRESS!**

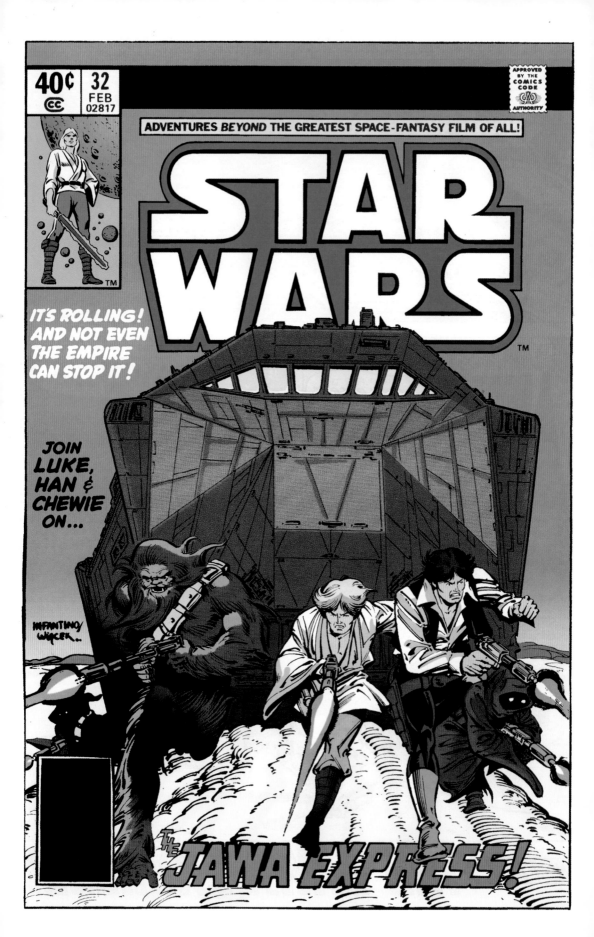

YOU DON'T HAVE TO TELL AN *EX-MOISTURE FARMER* WHAT THE MIDDAY HEAT HERE CAN *DO*, HAN.

BUT WITH A LITTLE MORE *WORK*, I THINK WE CAN *BYPASS* THESE FUSED PARTS.

IT'S *COOLANT* WE NEED, LUKE... TO REPLACE WHAT LEAKED AWAY. WITHOUT IT, ANY *REPAIRS* WILL MELT JUST LIKE THE *ORIGINAL* PARTS.

YEAH. I THOUGHT WE *ESCAPED* THOSE STORMTROOPERS IN MOS EISLEY FREE AND CLEAR... BUT *ONE* OF THEIR PARTING SHOTS FIXED US *GOOD!* *

* *LAST ISSUE.*--ARCHIE G.

AS LUKE AND HAN SOLO GRIMLY DISCUSS THEIR SITUATION... *CHEWBACCA* SUDDENLY COMES ALERT, NOSE TWITCHING...

NORRF?

...HE *RISES.*

AND MOVES SWIFTLY TO A NEARBY *RIDGE*...

WHAT HE SEES IN THE DISTANCE, THROUGH SHIMMERING HEAT, IS NOTHING TO *GLADDEN* A WOOKIEE'S HEART.

AND THE **NEWS** DOESN'T DO VERY MUCH FOR LUKE AND HAN'S MORALE EITHER.

IT'S A **BIG** PATROL. I GUESS WE SHOULD BE **FLATTERED**, KID.

I'M **SORRY**, HAN. I SEEM TO HAVE A **KNACK** FOR GETTING YOU TWO **INTO** MESSES LIKE THIS AND--

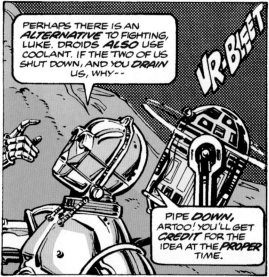

PERHAPS THERE IS AN **ALTERNATIVE** TO FIGHTING, LUKE. DROIDS **ALSO** USE COOLANT. IF THE TWO OF US SHUT DOWN, AND YOU **DRAIN** US, WHY--

VR-BLEET

PIPE **DOWN**, ARTOO! YOU'LL GET **CREDIT** FOR THE IDEA AT THE **PROPER** TIME.

SOON...

THANKS TO THREEPIO AND ARTOO-DETOO WE'RE **MOBILE**, KID... BUT I DUNNO FOR HOW **LONG**.

BEST WE CAN HOPE FOR IS TO GET A LITTLE **DISTANCE** BETWEEN US AND THOSE TROOPERS--

--BEFORE THIS THING DIES OF **STRAIN!**

WE CAN DO BETTER THAN **THAT**. THE DROIDS AND I DIDN'T **WALK** HERE FROM YAVIN, HAN.

WE'VE GOT A **SHIP** HIDDEN FURTHER OUT IN THE DUNES. EVEN **MY** REPAIRS SHOULD HOLD UP TILL WE **GET** THERE.

THEY **DO**. BUT AT THEIR DESTINATION... **MORE** BAD NEWS.

EASY, KID! WE'VE ALREADY GOT ENEMIES... RIGHT NOW WE COULD USE SOME FRIENDS. YOUR SHIP'S TOO FAR GONE TO HELP US NOW.

BUT, HAN--

FACE IT, LUKE... FINDERS KEEPERS IS ALL THESE GUYS KNOW. WITH THE LANDSPEEDER WHEEZIN' ITS LAST... IT'S TIME TO BE CHARMING.

SMILE! WE NEED A LIFT IN THEIR SANDCRAWLER...

AND THAT INVOLVES CHALLENGING THE JAWAS AT WHAT THEY DO BEST... HAGGLING.

THEY'RE NOT GOING FOR JUST THE 'SPEEDER, HAN... THEY WANT THE DROIDS TOO!

PROMISE 'EM ANYTHING, KID... LONG AS THEY AGREE TO GET US BACK TO MOS EISLEY.

THREEPIO AND ARTOO AREN'T JUST ROBOTS TO ME... THEY'RE FRIENDS! I'D FEEL LIKE A SLAVER!

CHEWIE AN' I STASHED PART OF OUR BONUS * FROM JABBA THE HUT ABOARD THE MILLENNIUM FALCON... WE CAN USE IT TO BUY BACK THE DROIDS!

MAKE A FAST DEAL AND GET US OUT OF HERE!

* SEE SW #28.--AG.

BUT THERE CAN BE DANGER IN FAST DEALS...

MOVIN' AT LAST, KID! NOT EXACTLY WARP SPEED... BUT MOVIN'.

BY THE TIME WE HIT MOS EISLEY, THE HEAT SHOULD BE OFF AND--

ONE PROBLEM, HAN... THIS ISN'T THE WAY TO MOS EISLEY.

UH... HAN, I BELIEVE THEY FEEL WE WEREN'T TOTALLY *HONEST* WITH THEM AND--

AND UNLESS WE DO SOMETHING *FAST*... OUR BARGAIN IS *OFF!* TELL 'EM TO *RELAX*, KID.

GOOD *NEWS*, CHEWIE! I THINK THERE'S A WAY WE CAN FINALLY *STAND UP* IN THIS ROLLING TORTURE CHAMBER.

MOMENTS LATER... TWO HATCHES ON THE SAND-CRAWLER ROOF ARE EASED SLOWLY *OPEN*.

WOWRK!

YEAH. IF WE MISS EVEN *ONE* TROOPER ON THE RIDGE... HE CAN BLOW US *AWAY*.

KA-POW!

VDAM!

THAT'S WHY YOU GOTTA FOLLOW MY *LEAD*--

DON'T SHOOT AT THE *TROOPERS*--

--BLAST THE *RIDGE* OUT FROM *UNDER* THEM!

RESULT: INSTANT *AVALANCHE*...

...THAT SWEEPS THE STORMTROOPERS *ABOVE* INTO THEIR COMPANIONS *BELOW*...

BA-WOM!

...CARRYING THEIR *ARMED* PROTON GRENADES *WITH* THEM!

BETTER HAVE OUR LITTLE PALS *BACK UP*, LUKE... THIS ISN'T MUCH OF A *THOROUGHFARE* ANYMORE.

THEY'RE *DOING* IT, HAN... BUT I GET THE FEELING THEY'RE NOT TOO *HAPPY* ABOUT IT.

APPARENTLY THEY'D HOPED TO *AVOID* THE JUNDLAND WASTES... NOW THEY *CAN'T*.

WHAT'S THE *PROBLEM?* ARE THEY AFRAID OF *SAND PEOPLE?*

NO. SOMETHING *ELSE*... BUT I THINK I CAN GUESS *WHAT*, HAN.

THE HOUSE OF *TAGGE* IS UP TO SOMETHING OUT HERE... AND THEY'RE DOING IT FOR THE *EMPIRE.*

THREEPIO, ARTOO, AND I *SAW* ENOUGH TO BE CERTAIN OF THAT *YESTERDAY* WHILE WE WERE MAKING OUR WAY INTO *MOS EISLEY.**

*LAST ISSUE.--ARCHIE.

MY MISSION FOR THE ALLIANCE IS TO RECRUIT *PILOTS* TO BECOME *BLOCKADE RUNNERS* FOR US, SO I COULDN'T TAKE TIME TO *INVESTIGATE,* BUT--

HEY! WE'RE *STOPPING* AGAIN!

THAT SEEMS TO BE WHAT THIS THING DOES *BEST.*

WHAT'S GOING *ON,* LUKE...? EVERYONE *ABANDONING SHIP* OR WHAT IT--

:OW!:

THE *ANSWER* LIES OUTSIDE...

MACHINERY, HAN...! LOOKS LIKE A GIANT *VAPORATOR!*

NO WONDER OUR SHORT FRIENDS ARE *EXCITED,* KID... THERE'S ANOTHER *SAND-CRAWLER.* THEY'VE GOT *COMPETITION* FOR THE LOOT.

WAIT, HAN. WHATEVER THIS *IS...* IT *ISN'T* A *VAPORATOR.* I'VE SEEN *TOO MANY* TO THINK THAT AND--

A CHILLING *TINGLE* GOES THROUGH LUKE...

HAN! CHEWBACCA!

WE'VE GOT TO GET THE JAWAS AND OURSELVES *AWAY* FROM THIS THING... *FAST!*

HUSTLE IT, HALF-PINTS! THE KID'S NOT GIVEN TO *PRACTICAL JOKES.*

AWRK!

?...WWL?!

THEN, WITH THE SUDDENESS OF LIGHTNING STRIKING... *SOMETHING* SWEEPS THE DESERT PLAIN BEFORE THE TOWER. SOMETHING *IMPOSSIBLE.*

AND ON THE *OPPOSITE* SIDE, BELOW THE RISE...

LUKE...! THE *WIND*... THE *SAND*...

I *KNOW,* HAN... THEY FEEL *COLD.*

MOMENTS PASS... NOTHING HAPPENS. CAUTIOUSLY, THE GROUP MOVES *FORWARD.*

YOU *SAID* IT, BIG BUDDY! BETWEEN HERE AN' THAT DISTANT TOWER... THE WHOLE PLAIN'S *FROZEN!*

WRAAG!

NOT *JUST* THE PLAIN... *LOOK!*

"THE OTHER *SANDCRAWLER*..! I-IT'S *COLLAPSING*...! THE COLD IS SO *GREAT*... EVEN THE *METAL* IS SHAT-TERING!"

SSHHRAAAAAAAAAAKKK!!!

THAT COULD'VE BEEN *US*, KID...IF YOU HADN'T *YELLED*. WAS THAT THE *FORCE* IN ACTION...?

NOT *THIS* TIME, HAN... I *FELT* THE TOWER STARTING TO GET *COLD*. IT REMINDED ME OF *YESTERDAY*--

--AND A FROZEN *BANTHA* THE DROIDS AND I DISCOVERED!*

*ALSO *LAST ISSUE*:--ARCH.

I THINK WE'VE FOUND--

DON'T BOTHER *TRANSLATING*, LUKE! THE *TONE* SOUNDS LIKE: EVERYBODY *DOWN*!

AND FOR GOOD REASON. THERE ARE *NEW* ARRIVALS ON THE SCENE...

EXCELLENT, SILAS... *EXCELLENT!* UNDER THE *MERCILESS* TWIN SUNS OF THIS HELLHOLE PLANET... YOU'VE ACHIEVED *THIS!*

IF YOU'LL EXAMINE THE *BODIES* OF THOSE LITTLE CREATURES WHO WERE *IN* THE MACHINE--

--YOU'LL FIND *THEY* WERE FROZEN AS WELL, ORMAN.

I BELIEVE IT'S SAFE TO SAY THAT *NOTHING* CAUGHT BETWEEN THE CONDUCTOR TOWERS CAN *SURVIVE*--

--NOT WHEN WE GENERATE THE *OMEGA FROST*, MY DEAR BROTHER.

YOU'LL BE ABLE TO *DUPLICATE* THIS SUCCESS ANYWHERE... IN ANY *ENVIRONMENT?*

PERHAPS NOT IN THE HEART OF A *NOVA*. BUT IF IT WORKS UNDER *THESE* ARID CONDITIONS... I'M CONFIDENT I CAN ADJUST IT FOR *WHATEVER* YOU REQUIRE.

THE *OMEGA FROST!* BRILLIANT, SILAS ....! IT'S GOING TO BE THE *CLUB* WITH WHICH WE BEAT *DARTH VADER* FROM THE EMPEROR'S FAVOR.

BARON TAGGE? WHAT ABOUT THE *REBELS*, SIR? THEY'RE STILL *OBSERVING* US.

GOOD, THEY HAVEN'T *GUESSED* THAT THE CONDUCTOR TOWER HAS A *SENSOR SYSTEM* THAT DETECTED THEM AND *ALERTED* US.

IF UNITS TWO AND THREE ARE IN *POSITION*...LET'S BEGIN HERDING THEM WHERE WE *WANT* THEM.

AND WITH TAGGE *ABOARD*, THE IMPERIAL TROOP CARRIER SUDDENLY, SWIFTLY *MOVES*...

...OPENING FIRE WITH ITS *LASER CANNON!*

NOT *TOO* CLOSE TO THEIR POSITION--

-- ONE OF THEM IS *LUKE SKYWALKER.*

I WANT HIM *ALIVE*...TO DEAL WITH *PERSONALLY!*

WHILE AHEAD...

HAN, SOMETHING'S *ROTTEN* ABOUT THIS.

YEAH. WE COULD GET *KILLED*--

--THAT *ALWAYS* DEPRESSES ME.

VWOOM!

NO, HAN. IF THEY *SUSPECTED* WE WERE SPYING ON THEM...WHY SUCH A *SLOPPY* ATTACK?

EVEN *IMPERIALS* KNOW TO CUT OFF OUR LINE OF *RETREAT* BEFORE MOVING IN!

SOUNDS LIKE YOU'VE BEEN SITTING IN ON SOME OF THOSE REBEL *STRATEGY* MEETINGS, KID.

HOW DO *YOU* FIGURE IT?

THEY'RE DRIVING US *INTO* SOMETHING. WE'VE GOT TO GET THE JAWAS TO *RESIST.*

NOW YOU'RE FLYING *BLIND*, LUKE. *SCROUNGING* AND *SCAVAGING* ARE THESE LITTLE CHARACTERS' SPECIALTIES.

BEFORE THEY *FIGHT*... THEY'LL TURN US OVER TO TAGGE AND COMPANY *THEMSELVES.*

ひげ─うじゃもで・ラッリ;ひ─:!!

THAT *MAY* HAVE BEEN THE CASE, HAN--

BUT *THIS* GUY IS GRATEFUL BECAUSE WE *SAVED* THEM...AND WANTS TO KNOW HOW *THEY* CAN HELP!

251

THUS, MOMENTS LATER, WHEN THE IMPERIAL TROOP CARRIER **TOPS** *THE RISE...*

...A **RUDE SURPRISE** IS WAITING!

BARON! THEY DIDN'T **FLEE**...THE MADMEN ARE **CHARGING US!**

WE'RE TOO **CLOSE** TO BLAST THEM, FOOL!

TURN BEFORE WE CRASH **HEAD ON...** **TURN!**

BUT EVEN **THAT** ALTERNATIVE LEAVES MUCH TO BE DESIRED! AND...

TAGGE BASE...THIS IS THE **BARON!** MY BROTHER AND I NEED **ASSISTANCE.**

UNITS TWO AND THREE...ABANDON **AMBUSH POSITIONS** AND GIVE **CHASE** TO FUGITIVE SAND-CRAWLER!—

TELL OUR HOSTS... **GREAT WORK,** LUKE! THE **JAWA EXPRESS** IS ON THE MOVE!

NEXT STOP... **MOS EISLEY!**

WE'RE PICKING UP TAGGE'S **TRANSMISSION BAND,** HAN—

—WE MAY HIT A COUPLE OF **OBSTACLES!**

YOU *CALLED* IT, KID! THE LANDSCAPE IS SUDDENLY FURNISHED WITH HOT AND COLD RUNNING *TROOP CARRIERS!*

HOT TO *CATCH* US... AND COLD *CERTAIN* TO DO IT AT THE SPEED *THEY* CAN TRAVEL!

HAN, HE SAYS THAT ALONG WITH THEIR *OTHER* PICKINGS... THEY HAVE SOME LOOSE DRUMS OF *SKYHOPPER PROPELLANT.* GIVE YOU ANY *IDEAS?*

THAT'S IT, CHEWIE! HEAVE 'EM *OUT!*

NOT *TOO CLOSE* TOGETHER... WE WANT 'EM *SPREAD* ACROSS THE PLAIN.

LUKE'S ON THE *ROOF* TO TAKE CARE OF THE *REST.*

BLAST THE WAY THIS LUMBERING MONSTROSITY *RATTLES* AND *SHAKES!*

STILL... THIS SHOULDN'T BE ANY TOUGHER THAN POTTING *WOMP RATS* FROM A LAND-SPEEDER WITH UNCLE OWEN'S OUTMODED OLD *ENERGY RIFLE.*

COME TO *THINK* OF IT... THAT WAS PRETTY *TOUGH!*

FTOOM! FTOOM! FTOOM!

BUT DESPITE CONCERN...LUKE'S SHOTS ARE *TRUE*. PROPELLANT DRUMS *EXPLODE* IN A FIERY SPRAY...

...PRODUCING A *CHAIN REACTION* THAT TOUCHES *ALL* THE DRUMS SPREAD ACROSS THE PLAIN...

...UNTIL A MASSIVE WALL OF *FLAME* RISES BEFORE THE PURSUING CARRIERS OF THE EMPIRE'S TROOPS! THE WARRIORS ARE LEFT BUT ONE CHOICE. *HALT*...

...OR BE *DESTROYED!*

KA-VWOOM!

THAT SAVED US, LUKE... FOR THE *MOMENT.* BUT THEY'RE *BOUND* TO HAVE SIGNALLED AHEAD TO *MOS EISLEY*--

--AND WE CAN'T EXACTLY *SNEAK* INTO THERE WITH A *SANDCRAWLER!*

BUT, HAN, IT'S MORE IMPORTANT THAN *EVER* THAT WE REACH THE MILLENNIUM FALCON AND *GET OFF* TATOOINE!

THE ALLIANCE *HAS* TO KNOW WHAT THE HOUSE OF TAGGE HAS *CREATED* HERE!

MAY *WE* MAKE A SUGGESTION, SIR?

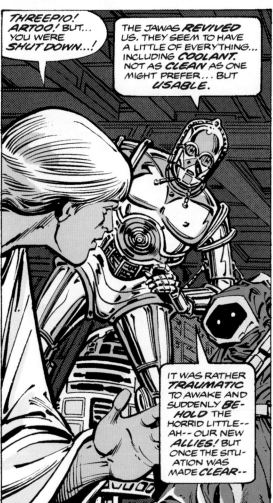

THREEPIO! ARTOO! BUT... YOU WERE *SHUT DOWN...!*

THE JAWAS *REVIVED* US. THEY SEEM TO HAVE A LITTLE OF EVERYTHING... INCLUDING *COOLANT.* NOT AS *CLEAN* AS ONE MIGHT PREFER... BUT *USABLE.*

IT WAS RATHER *TRAUMATIC* TO AWAKE AND SUDDENLY *BE-HOLD* THE HORRID LITTLE-- AH-- OUR NEW *ALLIES!* BUT ONCE THE SITUATION WAS MADE *CLEAR*--

--I REASONED THAT IF THEIR COOLANT WORKS IN *US*... IT WILL REVIVE OUR AILING *LAND-SPEEDER* TOO!

VREET!

OH, VERY WELL, ARTOO... *YOU* REASONED IT! THE MAIN THING IS WE *CAN* REACH MOS EISLEY.

AND...

SINCE THE IMPERIALS ARE AFTER A *SANDCRAWLER*... THIS SHOULD DO THE TRICK, KID.

RIGHT, HAN! AND OUR FRIENDS, THE *JAWAS,* CAN *LOSE* THEMSELVES IN THE DUNE SEA.

TAGGE'S *SCHEME* MAY NOT BE FINISHED... BUT NEITHER ARE *WE!*

NEXT ISSUE: IN THE DEPTHS OF SPACE... LUKE SKYWALKER VS. BARON TAGGE!

SABER CLASH!

Long ago in a galaxy far, far away. . .there exists a state of cosmic *civil war*. A brave alliance of *underground freedom fighters* has challenged the tyranny and oppression of the awesome *Galactic Empire*. This is their story!

LucasFilm PRESENTS: **STAR WARS**™ THE GREATEST SPACE FANTASY OF ALL!

CONTINUING THE SAGA BEGUN IN THE FILM BY GEORGE LUCAS RELEASED BY TWENTIETH CENTURY-FOX

ARCHIE GOODWIN
WRITER/EDITOR

CARMINE INFANTINO and GENE DAY
ARTISTS

JOHN COSTANZA
LETTERER

PETRA GOLDBERG
COLORIST

JIM SHOOTER
CONSULTING EDITOR

IT'S THE SAME *HOUSE OF TAGGE* SHIP THAT WAS FERRYING *TIE FIGHTERS* TO YAVIN TO ATTACK THE *REBEL BASE* THERE!*

NOT *SURPRISING,* KID... CONSIDERING THAT *BARON TAGGE* WAS BEHIND ALL THE *TROUBLE* WE HAD BACK ON TATOOINE.

* BACK IN *STAR WARS* #25 --ARCHIE G.

WOWRK!

YEAH, I SEE THE *SCOPE* TOO, CHEWIE! CHECK IT *OUT,* LUKE--

"-- THERE'S A *SHUTTLE CRAFT* APPROACHING THAT LUMBERING *SPICE SNIFFER.*

"NOT A *CARGO ORBITER...* THEY MUST BE TAKING ON *PASSENGERS,* GETTING READY TO *EMBARK.*"

HAN, IT *HAS* TO BE THE *BARON!* WHO *ELSE* WOULD THEY BE TAKING ABOARD?

EVERYTHING SEEMS TO BE WORKING TO TAKE ME FURTHER AWAY FROM MY *ORIGINAL* MISSION FOR THE ALLIANCE, BUT--

WE'VE *GOT* TO FOLLOW HIM!

WHAT WE WITNESSED OUT IN THE *JUNDLAND WASTES* * MAKES IT TOO *IMPORTANT* FOR US NOT TO!

* *LAST ISSUE* -- ARCH AGAIN.

258

IT IS CALLED THE *OMEGA FROST.* IT IS GENERATED FROM TWO *CONDUCTOR TOWERS.* ANYTHING CAUGHT IN ITS PATH CONTAINING EVEN MINUTE QUANTITIES OF *MOISTURE...* FREEZES AND SHATTERS.

SINCE MOST THINGS IN THIS GALAXY CONTAIN *SOME* MOISTURE... IT IS *AWESOME.*

WHAT WE SAW WAS OBVIOUSLY ONLY AN *EXPERIMENT.* NOW BARON TAGGE'S PROBABLY MOVING TO *REALLY* USE IT!

IT'S UP TO US TO *STOP* HIM!

KID, YOU'RE A *BAD INFLUENCE...*

... EVERY TIME I'M AROUND YOU, I GET TURNED INTO A *HERO* IN SPITE OF MYSELF.

OKAY, CHEWIE. CUT OUR *ACCELERATION.* WE'LL MANEUVER SO THAT *ASTEROID CLUSTER* IS BETWEEN US AND THE *TAGGE* SHIP...

WE'LL WAIT 'EM OUT AND SEE WHERE THEY'RE *HEADED.*

MEANTIME, IN THE *DOCKING BAY* OF THE SPICE EXPLORER...

REALLY, ORMAN... THIS EMOTIONAL *OUTBURST* IS UNWARRANTED.

WE WERE REMARKABLY *SUCCESSFUL* ON TATOOINE.

SHRAAAAAAAAK

SUCCESSFUL WITH THE *OMEGA FROST*, SILAS... BUT *NOT* IN CAPTURING *LUKE SKYWALKER!*

HE TURNED ONE OF OUR *TRIUMPHS* INTO *HUMILIATION!* I WON'T LET HIM GO *UNPUNISHED!*

*SHOWN IN *STAR WARS* #26 --ARCHIE.

ALL THESE *VENDETTAS*, MY DEAR BROTHER... THE YOUNG *REBEL*, DARTH *VADER* FOR BLINDING YOU... WE TAGGES SHOULD BE *ABOVE* THAT.

ABOVE *PRIDE* AND *FAMILY HONOR...?* WE WOULDN'T *BE* TAGGES THEN, SILAS. WE WOULDN'T EVEN BE *MEN.*

ROMANTIC, ORMAN... BUT SOMEWHAT LACKING IN *LOGIC.* I SUPPOSE THAT'S WHY *YOU* HAVE THE TITLE AND I'M CONTENT TO BE A MERE *SCIENTIST.*

CHIEF SCIENTIST... OF ALL THE TAGGE INDUSTRIES.

SHANKS, CONTACT MY *YOUNGER* BROTHER. TELL THE GENERAL WE'RE READY TO *RENDEZVOUS* WITH HIM.

A VERITABLE *FAMILY REUNION*, ORMAN. PITY OUR DEAR LITTLE *SISTER* DOESN'T HAVE A *ROLE* IN OUR SCHEME.

SILAS, YOUR *BANTER* IS NOT TO EXTEND TO HER. *EVER.*

BE CONTENT THAT THIS MEETING SHOULD SPELL *DOOM* FOR THE REBEL ALLIANCE.

THERE THEY *GO!* NOT MUCH HOPE OF FOLLOWING THEM THROUGH HYPERSPACE--

--UNLESS YOU AND YOUR *STUBBY FRIEND* HAD SOME LUCK, THREEPIO.

NATURALLY IT WAS A *DIFFICULT* TASK, CAPTAIN SOLO... EVEN WITH ARTOO AUGMENTING YOUR *BROADCAST MONITER.*

OF COURSE, HE HAD *ME* DIRECTING HIM, SO--

THE *BOTTOM LINE,* BRIGHT EYES, DID YOU *PICK UP* ANYTHING?

THE FRAGMENT OF A *TRANCEIVER* COMMUNICATION. THEIR DESTINATION IS APPARENTLY *JUNCTION.*

JUNCTION...?! *WE* KNOW THAT PLACE! SINCE THE *IMPERIAL BLOCKADE*... IT'S ONE OF YAVIN BASE'S CHIEF SOURCE OF *SUPPLIES.*

WHAT COULD *TAGGE* BE PLANNING *THERE?*

GUESS WE WON'T KNOW UNTIL WE *REACH* THE PLACE, LUKE--

--BUT I'LL BET ALL THE *SAND* ON TATOOINE IT'S *NOTHING* THAT WE'LL LIKE!

THE MILLENNIUM FALCON LEAPS INTO HYPERSPACE... AND A LONG *JOURNEY* BEGINS.

WORO-ARRK!

IT'S *AMAZING,* ARTOO. YOU'D THINK HE'D GROW *TIRED* OF CONSTANTLY WINNING.

TRY ONE MORE *GAME.* AN EVEN *TWENTY* VICTORIES WILL SURELY PUT HIM IN A MOOD TO LET SOMEONE *ELSE* PLAY.

KID, YOU'RE A LOT *BETTER* AT THAT THAN THE *FIRST TIME* I SAW YOU DO IT.

I'VE HAD A LOT MORE *PRACTICE,* HAN, WITH THE SABER... *AND* THE *FORCE!*

AND THE LONG JOURNEY CONTINUES UNTIL...

A SHIP TO SHIP *TRANSFER* IS UNDERWAY. CARGO HANDLERS FROM THE TAGGE MINING EXPLORER GUIDE *MODULE PACKS* TOWARD THE IMPERIAL STAR DESTROYER BELOW...

IT IS AN *OLD FASHIONED* OPERATION, SOMETIMES STILL NECESSARY WHEN ONE SHIP CANNOT FIT IN ANOTHER'S DOCKING BAY...

...AND MATERIALS ARE TOO DELICATE-- OR *DANGEROUS*-- TO TRUST TO *TRACTOR BEAMS.*

I'M NOT SURE I *LIKE* THIS, ORMAN, THERE'S TOO MUCH *TRAFFIC* AROUND JUNCTION.

THIS OPERATION IS STIRRING UP *CURIOSITY...* MAKING THE LOCALS HOVER AROUND US LIKE *TOURISTS.*

AND NO DOUBT SOME OF THEM ARE *SPIES...* REBELS, SURELY. PERHAPS EVEN SOME FROM OUR FRIEND, THE *SITH LORD.*

IT'S TO BE *EXPECTED,* LITTLE BROTHER. INDEED, ULRIC... JUST ONE MORE PART OF OUR *PLAN.*

A GOOD PLAN SHOULDN'T BE *COMPLICATED--*

"--SOMETHING *UNEXPECTED* IS LIKELY TO HAPPEN."

NO ONE SEEMS TO HAVE PICKED UP MY *APPROACH*... THEIR MONITORS MUST BE CONCENTRATED ON THE *TRANSFER.*

TIME TO JOIN THE *WORK FORCE*... AND TUNE IN ON THE *INTERCOM GOSSIP*.

--ASTED *STORMTROOPERS* OUGHT TO BE HELPING! THEY'RE THE ONES WHO'LL BE *USING* THIS STUFF.

QUIT *GRIPING*. THE BARON'LL DUMP YOU ON *JUNCTION*. YOU WOULDN'T WANT TO BE *THERE* WHEN THIS IS ASSEMBLED AND WORKING.

YOU *SAID* IT! SAW ONE OF THE *DEMON-STRATIONS* ON THAT DESERT PLANET.

OMEGA FROST. I DON'T EVEN LIKE THE *NAME*... MUCH LESS THINKING ABOUT WHAT IT'D DO TO AN *ENTIRE WORLD*.

NO TIME TO BE *SUBTLE*! GOT TO GET BACK TO THE *FALCON*... ALERT THE *ALLIANCE* AT ALL COSTS!

HEY! NO ONE CALLED A *BREAK*!

AND LUKE GETS *NONE*...

STORMTROOPERS! THEY WEREN'T THERE *BEFORE*--!

HAN! CHEWIE! I'M *CAUGHT*! THE EMPIRE'S GOING TO *USE* THAT THING WE SAW ON TATOOINE--

--USE IT ON *JUNCTION*! GET *HELP*! GET-- ::UNGHHHH!::

AW...*NO*, KID!

WHY DIDN'T YOU LET ME TALK YOU *OUT* OF THIS CRAZY STUNT LIKE I *TRIED* TO DO?

HRAAWRUH

YEAH, YEAH, YOU'RE *RIGHT*, CHEWIE. MAYBE THEY ONLY *STUN-BLASTED* HIM.

WHATEVER'S HAPPENED, I GOTTA GET *HOLD* OF MYSELF... GET US *AWAY* FROM HERE.

WE'LL BRING WORD TO THE *REBELS* LIKE LUKE WANTED IF WE HAVE TO WARP STRAIGHT *THROUGH* HALF THE BATTLE WAGONS IN THE *IMPERIAL BLOCKADE!*

BUT THERE'S ONE *PARTICULAR* REBEL I DON'T RELISH BREAKING THE *NEWS* TO.

I CAN'T *BELIEVE* IT, HAN SOLO! LUKE HAS THE EXCUSE OF BEING *YOUNG* AND *EAGER*... BUT *YOU* SHOULD HAVE KNOWN BETTER!

HOW DID I EVER BECOME INVOLVED WITH TWO MEN SO *BRAVE*... AND SO *STUPID?!*

I DON'T THINK YOU *MEAN* THAT, YOUR *ROYALNESS*. BUT IF BEING ANGRY *HELPS*... LAY IT ON.

PERHAPS IT SHOULD BE DIRECTED AT *ME*, PRINCESS LEIA--

IT WAS *MY* DECISION TO SEND HIM OUT TO RECRUIT *BLOCKADE RUNNERS*... RATHER THAN HAVE HIM MOON AROUND THE BASE WAITING FOR *YOU* TO COMPLETE YOUR MISSION ON *METALORN*. *

I THINK *HAN* DIFFUSED MY NEED TO *ATTACK*, GENERAL DODONNA--

* CHRONICLED IN SW #30 -- ARCHIE.

--BUT IT SEEMS LIKE AN ASSIGNMENT *ANYONE* MIGHT HAVE HANDLED, WITH LUKE'S WAY OF STUMBLING INTO *TROUBLE*...

I *CONSIDERED* THAT, YOUR HIGHNESS. BUT *DOES* HE STUMBLE... OR IS HE *GUIDED*?

WE ALL *SPEAK* OF THE FORCE... BUT SKYWALKER SEEMS TRULY *TOUCHED* BY IT. PERHAPS IN MORE WAYS THAN WE *KNOW*.

WELL, *I* KNOW WHILE WE STAND HERE *TALKIN'*... A LOT OF FOLKS ON *JUNCTION* ARE THAT MUCH NEARER THE *BIG FREEZE*.

BESIDES BEING A VALUABLE SOURCE OF *SUPPLIES*... THAT OUTPOST WORLD ATTRACTS A LOT OF HOT-SHOT *STAR HOPPERS*.

GOOD POTENTIAL *BLOCKADE RUNNERS*... ESPECIALLY ONCE THEY LEARN WE'RE SAVING THEIR *TAILS*!

VA-BLEET! DA-TOOT!

FOR A CHANGE, I COULDN'T *AGREE* MORE, ARTOO. *WHATEVER* ACTION THEY DECIDE UPON... I HOPE IT REVEALS *SOON* WHETHER POOR LUKE IS *ALIVE* OR *DEAD*!

WE'VE REACHED THE *ASTEROID CORRIDOR*, BARON TAGGÉ.

PROCEED ACCORDING TO *PLAN*, MY BROTHER, *SILAS*, WILL DIRECT THE OPERATION.

I WISH TO CHAT WITH OUR YOUNG *GUEST* NOW THAT HE'S AWAKE.

YOU'RE *AUDACIOUS*, REBEL. IF I HADN'T BEEN FAMILIARIZING MYSELF WITH YOUR *FACE* FROM OFFICIAL RECORDS... I MIGHT HAVE *MISSED* YOU ON THE MONITORS DURING THE *TRANSFER* AT JUNCTION.

INTERESTING. YOU DRESS LIKE A *FARM BOY*... YET YOU CARRY *THIS*. THE WEAPON OF A *JEDI KNIGHT*.

I HOPE YOU'RE AS *SKILLFUL* WITH IT AS YOU WERE WITH AN *X-WING FIGHTER* DURING MY OPERATION ON YAVIN... * BECAUSE I HAVE IN MIND A LITTLE *GAME* AS MY WAY OF *AVENGING* THAT BUSINESS.

* ISSUE #26 -- ARCHIE.

BEFORE LUKE CAN RESPOND IN ANY WAY... A GREAT VIBRATION SHAKES THE TAGGE MINING EXPLORER!

DON'T BE *ALARMED*, SKYWALKER... WE'RE JUST PLANTING ONE OF THE *OMEGA FROST CONDUCTOR TOWERS* INTO ONE OF THE CORRIDOR'S MAJOR ASTEROIDS.

IT'S A CONSIDERABLY *LARGER* MODEL THAN YOU SAW IN OPERATION ON YOUR HOMEWORLD OF *TATOOINE*... ALMOST *UNLIMITED* IN RANGE.

YOUR ALLIANCE FRIENDS MAKE GREAT *USE* OF THE ASTEROID CORRIDOR IN BREAKING THE *BLOCKADE*...IT'S ALMOST *IMPOSSIBLE* FOR THE MASSIVE IMPERIAL CRUISERS TO *PATROL* HERE.

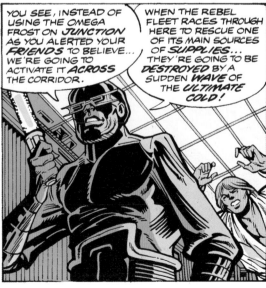

YOU SEE, INSTEAD OF USING THE OMEGA FROST ON *JUNCTION* AS YOU ALERTED YOUR *FRIENDS* TO BELIEVE... WE'RE GOING TO ACTIVATE IT *ACROSS* THE CORRIDOR.

WHEN THE REBEL FLEET RACES THROUGH HERE TO RESCUE ONE OF ITS MAIN SOURCES OF *SUPPLIES*... THEY'RE GOING TO BE *DESTROYED* BY A SUDDEN *WAVE* OF THE *ULTIMATE COLD!*

NO!

IT IS A *RASH ACT* OF ANGER AND DESPERATION. AGAINST A MAN OF THE SKILL AND EXPERIENCE OF *BARON TAGGE*, IT SHOULDN'T *SUCCEED*...

...YET, SOMEHOW, IT *DOES*.

PERHAPS.

MY PRISONER HAS *ESCAPED*... AS I *PLANNED*. ALERT ALL PERSONNEL TO STAY OUT OF HIS WAY AND MAKE NO ATTEMPT TO *INTERFERE*.

MEANTIME, TELL MY *CREW* TO PROCEED TO THE FAR SIDE OF THE *ASTEROID CORRIDOR*... MY LITTLE GAME SHOULDN'T INTER- RUPT GETTING THE *FINAL* CONDUCTOR TOWER INTO POSITION.

LIGHTSABER OPPONENTS ARE DIFFICULT TO *FIND* IN THIS AGE OF BLASTERS, LUKE SKYWALKER... I HOPE YOU CAN PROVIDE ME WITH VALUABLE *PRACTICAL EXPERIENCE*.

WHEN THE DAY COMES THAT I CHALLENGE *DARTH VADER* WITH THE VERY SAME WEAPON HE USED TO *BLIND* ME--

--IT WILL BE MOST USEFUL TO KNOW THAT MY *KILLING TECHNIQUES* WORK--

--BECAUSE I HAVE *PROVEN* THEM ON *YOU*!

LUKE HAS MOVED AS QUICKLY AS HE CAN THROUGH THE STRANGE SHIP, USING ACCESS CORRIDORS AND REPAIR TUBES, AT LAST FINDING HIS WAY TO...

THE *DOCKING BAY...!* GOT TO GRAB A SHIP AND GET OUT OF HERE TO WARN THE *ALLIANCE.*

THAT *TIE FIGHTER* LOOKS LIKE MY BEST BET!

UNFORTUNATELY, SKYWALKER.... THERE IS AN *OBSTACLE* IN REACHING IT. ME.

SO FAR, I FIND YOU A BIT *PREDICTABLE,* MY YOUNG REBEL FRIEND, I HOPE THAT DOESN'T EXTEND TO WIELDING THE *LIGHTSABER--*

--FOR YOUR SAKE!

YOUR *REFLEXES* ARE EXCELLENT... YOU SHOW SOME *SKILL*... BUT YOUR *TECHNIQUE* IS PRIMITIVE. ALMOST *NONEXISTENT.*

A TALENTED *AMATEUR*...WITH THE BENEFIT OF ONLY A *FEW* LESSONS.

THAT'S JUST *NOT GOOD ENOUGH,* YOUNGSTER.

NOT *NEARLY!*

PICK UP YOUR *LIGHT-SABER*, SKYWALKER. I'LL END THIS *SWIFTLY*.

EVEN FOR *VENGEANCE*... THERE'S NO SPORT IN TORMENTING A *NOVICE*.

LUKE FIGHTS A GROWING *PANIC*. SOMEHOW THIS IS *DIFFERENT*, FAR DIFFERENT, THAN ALL THOSE SESSIONS WITH THE *PRACTICE SPHERE*.

YES, A LIVING FOE *IS* DIFFERENT, YOUNG LUKE... ESPECIALLY IF YOU ATTEMPT TO FIGHT *HIS* WAY, CON-SCIOUSLY MATCH *HIS* MOVES.

THEN, A FAMILIAR *VOICE* SOUNDS WITHIN HIS MIND...

YOUR WAY MUST BE THE WAY OF *FEELING*... COMING FROM *WITHIN*. THE WAY OF THE *FORCE*.

NOT EVEN RAISING YOUR BLADE IN *DEFENSE*...? PERHAPS THAT'S JUST AS *WELL*.

AND TAGGE LUNGES... A SURE *KILLING* LUNGE...

...THAT SOMEHOW IS *NOT*.

ZRAAAK!

W-WHAT--?

VRAAAMP!

REACTIONS HONED IN COUNTLESS HOURS OF PRACTICE AND TRAINING *SAVE* THE BARON...

BUT SUDDENLY HE REALIZES A MUCH *DIFFERENT BATTLE* IS BEING FOUGHT THAN THE ONE HE BEGAN...

...AND TO *WIN* THAT BATTLE, EVEN WITH *ALL HIS* CONSIDERABLE SKILL...

...HE MUST FIGHT FOR HIS *LIFE!*

YET FOR EVERY STUNNING ATTACK AND COUNTER-ATTACK PATTERN TAGGE LAUNCHES...THE BOY'S LIGHT BLADE IS *THERE!*

LUKE'S STROKES ARE AWKWARD...UNORTHO-DOX...COMING FROM NO TRAINING PRINCIPLES OR FIGHTING SYSTEMS THE BARON HAS EVER EN-COUNTERED...

...AND HIS *MIND* SEEMS FOCUSED ON SOMETHING *BEYOND* THE COMBAT.

FOR THE FIRST TIME SINCE HE ACHIEVED *MASTERY* OF THE LIGHTSABER...BARON TAGGE FEELS THE NEED TO GIVE *GROUND!*

THERE'S MORE TO YOU THAN MEETS THE *EYE*, SKYWALKER... YOU'VE THE TOUCH OF THE *WIZARD* ABOUT YOU, LIKE THAT BLASTED *DARTH VADER!*

TIME FOR A *NEW* STRATEGY--

VER-RAAAN!

--THE *FINAL* STRATEGY I WAS SAVING TO DISPATCH THE *DARK LORD* HIMSELF!

WITH THE SUDDEN FLARE OF SHORTED CIRCUITRY...THE DOCKING BAY PLUNGES INTO *DARKNESS.*

DARKNESS PIERCED ONLY BY THE GLOW OF A SOLITARY *LIGHT-SABER.*

THAT... AND THE *CYBER-VISION* OF BARON TAGGE.

MECHANIZED SIGHT HAS *SOME* ADVANTAGES, MY YOUNG FRIEND...

...BUT I WON'T UNDERESTIMATE YOU *TWICE.* TO FIGHT AS YOU HAVE SO FAR, *ALL* YOUR SENSES MUST BE EXCEPTIONAL.

AND SINCE YOU'RE SO *INTENT*--

--I'M *GIVING* THOSE SENSES SOMETHING TO *DETECT!*

THE WHISPER OF *CLOTH.* SLIGHT, BUT ENOUGH. ENOUGH TO MAKE LUKE *REACT*...

...ENOUGH TO GIVE TAGGE THE *UNPROTECTED TARGET* HE HAS BEEN WAITING FOR!

LIGHTSABER CLICKED ON... THE BARON LUNGES FOR THE *KILL!*

BUT HIS BLADE STRIKES *THIN AIR!* HIS TARGET HAS MOVED, NOT *STOPPING* WITH THE CUT OF THE CLOTH AS EXPECTED, BUT *CONTINUING* THE SWING...

VRAAAAMMP!

...CONTINUING IN A PERFECT ARC THAT *ENDS* AT THE FACE OF BARON TAGGE!

MOMENTS LATER, A *TIE FIGHTER* BLASTS OUT OF THE DOCKING BAY...

IT IS PILOTED BY A BOY WHO HAS LEARNED ONCE AGAIN *HOW MUCH* HE CAN DO WITH THE *FORCE* AWAKENED IN HIM BY OBI-WAN KENOBI...

...AND HAS ALSO DISCOVERED AT WHAT POINT HE *PREFERS* TO STOP.

...H-HE DIDN'T *KILL* ME...! DIDN'T... *NEED* TO...! CONTROLLED STROKE SO *PERFECTLY...* DESTROYED MY *CYBER-VISION...* WITHOUT HARMING *ME...!*

HE...WAS *THAT* GOOD...! TH-THAT... *GOOD...!*

THE BARON'S IN *SICK BAY,* SILAS... BEING TREATED FOR *SHOCK.* I'M ORDERING OUT A FLIGHT TO *PURSUE* THE REBEL GO--

IT'S *UNNECESSARY,* SHANKS. WHEN I LEARNED OF THE *'GAME'* MY BROTHER PLANNED... I ORDERED SOME *PRECAUTIONS* TAKEN.

SKYWALKER'S SHIP HAS *NO ARMAMENT, NO COMMUNICATIONS...* AND JUST ENOUGH *FUEL* TO CARRY HIM TO *DISASTER.*

ORMAN IS THE *ROMANTIC.* I AM *NOT.*

NEXT ISSUE: THUNDER IN THE STARS

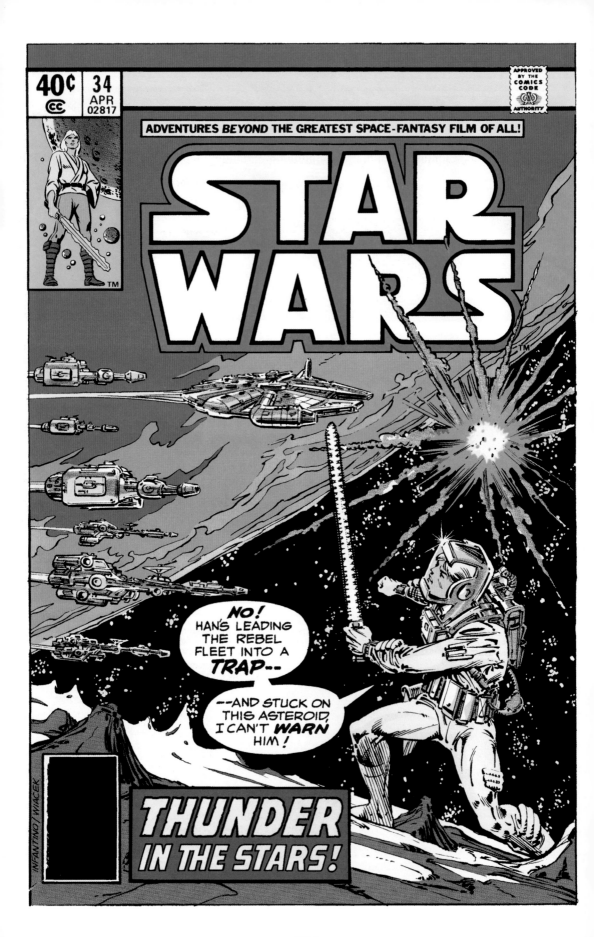

THUNDER IN

THE STARS!

I *HOPE* SO, MR. SOLO, THE REBEL ALLIANCE DOESN'T HAVE SHIPS TO *SPARE*.

LADY, I DON'T HAVE ANY *LIVES* TO SPARE. I'M NOT ABOUT TO *WASTE* THE ONE I'VE GOT BUTTING HEADS WITH AN *ASTEROID*.

TENSION HAS TEMPERS RUNNING HIGH IN THE COCKPIT, ARTOO. AT TIMES LIKE *THESE* I'M GRATEFUL TO HAVE THE MECHANICAL CALM AND LOGIC OF--

CHECKMATE?! HOW DARE YOU, YOU ROLLING SCRAP BIN! YOU *KNOW* I'M TOO CONCERNED OVER MASTER LUKE'S FATE TO *CONCENTRATE!*

VREEE-DLIT!

WHAT DO YOU *MEAN* I PLAYED *BETTER* THAN WHEN I *DO* CONCENTRATE?

IF YOU'RE GOING TO BE *INSOLENT* PERHAPS YOU SHOULD HAVE A MORE *WORTHY* OPPONENT! LET ME CALL *CHEWBACCA* AND--

YOU DROIDS BETTER GET *SET*... WE'RE APPROACHING *WARP TIME*.

PRINCESS, LET'S BREAK *COMMUNICATIONS SILENCE* LONG ENOUGH TO CLUE IN THE REST OF THE *FLEET*--

NEXT STOP: THE *ASTEROID CORRIDOR!*

BUT *AHEAD*, IN THAT VERY SECTOR OF SPACE...

TARGET IN *SIGHT*--

--*LAUNCH!*

THE TAGGE TECHNICIANS REPORT THAT THE *CONDUCTOR TOWER* HAS BEEN SUCCESSFULLY *IMPLANTED*, SIR.

YOU STILL THINK WE SHOULD GO *AHEAD*, SILAS, EVEN THOUGH THE BARON IS...AH... *DISABLED*?

CERTAINLY, SHANKS. THE PLAN NOW DEPENDS UPON MY *CREATION*...NOT MY OLDER BROTHER.

BELIEVING THEIR SUPPLY PLANET OF *JUNCTION* TO BE THE OBJECT OF OUR *EVIL INTENTIONS*...THE REBELS WILL SEND *SHIPS* TO STOP US.

DAREDEVILS THAT THEY ARE, THEY WILL USE THE TREACHEROUS *ASTEROID CORRIDOR* TO AVOID THE IMPERIAL *BLOCKADE*... KNOWING THE EMPIRE'S GREAT *BULK CRUISERS* CANNOT PATROL THERE.

" UNFORTUNATELY FOR THEM, OUR CONDUCTOR TOWERS NOW *BRACKET* THE CORRIDOR. ONCE THEY ARE *MIDWAY*, I SHALL *ACTIVATE* THE TOWERS...

"...AND THE ALLIANCE FLEET AND CREWS WILL BE SWEPT BY THE *ULTIMATE COLD* OF MY MODEST CONTRIVANCE...*THE OMEGA FROST!*"

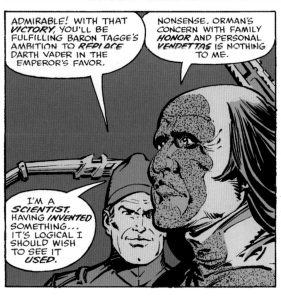

ADMIRABLE! WITH THAT *VICTORY*, YOU'LL BE FULFILLING BARON TAGGE'S AMBITION TO *REPLACE* DARTH VADER IN THE EMPEROR'S FAVOR.

NONSENSE, ORMAN'S CONCERN WITH FAMILY *HONOR* AND PERSONAL *VENDETTAS* IS NOTHING TO ME.

I'M A *SCIENTIST*. HAVING *INVENTED* SOMETHING... IT'S LOGICAL I SHOULD WISH TO SEE IT *USED*.

STILL...THERE'S *SOMETHING* IN WHAT YOU SAY, SHANKS. WITH MY OLDER BROTHER *INDISPOSED* I AM NEXT IN LINE FOR THE *TITLE*.

HAVING LABORED WELL AS *CHIEF SCIENTIST* FOR THE HOUSE OF TAGGE... PERHAPS IT'S *TIME* FOR SOME *GREATER* HONOR.

BUT THE YOUNG *REBEL* WHO ESCAPED, SILAS... THERE'S NO CHANCE HE COULD *SPOIL* THINGS?

ANYONE WHO DEFEATED BARON TAGGE IN A *LIGHTSABER DUEL** SHOULDN'T BE UNDER-ESTIMATED.

I *HAVEN'T*, SHANKS. REMEMBER, I WAS THE ONLY ONE ON THE SHIP TO EVEN *CONSIDER* THAT THE BOY MIGHT *WIN*...AND TAKE *PRECAUTIONS*.

**SHOWN LAST ISSUE-- ARCHIE.*

HAD BROTHER *ORMAN* SHOWN SUCH *FORESIGHT*...HE MIGHT NOT BE AS WE SEE HIM *NOW*, DEVASTATED BY THE YOUNG MAN'S *SKILL*...REDUCED TO A *STATE OF SHOCK*.

AS FOR *LUKE SKYWALKER*...

"...HE CAN'T BE *ENJOYING* HIS VICTORY. NOT SINCE HE'S UNDOUBTEDLY DISCOVERED THE *ADJUSTMENTS* I HAD MADE IN HIS *ESCAPE CRAFT!*"

THE GUNS AREN'T *ENERGIZED*...THE COMMUNICATIONS SYSTEM IS *OUT*...AND I JUST HAD TO *EXHAUST* WHAT LITTLE *FUEL* THIS CRATE HAS--

--TO GET IT ON THE *COURSE* I WANT!

SOMEBODY FIXED IT SO THERE'S NO WAY I CAN *WARN* THE ALLIANCE OR TURN THIS FIGHTER AGAINST THAT *TAGGE SHIP!*

HAVE TO ACT *MYSELF*...! CRAFT WON'T LOSE ITS *THRUST* OUT HERE IN SPACE,...BUT WITHOUT FUEL, I CAN'T *MANEUVER*.

WHICH MAKES *FLYING* IT A GREAT WAY TO COMMIT *SUICIDE*...! 'CAUSE IN A PLACE LIKE THE *ASTEROID CORRIDOR*--

--SOMETHING'S *BOUND* TO GET IN THE WAY!

AND AS ROCKY *DEATH* LOOMS BEFORE THE ONRUSHING *TIE FIGHTER*...LUKE HITS THE *EJECTION BUTTON!*

P-VOW!

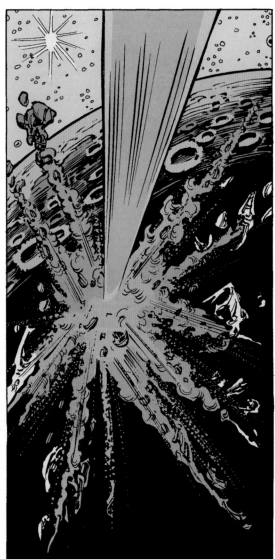

THIS IS CARRYING ME FARTHER AND *FARTHER* FROM THE WAY I *WANT* TO GO...!

GOT TO GET OUT OF THIS *SEAT*... *FAST!*

MY FIRST *BREAK*....! THE *TAMPERING* DIDN'T EXTEND TO THE SURVIVAL ARMOR'S *JET PACK.*

MUST'VE FIGURED ONE *EX-FARM BOY* FLOATING AMONG THE ASTEROIDS COULDN'T *HURT* THEM MUCH...AND THEY MAY BE *RIGHT!*

BUT I CAN'T THINK OF THE ODDS *AGAINST* ME... GOT TO CLEAR MY *MIND*. TRUST MY *FEELINGS*...

LET THE *FORCE* GUIDE ME IN THE RIGHT *DIRECTION*...

AND PRAY MY JET PACK HOLDS OUT *LONG* ENOUGH!

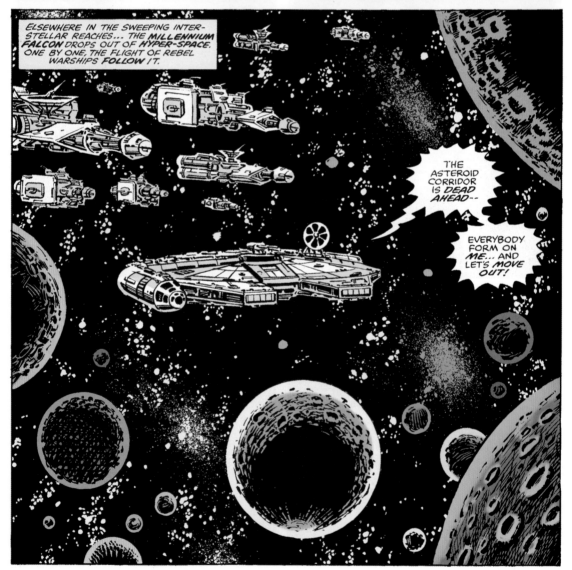

ELSEWHERE IN THE SWEEPING INTER-STELLAR REACHES... THE *MILLENNIUM FALCON* DROPS OUT OF *HYPER-SPACE*. ONE BY ONE, THE FLIGHT OF REBEL WARSHIPS *FOLLOW* IT.

THE ASTEROID CORRIDOR IS *DEAD AHEAD*--

EVERYBODY FORM ON *ME*... AND LET'S *MOVE OUT!*

WAARGH!

YEAH, THIS *IS* GONNA BE A LOT *DIFFERENT* THAN DODGING AROUND THOSE KING-SIZE BOULDERS ON OUR *LONESOME*, CHEWIE. BUT LOOK AT THE *BRIGHT* SIDE--

--SO FAR THIS TIME, NOBODY'S *CHASIN'* US! PRINCESS, BETTER GO BACK AND *STRAP IN*...JUST IN CASE WE *SCRAPE* SOMETHING.

IF YOU'RE AS GOOD AS YOU ALWAYS *SAY* YOU ARE, YOU SHOULDN'T *NEED* THIS, FLYBOY--

--BUT *GOOD LUCK* ANYWAY.

DR. TAGGE, THE LONG RANGE SCANNERS HAVE PICKED UP A GROUP OF *REBEL* SHIPS--

DESPITE AN ATTEMPT AT *JAMMING*...IT'S DEFINITE THEY'RE MOVING INTO THE *CORRIDOR.*

UH...*SILAS*? ARE WE FAR ENOUGH *REMOVED* FROM THE ASTEROIDS NOT TO BE AFFECTED BY THE *OMEGA FROST*...?

A MILITARY MAN SHOULDN'T ALLOW *NERVES* TO SHOW, SHANKS. AND IF I WERE A LESS *LOGICAL* MAN... I MIGHT BE *DISTURBED* BY YOUR LACK OF FAITH.

THERE'S NO *FALLOUT* FROM MY CREATION. SO LONG AS YOU AREN'T CAUGHT *BETWEEN* THE CONDUCTOR TOWERS... IT'S PERFECTLY *SAFE.*

WE'LL *ACTIVATE* WHEN THE REBELS ARE AT THE HALF-WAY MARK. PERHAPS YOU SHOULD CONTACT YOUR *COMMANDER,* SHANKS--

MY LITTLE BROTHER, *GENERAL TAGGE,* MAY WANT TO MOVE HIS *CRUISER* NEAR TO THE SCENE...SO HE CAN *RECORD* OUR SUCCESS FOR THE EMPEROR.

VISUALS ADD SO *MUCH* TO A REPORT...AND WE *DO* WANT TO MAKE AN *IMPRESSION!*

THAT'S *IT*...! THE EDGE OF THE CORRIDOR... AND THE *FIRST* TOWER SET UP BY TAGGE'S PEOPLE!

I'VE GOTTEN *WHERE* I WANTED... BUT I'VE *EXHAUSTED* MY JET PACK *DOING* IT.

WHICH LEAVES ME WITH LOADS OF *MOMENTUM*... AND NO WAY OF *BRAKING!* I COULD WIND UP SMEARED INTO *THIS* ASTEROID JUST LIKE THAT *TIE FIGHTER* I ABANDONED HIT THE *OTHER* ONE!

UNLESS...

ZAMP!

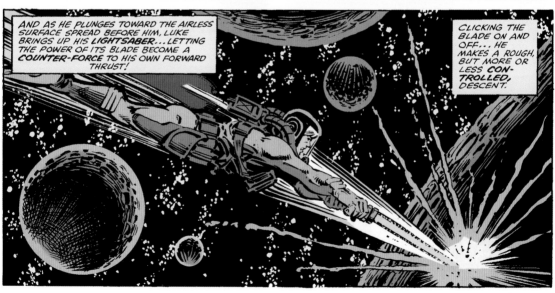

AND AS HE PLUNGES TOWARD THE AIRLESS SURFACE SPREAD BEFORE HIM, LUKE BRINGS UP HIS *LIGHTSABER*... LETTING THE POWER OF ITS BLADE BECOME A *COUNTER-FORCE* TO HIS OWN FORWARD THRUST!

CLICKING THE BLADE ON AND OFF... HE MAKES A ROUGH, BUT MORE OR LESS *CONTROLLED*, DESCENT.

UNTIL...

THE *TOWER*...! IT'S A LOT *BIGGER* THAN THE EXPERIMENTAL ONES HAN, CHEWIE, AND I SAW *TESTED* BACK ON TATOOINE! *

BUT THEN, TO GENERATE THE *OMEGA FROST* ACROSS THE ASTEROID CORRIDOR... IT'D *HAVE* TO BE.

*STAR WARS #32-- ARCH.

ONLY IT'S *NOT GOING TO!* NOT WHEN THE REBEL ALLIANCE PROBABLY ALREADY HAS A *RESCUE FORCE* MOVING THROUGH THE CORRIDOR--

NOT WHEN MY *FRIENDS* MAY VERY WELL BE *LEADING* IT!

BARON TAGGE *TRICKED* ME INTO BROADCASTING THE INFORMATION THAT WOULD *BRING* THEM HERE-- *

VRAAMP!

BUT NOW I'M GOING TO *MAKE UP* FOR THAT! NOW I'M--

*LAST ISSUE--ARCH AGAIN.

SHRA-DAAAAAAK!

THE BLINK OF AN EYE. SUDDENLY, THE *MILLENNIUM FALCON'S* FORWARD SCANNERS GO *WILD* AS...

THE ASTEROIDS *AHEAD* OF US HAVE TURNED TO *ICE,* HAN....! AS IF THEY'D BEEN SWEPT BY SOME KIND OF... *IMPOSSIBLE COLD!*

IT'S A TRAP! THAT TAGGE DEVICE LUKE THOUGHT WAS GOING TO BE USED ON *JUNCTION* HAS BEEN SET UP FOR US *HERE,* PRINCESS --

-- AND WE'LL BE IN ITS *RANGE* IN SECONDS!

WHILE ON THE BRIDGE OF THE TAGGE MINING EXPLORER...

WE'VE ACTIVATED *MOMENTS* TOO EARLY... THE ALLIANCE SHIPS ARE JUST *SHY* OF THE OMEGA FROST'S EFFECTIVE BAND, DOCTOR!

MAINTAIN THE *POWER.* EVEN WITH THEIR MUCH VAUNTED *MANEUVERABILITY,* THE REBEL CRAFT CAN'T DO A *FULL REVERSE* AMID THOSE ASTEROIDS --

-- NOT WITHOUT COLLISION AND *DISASTER.* EITHER WAY, WE *WIN.*

YOU SEE THE VALUE OF THE *SCIENTIFIC MIND,* SHANKS? I'VE CONSIDERED *ALL* CONTINGENCIES SO--

YOU'VE FORGOTTEN *SKYWALKER!* LOOK AT THE *MONITOR...* HE *HASN'T* GIVEN UP!

IT IS HIS LAST CHANCE. HIS ARMOR'S *AIR* RESERVES ARE NEARLY SPENT. EACH DRIVING SWING OF THE LIGHTSABER IS TORTUROUS *EFFORT...*

...BUT HE HAS *MEDITATED,* AND THIS WAY SEEMS *RIGHT.*

THERE...! THE *BASE* OF THE TOWER...! NOW WE *TEST* MY THEORY--

-- THAT THEY WOULDN'T EXTEND THE TOWER'S PRO-TECTIVE FORCE FIELD *BELOW* THE ASTEROID'S SURFACE!

ZOAK!

AND THE ANSWER *LUKE* SEEKS... IS LEARNED ABOARD THE *MILLENNIUM FALCON* AS WELL!

THAT'S *RIGHT*, CHEWIE! WE SHOULD BE *ICICLES*... BUT WE'RE *NOT*! SOME-THING'S *SPOILED* THE HOUSE OF TAGGE'S *COLD WAVE!*

VROWRRK!

LONG AS WE'VE GOTTEN OUR *LIVES* HANDED BACK TO US... LET'S KEEP ON *PRESERVING* THEM.

SINCE THE JUNCTION BUSINESS WAS A *SET UP*, WE DON'T HAVE TO CONTINUE ON IN THE *CORRIDOR*. I'LL TELL THE OTHER SHIPS TO *SCATTER* OUT OF IT AND--

NO, HAN. WE'LL BE *MISSING* AN OPPORTUNITY...

THE CONDUCTOR TOWER HAS BEEN *SHORTED OUT*, DOCTOR TAGGE! THE *OMEGA FROST* CAN NO LONGER BE GENERATED. WHAT DO WE DO *NOW?*

THAT BOY... THAT BOY *SKY-WALKER...!* THIS IS *ALL* HIS FAULT! CONTACT MY *YOUNGER* BROTHER... HAVE HIM SEND A *TIE FIGHTER* FROM HIS CRUISER TO *DESTROY* SKYWALKER AND...AND...

NONE OF MY PLANS *INCLUDED* THIS...! I-IT'S...SO *CONFUSING*. NOT LIKE DOING *EXPERIMENTS* IN THE LABORATORY...! I-I--

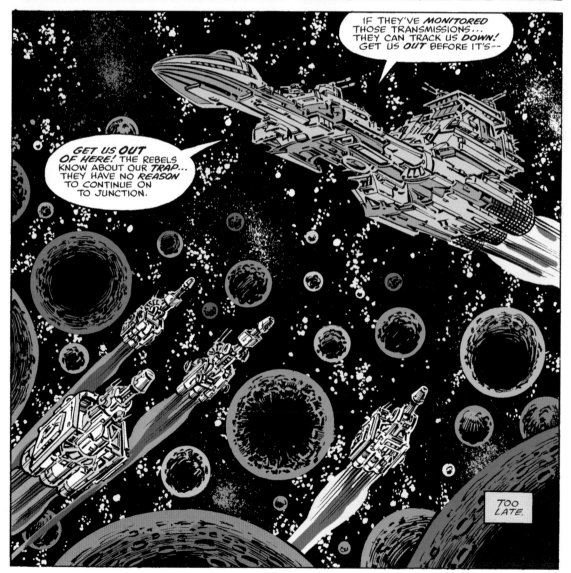

THE THUNDER IS *ECHOED* IN A *TIE* FIGHTER'S APPROACH ON A HUMAN TARGET. A TARGET THROWN TO THE GROUND BY THE AFTERSHOCK OF DISRUPTING THE *OMEGA FROST*...

...A TARGET RENDERED TOTALLY *HELPLESS* AS HE FIGHTS FOR THE LAST BITS OF *AIR* HIS SUIT PROVIDES.

HELPLESS... BUT NOT WITHOUT *HELP.*

NO *SCORE* TODAY, IMPERIAL. THE SAME TRANSMISSION THAT BROUGHT *YOU* HERE... BROUGHT *US* TOO!

HAN, SENSORS INDICATE LUKE'S STILL *ALIVE* DOWN THERE BUT--

UNFURROW YOUR *BROW,* PRINCESS... I'VE NEVER MISSED A LAST MINUTE *RESCUE* YET. CHEWIE WILL TAKE OVER WHILE I PICK UP THE KID.

DESPITE MY CYNICAL SOUL, EVEN *I* ENJOY AN OCCASIONAL *HAPPY* ENDING.

NEXT ISSUE: **DARK LORD'S GAMBIT!**

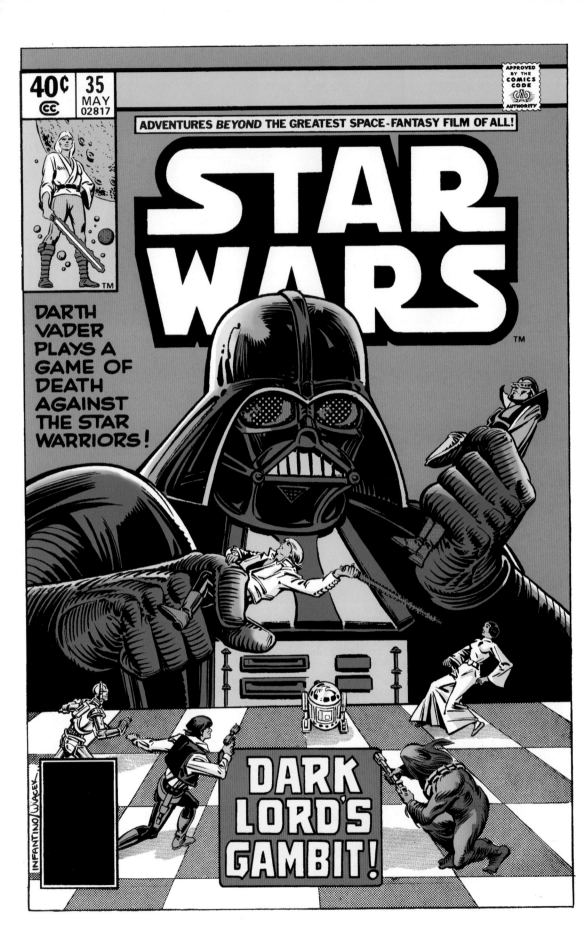

LUKE SKYWALKER. A LONG BREATH RASPS FROM THE SITH LORD'S MASK. IN SOMEONE LESS AWESOME, IT MIGHT ALMOST HAVE BEEN A *SIGH*. TWO WORDS; ONE NAME. ALMOST *ANTICLIMACTIC* CONSIDERING THE LONG TIME IT HAS TAKEN HIM TO LEARN IT.

STILL, THE *IMPORTANT* THING IS THAT HE HAS IT AT LAST.

CAPTAIN WERMIS, WE ARE RETURNING TO THE *CRUISER*...MAKE READY TO *DEPART*. THE REBELS NO LONGER HAVE A *REFUELING STATION* HERE--

--AND THE NAME OF THE T-65 PILOT WHO DESTROYED THE *DEATH STAR* IS NO LONGER A *SECRET*.

AND HAVING ACQUIRED THAT INFORMATION... WE SHALL NOW TAKE *ACTION*.

M-MY OLDER BROTHERS-- ORMAN, THE *BARON*, AND SILAS, *CHIEF SCIENTIST* OF THE FAMILY INDUSTRIES-- CONVINCED ME TO TRY AN *INVENTION* OF THEIRS AGAINST THE REBELS. *

WE SET A *TRAP* THAT, IF SUCCESSFUL, WOULD HAVE WON THE EMPEROR'S *FAVOR* AWAY FROM *YOU*.

*SEE STAR WARS # 31-34 --ARCHIE

BUT... SOMETHING WENT *WRONG!* THE INVENTION *FAILED*... AND THE ALLIANCE FLEET IT WAS INTENDED TO *CRUSH* TURNED THE TRAP AGAINST US!

MY BROTHER'S VESSEL WAS SWIFTLY *DESTROYED*. AND BEFORE MY CRUISER COULD *RETREAT* FROM THE SECTOR--

"-- THE REBELS CAME SWEEPING *IN* ON US! STILL, I GOT MY DEFENSIVE FIGHTERS INTO ACTION AND WE WERE HOLDING OUR OWN--

"-- WHEN *ANOTHER SHIP* SURGED INTO THE FRAY!

"IT LOOKED LIKE A FREIGHTER, BUT ITS *SPEED* AND *MANEUVERABILITY* EQUALLED ANY CRAFT IN THE BATTLE... AND *THEN* SOME!

THE ACCURACY OF ITS FIRE PIERCED ONE OF OUR *SHIELDS*... A RESERVE *REACTOR* EXPLODED!

MY STAFF AND I WERE FORCED TO *FLEE* IN AN ESCAPE CRAFT... EVERYTHING ELSE WAS *LOST.*

OUR MONITORS PICKED UP SOME OF THE REBELS' SHIP-TO-SHIP *COMMUNICATION.*

IT LEFT NO DOUBT THAT PRINCESS *LEIA ORGANA* WAS ABOARD THAT FREIGHTER... AND THAT ITS DEADLY WORK WITH THE *LASER CANNON* WAS BY INDIVIDUALS NAMED *SOLO* AND *SKYWALKER.*

YOU HAD *ALL* THAT...! THE ONE I'VE BEEN *SEEKING*... THE SHIP THAT *RUINED* MY DEFENSE OF THE DEATH STAR... AND YOU *LOST* IT!

I'M *WEARY* OF YOUR FAMILY WORKING AT *CROSS PURPOSES* TO ME, TAGGE!

WE'RE PUTTING AN *END* TO IT! *RIGHT NOW!*

BEHOLD!

IT CAN'T BE...! M-MY *BROTHERS*...! ORMAN... SILAS...! BUT... THEY'RE *DEAD*... SLAIN BY THE REBELS... DESTROYED WITH THEIR SHIP!

NO, EVIDENTLY THEIR *COMPARTMENT* SUFFERED NO DAMAGE... THE EMERGENCY SEALS KEPT IT *AIRTIGHT*.

STILL, THEY HAD NEARLY *SUFFOCATED* WHEN MY SPIES INVESTIGATED THE WRECKAGE AND *FOUND* THEM... BUT, IN TIME, THESE MACHINES CAN RESTORE THEIR LIFE FUNCTIONS TO *NORMAL*.

YOU MEAN TO *REVIVE* THEM...?

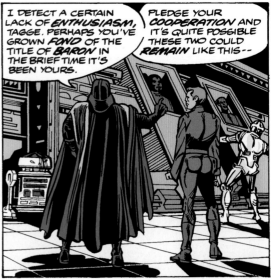

I DETECT A CERTAIN LACK OF *ENTHUSIASM*, TAGGE. PERHAPS YOU'VE GROWN *FOND* OF THE TITLE OF *BARON* IN THE BRIEF TIME IT'S BEEN YOURS.

PLEDGE YOUR *COOPERATION* AND IT'S QUITE POSSIBLE THESE TWO COULD *REMAIN* LIKE THIS--

--CONTINUE TO OPPOSE ME AND I'LL HAVE THE *THREE* OF YOU BROUGHT BEFORE THE *EMPEROR* WITH A FULL ACCOUNT OF YOUR *FIASCO* AGAINST THE REBELS!

I MEAN TO GO FORWARD WITH PLANS OF MY *OWN*, GENERAL TAGGE...AND I WANT *NO SCHEMING* BEHIND MY BACK WHEN I DO!

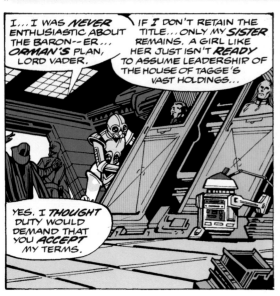

I...I WAS *NEVER* ENTHUSIASTIC ABOUT THE BARON--ER... *ORMAN'S* PLAN, LORD VADER.

IF *I* DON'T RETAIN THE TITLE...ONLY MY *SISTER* REMAINS, A GIRL LIKE HER JUST ISN'T *READY* TO ASSUME LEADERSHIP OF THE HOUSE OF TAGGE'S VAST HOLDINGS...

YES. I *THOUGHT* DUTY WOULD DEMAND THAT YOU *ACCEPT* MY TERMS.

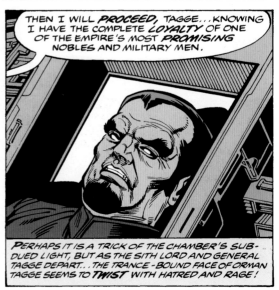

THEN I WILL *PROCEED*, TAGGE...KNOWING I HAVE THE COMPLETE *LOYALTY* OF ONE OF THE EMPIRE'S MOST *PROMISING* NOBLES AND MILITARY MEN.

PERHAPS IT IS A TRICK OF THE CHAMBER'S SUBDUED LIGHT, BUT AS THE SITH LORD AND GENERAL TAGGE DEPART...THE TRANCE-BOUND FACE OF ORMAN TAGGE SEEMS TO TWIST WITH HATRED AND RAGE!

SHORTLY, A **SHUTTLE CRAFT** ROARS OUT OF THE DOCKING BAY OF DARTH VADER'S CRUISER... CARRYING THE **NEW** BARON TAGGE BACK TO HIS OWN SHIP.

PEACE WITH AN **ENEMY**, SIR...? I'M MOST **SURPRISED**.

I EXPECTED YOU TO TAKE THIS OPPORTUNITY TO **CRUSH** THE TAGGE LINE FOREVER.

ANY PETTY TYRANT CAN **OBLITERATE** A FOE, WERMIS... I AM A **MASTER OF THE FORCE**.

FROM THIS MOMENT ON, AN ENTIRE **FAMILY** WHICH STRUGGLED AGAINST ME WILL NOW SERVE AS... MY **PAWNS**.

TIME PASSES. TIME IN WHICH THE FALLEN JEDI MOVES AT HIS OWN PACE ON HIS OWN DARK COURSE. TIME IN WHICH A FORMER MOISTURE FARMER FROM TATOOINE SERVES THE **REBEL ALLIANCE** ANY WAY HE CAN.

BLUE LEADER TO BLUE FLIGHT... I FIGURE WE'RE GOOD FOR FIVE MINUTES MORE **PATROL** WITHOUT TAXING OUR FUEL. DO YOU **COPY?** OVER.

ROGER, BLUE LEADER, BUT ARE YOU CONCERNED ABOUT **FUEL**... OR THE FACT THAT **HAN SOLO** IS BACK AT THE BASE WITH THE **PRINCESS?**

IT IS A QUESTION LUKE SKYWALKER IS *SPARED* ANSWERING... AS SCANNING SCOPES SUDDENLY COME TO *LIFE* WITH THE PRESENCE OF OTHER SHIPS!

TIE FIGHTERS AND THEIR PREY... ON THE EDGE OF THE YAVIN SYSTEM!

BUT NOT FOR *LONG*... AS LUKE'S PATROL MOVES IN *FAST*, LASER CANNONS *BLAZING!*

WE CAUGHT 'EM *NAPPING*, BLUE FLIGHT! ESCORT THAT *CIVILIAN* THEY WERE TRYING TO ZAP--

--I'M FOLLOWING THE LAST *STRAGGLER* TO SEE WHERE HE *CAME* FROM!

THE *ANSWER* IS NOT LONG COMING.

IMPERIAL BATTLE CRUISER....! BUT THEY'RE ALREADY BUILDING UP SPEED TO JUMP INTO *WARP*... THEY'LL BE *GONE* BEFORE I CAN GET *HELP* HERE.

GENERAL DODONNA ORDERED US TO *AVOID* ONE-SIDED ENGAGEMENTS... MIGHT AS WELL HEAD *BACK* AND SEE JUST *WHO* WE SAVED!

THERE SEEMS TO BE A *COMMOTION* OUTSIDE ON THE LANDING STRIP, HAN. I'D LIKE TO SEE WHAT'S HAPPENING.

IN THE *MIDDLE* OF MY STORY OF HOW CHEWIE AN' ME TRICKED *JABBA THE HUT* INTO TRADING A KILO OF SPICE FOR A THREE-LEGGED *BAN-THA?*

THIS IS THE LAST TIME I TRY TO ENTERTAIN INVALID *ROYALTY!*

MY LEG'S ALMOST *HEALED* SINCE IT WAS INJURED ON THAT LAST MISSION...✱ I DON'T THINK I NEED ANY *HELP* WALKING.

YOU'RE TOO *VALUABLE* TO THE ALLIANCE TO RISK A *RELAPSE*, PRINCESS. RELAX AND *ENJOY* IT...LIKE *ME.*

✱ONE WE'VE YET TO CHRONICLE -- ARCHIE.

SHORTLY, ON THE LANDING FIELD IN FRONT OF THE GREAT STONE RUINS WHICH HOUSE REBEL HEADQUARTERS, ON THE FOURTH MOON OF YAVIN...

WHERE DID THAT *SHIP* COME FROM, THREEPIO?

MASTER LUKE AND HIS PATROL SEEM TO HAVE *RESCUED* IT, YOUR HIGHNESS--

--ARTOO WAS SO ANXIOUS TO SEE THE *PASSENGERS*, HE BARELY TOOK TIME TO BLEEP OUT THE DETAILS TO ME.

I AM *SISTER DOMINA*... PRIESTESS IN THE *ORDER OF THE SACRED CIRCLE.*

WE HAVE RISKED VIOLATING THE IMPERIAL BLOCKADE TO SEEK YOUR *COUNCIL*... AND, PERHAPS, YOUR *AID.*

AND JUDGING BY *YOUR* SWIFT ACTIONS AGAINST OUR IMPERIAL PURSUERS, AS WELL AS THE PERSONAL *AURA* I SENSE ABOUT YOU--

--COMING HERE WAS *NOT* A MISTAKE.

WELL...UH... I WAS ONLY DOING MY *JOB*....! BUT... IF YOU'RE ON A DIPLOMATIC MISSION ....YOU'LL WANT TO SEE...UH... GENERAL DODONNA OR...ER... SENATOR ORGANA...!

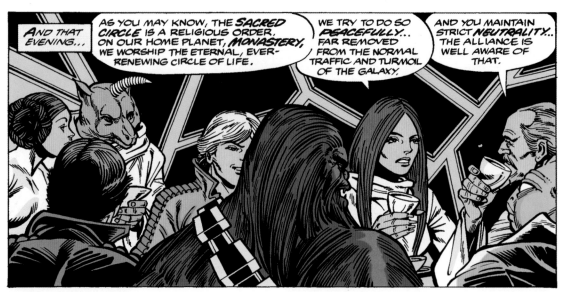

AND THAT EVENING...

AS YOU MAY KNOW, THE *SACRED CIRCLE* IS A RELIGIOUS ORDER, ON OUR HOME PLANET, *MONASTERY,* WE WORSHIP THE ETERNAL, EVER-RENEWING CIRCLE OF LIFE.

WE TRY TO DO SO *PEACEFULLY...* FAR REMOVED FROM THE NORMAL TRAFFIC AND TURMOIL OF THE GALAXY.

AND YOU MAINTAIN STRICT *NEUTRALITY...* THE ALLIANCE IS WELL AWARE OF THAT.

UNTIL *RECENTLY,* GENERAL. THE EMPIRE HAS SENT AN *ENVOY* TO MONASTERY... OVERTURES ARE BEING MADE TO PERSUADE US TO *SIDE* WITH THEM.

A GALACTIC WAR, SUCH AS YOU HAVE BEGUN, COULD WELL *SUNDER* THE CIRCLE OF LIFE ...WITH OUR MANY FOLLOWERS IN MANY SYSTEMS, OUR INFLUENCE MIGHT TIP THE BALANCE TO *END* SUCH A WAR SWIFTLY.

SISTER DOMINA, IMPERIAL *TYRANNY* CAN BE EVEN *MORE* CORRUPTING AND DANGEROUS TO THE NATURAL CYCLE THAN OUR *REBELLION!*

YOU CAN *SEE* THE RESULTS ON WORLDS WHERE THEY HOLD *FULL SWAY!* IF YOUR ORDER NEEDS *PROOF,* I'M CERTAINLY *WELL* ENOUGH TO TRAVEL TO--!

THAT'S THE *RESPONSE* WE HOPED FOR, SENATOR.

THE ORDER WISHED TO HEAR FROM *BOTH* SIDES BEFORE MAKING A DECISION. BUT THE EMPIRE HAS A STRONG AND *PERSUASIVE* REPRESENATIVE...A LARGE FACTION HAS BEEN *IMPRESSED.*

AND HE IS NOT THE SORT TO LET HIS WORK BE *UNDONE!*

DARTH VADER!

GENERAL DODONNA, YOU'VE GOT TO SEND *ME* ON THIS MISSION...!

THIS IS *DIPLOMACY*, LUKE... *POLITICS*. PRINCESS LEIA'S TIME IN THE IMPERIAL SENATE MAKES *HER* THE BEST QUALIFIED.

I SUPPOSE SHE COULD USE A *BODYGUARD*...

THERE IS A *PROBLEM*, I FEAR. MONASTERY IS A *CLOISTERED* WORLD... USUALLY NOT *OPEN* TO VISITORS. WE ALLOWED THE EMPIRE ONLY A *SINGLE* REPRESENTATIVE--

--THE SAME MUST BE TRUE FOR THE *ALLIANCE.* HOWEVER--

--I SENSE IN LUKE SKYWALKER AN *OPENESS* AND *SINCERITY* THE MOST SKILLFUL DIPLOMATS RARELY POSSESS.

THIS WOULD MAKE A MARKED *CONTRAST* TO LORD VADER...A CONTRAST THE ELDERS OF THE SACRED CIRCLE--WITH THEIR APPRECIATION OF THE NATURAL, UNCOMPLICATED FLOW OF LIFE--WOULD FIND *IMPRESSIVE.*

CERTAINLY, I *PERSONALLY* FIND THIS SO... BUT, OF COURSE, WHO *FINALLY* ACCOMPANIES US BACK TO MONASTERY IS YOUR *OWN* DECISION.

AND THE FOLLOWING MORNING... THAT DECISION IS MADE.

GENERAL DODONNA...! HOW COULD YOU AND THE COUNCIL *DO* THIS?!

PERHAPS WE THOUGHT YOUR ARGUMENTS WERE *TINGED* SLIGHTLY WITH JEALOUSY, YOUR HIGHNESS.

DON'T *WORRY*... ARTOO DEETOO IS *WITH* LUKE, PROGRAMMED WITH A MOST *CONVINCING* SET OF PROOFS AGAINST THE EMPIRE.

THAT-- PLUS THE FACT THAT HE SEEMS THE *CHOICE* THE ORDER'S REPRESENTATIVE FAVORS-- SHOULD ENABLE HIM TO DO THE JOB *WELL.*

BUT JUST IN CASE... WE'RE TAKING *OTHER* MEASURES. *MONASTERY* MAY BE OFF-LIMITS, BUT THAT DOESN'T MEAN WE CAN'T HAVE A *SHIP* IN THE SYSTEM...

"...ONE THAT'S NOT TOO *CONSPICUOUS...* LIKE A *SPICE FREIGHTER.*"

WE'RE COMING OUT OF *WARP,* YOUR ROYALNESS... ONE MORE *ITEM* FOR A VERY LONG BILL I'M GOING TO SUBMIT TO YOUR ALLIANCE *ACCOUNTANTS* ONE OF THESE DAYS!

AND I THOUGHT YOU WERE DOING THIS IN CASE *LUKE* NEEDED *HELP,* HAN.

FOR *SURE,* PRINCESS... BUT I'M STILL *MERCENARY* ENOUGH THAT I'D LIKE TO TURN A *PROFIT* ON IT IF I CAN.

THE RINGED PLANET IS *MONASTERY,* BY THE WAY. THE KID SHOULD BE *DOWN* THERE BY NOW... IF HE'S IN *TROUBLE,* WE OUGHT TO LEARN ABOUT IT *SOON!*

WE WON'T IF THE ULTRA-FREQUENCY LASERWAVE LINK THE TECHNOS ON YAVIN DEVISED DOESN'T *FUNCTION* PROPERLY.

THREEPIO, WE'D BETTER *TEST* IT NOW.

AS YOU *WISH*, YOUR HIGHNESS ...THOUGH IT'S AN ODD SENSA-TION TO FIND ALL MY CIRCUITS SUDDENLY LOCKED INTO A *COMMUN-ICATIONS SYSTEM.*

ARTOO...? ARE YOU *RECEIVING* ME? COME IN, ARTOO... WE *MUST* KNOW IF THE *CONTACT* IS ESTABLISHED. ARTOO DEETOO, YOU MALICIOUS LITTLE MASS OF MICROCIRCUITRY,...*ANSWER* ME!

VIROOOP-A-DEET!

"OF ALL THE *ARROGANCE!* HE SAYS THE CONNECTION IS FINE... BUT HE'S TOO *BUSY* TO COMMUNICATE NOW!"

SISTER DOMINA....! *DOWN!*

BLEEET!

CERTAINLY IT DEMONSTRATES THEIR LACK OF *RESPECT* FOR THE ORDER OF THE SACRED CIRCLE... BY SENDING AN UNRULY *CHILD* INSTEAD OF A SEASONED *DIPLOMAT!*

DARTH VADER!

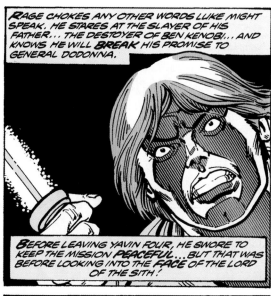

RAGE CHOKES ANY OTHER WORDS LUKE MIGHT SPEAK. HE STARES AT THE SLAYER OF HIS FATHER... THE DESTROYER OF BEN KENOBI,... AND KNOWS HE WILL *BREAK* HIS PROMISE TO GENERAL DODONNA.

BEFORE LEAVING YAVIN FOUR, HE SWORE TO KEEP THE MISSION *PEACEFUL*... BUT THAT WAS BEFORE LOOKING INTO THE *FACE* OF THE LORD OF THE SITH!

BUT IF THE URGE TO *REVENGE* MAKES LUKE FORSAKE EVERYTHING... SOMEONE *ELSE* IS READY TO REMIND HIM!

FREEDA-BRRRT!

THE NUDGE IS ENOUGH. LUKE'S ANGER REMAINS... BUT IT COMES UNDER CONTROL.

ONCE THIS BUSINESS IS *SETTLED*, JUST AS SOON AS YOU'RE OFF *MONASTERY*... WE'LL *MEET*, LORD VADER. THAT'S A *PROMISE!*

YOUR PROMISES ARE OF NO *IN-TEREST* TO ME, STRIPLING... I CHOOSE MY *OWN* TIME PLACES. AND I DIDN'T COME HERE TO IDLY *BANTER* WITH A YOUNG HOTHEAD--

--BUT TO WELCOME *SISTER DOMINA* BACK. WE'VE BEEN ,AT *ODDS* IN THE PAST... BUT SHE'S DONE ME A GREAT *SERVICE* TODAY.

THIS,...*REPRESENTATIVE* YOU'VE BROUGHT BACK FROM THE ALLIANCE SHOULD MAKE MY PRESENTATION TO THE HIGH CIRCLE OF ELDERS APPEAR ALL THE *BETTER.*

BLAST IT ALL! HE'S *RIGHT*... PRINCESS LEIA SHOULD BE DOING THIS, NOT *ME*. I'M *WAY* OUT OF MY DEPTH!

NO, LUKE SKYWALKER--

IN ALL THE REBEL ALLIANCE, ONLY *YOU* CAN FULFILL WHAT MUST BE *DONE* HERE.

I *KNOW* THIS...AS A *PRIESTESS*... AS A *WOMAN!*

AND MOVING TO A *SLIDEWAY*... SISTER DOMINA, JOINING THE GREETING PARTY, LEADS THE BOY FROM *TATOOINE* TOWARD THEIR *DESTINATION.*

THE *TEMPLE* OF THE SACRED CIRCLE...! IT IS WHERE WE WORSHIP AND ABIDE.

QUARTERS HAVE BEEN ARRANGED FOR YOU, LUKE... REST *WELL.* TOMORROW YOU WILL FACE THE *HIGH ELDERS.*

SOON...

QUITE A *PLACE,* ARTOO... AND THAT SISTER DOMINA'S QUITE A LADY. KIND OF MAKES ME BELIEVE I CAN PULL THIS *OFF*...!

SHE'S *BEAUTIFUL,* TOO!

--ALMOST AS BEAUTIFUL AS THE *PRINCESS.* NOT THAT I'D *FORGET* LEIA... IT'S JUST THAT SOMETIMES I CAN'T FIGURE WHERE I *STAND* WITH HER, ESPECIALLY WHEN *HAN'S* AROUND...

TURN IT *OFF,* THREEPIO! OBVIOUSLY GENERAL DODONNA DIDN'T *TELL* LUKE ABOUT THE LASERWAVE LINK WITH ARTOO...! PROBABLY SO WE COULD *AID* HIM--

--WITHOUT ANY...ER... *EMBARRASSMENT.*

NIGHT FALLS ON THE PLANET OF MONASTERY; A SHOWER OF MOONS, PART OF THE PLANET'S GREAT RING, GLOW LUSHLY. ONE BY ONE THE TEMPLE LIGHTS DIM... EXCEPT IN A TOWER ROOM.

YOU USED THE *FORCE* TO MAKE THAT NIGHTSHRIKE ATTACK, LORD VADER,... IT WILL *IMPRESS* THE MORE *SUPERSTITIOUS* OF OUR FOLLOWERS.

BUT WEREN'T YOU AFRAID YOUNG SKYWALKER WOULD *EXPOSE* IT...? MY INSTINCTS AS A PRIESTESS TELL ME HE, *TOO*, IS FAMILIAR WITH THE FORCE.

TRUE. BUT HE IS STILL A *NOVICE*. WORSE YET... HE IS A *ROMANTIC*. YOUR OVERTURES TO HIM *PLAY* ON THAT,... IT CONFUSES HIS *THOUGHTS* AND ULTIMATELY, HIS *ABILITIES*.

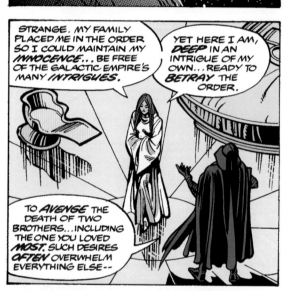

STRANGE. MY FAMILY PLACED ME IN THE ORDER SO I COULD MAINTAIN MY *INNOCENCE*... BE FREE OF THE GALACTIC EMPIRE'S MANY *INTRIGUES*.

YET HERE I AM, *DEEP* IN AN INTRIGUE OF MY OWN... READY TO *BETRAY* THE ORDER.

TO *AVENGE* THE DEATH OF TWO BROTHERS...INCLUDING THE ONE YOU LOVED *MOST*. SUCH DESIRES *OFTEN* OVERWHELM EVERYTHING ELSE--

--PARTICULARLY IN A LONG, PROUD LINE LIKE *YOURS*.

YES. WHY *ELSE* WOULD I HAVE ALLIED MYSELF WITH THE MAN MY BROTHER, *BARON TAGGE*, HATED?

BUT FOR *ALL* YOU DID AGAINST ORMAN, YOU WEREN'T RESPONSIBLE FOR HIS *DEATH*... LUKE SKYWALKER WAS!

THE LORD OF THE SITH *LEAVES* THE YOUNGEST MEMBER OF THE HOUSE OF TAGGE, STRIDING SWIFTLY TO A BALCONY WHERE HE CAN BE *ALONE*.

MY OPENING MOVES ARE *COMPLETE*, WERMIS... THE PLAYERS ARE *ALL* IN POSITION.

LET THE GAME *TRULY* BEGIN!

NEXT ISSUE: RED QUEEN RISING!

Long ago in a galaxy far, far away. . .there exists a state of cosmic *civil war*. A brave alliance of *underground freedom fighters* has challenged the tyranny and oppression of the awesome *Galactic Empire*. This is their story!

LucasFilm PRESENTS: **STAR WARS** THE GREATEST SPACE FANTASY OF ALL!

CONTINUING THE SAGA BEGUN IN THE FILM BY GEORGE LUCAS RELEASED BY TWENTIETH CENTURY-FOX

ARCHIE GOODWIN *writer/editor* • CARMINE INFANTINO and GENE DAY *artists* • JOHN COSTANZA *letterer* • PETRA GOLDBERG *colorist* • JIM SHOOTER *consulting ed.*

THE *MILLENNIUM FALCON* FLOATS IN WIDE ORBIT AROUND A RINGED WORLD CALLED *MONASTERY.* AND TO HAN SOLO'S *DISMAY... IT* NO LONGER DOES THIS *ALONE!*

ATTENTION, FREIGHTER! STAND BY FOR IMPERIAL INSPECTION!

WELL, KIDS, IT'S NICE TO KNOW OUR *SCANNERS* ARE WORKING PERFECTLY--

--THIS MAKES IT PRETTY *DEFINITE* THAT ONE OF THE EMPIRE'S *BATTLE CRUISERS* IS MOVING IN ON US!

Red Queen Rising!

YOU KNOW WE COULDN'T TAKE *FLIGHT*... NOT WHEN OUR MISSION IS TO BE LONG RANGE *BACK-UP* FOR LUKE WHILE HE'S DOWN ON THAT PLANET.

YEAH, *I KNOW.* THAT DOESN'T MEAN I HAVE TO BE *HAPPY* ABOUT IT.

OUR ONLY HOPE NOW IS THAT THEY BUY OUR *COVER STORY*--

--BUT IT MAY BE HARD FOR THEM TO *BELIEVE* WE'RE A SIMPLE FREIGHTER MAKING *REPAIRS* IF THEY FIND AN ACKNOWLEDGED *LEADER* OF THE REBEL ALLIANCE ABOARD.

TIME TO GO INTO *HIDING,* PRINCESS!

VOWROWRK!

YOU *HEARD,* CHEWIE... THEY'RE PULLING US IN WITH THEIR *TRACTOR BEAM.*

DOWN INTO THE *BIN,* YOUR ROYALNESS... PRETEND YOU'RE A CONTAINER OF *SPICE.*

I BEG YOUR PARDON, CAPTAIN SOLO... BUT WHAT SHOULD *I* DO WHEN THE IMPERIALS COME ABOARD?

YOU SHOULD BE ABLE TO KEEP THAT ULTRA-FREQUENCY *LASER-WAVE LINK* TO ARTOO DETOO *OPEN,* BRONZE BRITCHES--

TELL THE STORM-TROOPERS YOU'RE RECHARGING YOUR *FRAMISTATS* OR SOMETHIN'.

BE *BOLD...* BE *CREATIVE!* YOU KNOW... *LIE!*

THIS IS IMPERIAL CAPTAIN *WERMIS,* FREIGHTER. LOWER YOUR *RAMP* AND STAND READY TO BE *BOARDED*--

ON THE WORLD OF MONASTERY, IT IS DAWN. BEYOND THE TEMPLE OF THE ORDER OF THE SACRED CIRCLE LIES A GREAT RAIN FOREST... AND HERE, A RESTLESS LUKE SKYWALKER HAS CHOSEN TO WANDER.

I CAN'T SLEEP, ARTOO... NOT WHEN WE'VE GOT TO PRESENT OUR CASE AGAINST THE EMPIRE TO THE TEMPLE ELDERS THIS MORNING.

THIS RELIGIOUS ORDER HAS A LOT OF INFLUENCE AROUND THE GALAXY... IF WE MESS UP, THEY MAY SEE THE REBELLION AS A THREAT TO THE NATURAL CIRCLE OF LIFE THAT THEY WORSHIP.

BLIIT-DA VOOP!

ARE YOU TRYING TO REMIND ME THAT YOU'VE BEEN PROGRAMMED WITH ENOUGH PROOF TO SHOW THE EMPIRE IS AN EVEN BIGGER THREAT...? THAT'S FINE, ARTOO--

--BUT IT'S ME, I'M WORRIED ABOUT... BEING IN WAY OVER MY HEAD PLAYING DIPLOMAT! ESPECIALLY SINCE THE IMPERIAL REPRESENTATIVE HERE... IS DARTH VADER!

STILL... SISTER DOMINA OF THE ORDER THOUGHT MY LACK OF EXPERIENCE MIGHT BE A VIRTUE, FIGURED SINCERITY WOULD COUNT FOR MORE WITH THE ELDERS THAN--

WHAT'S THAT AHEAD OF US?

IT IS A GLADE AMID THE TALL TREES THAT STAND LIKE CATHEDRAL COLUMNS... AND BEFORE THE CALM POOL IN ITS CENTER, THE PRIESTESS KNOWN AS SISTER DOMINA SEEMS TO MEDITATE.

CERTAINLY THE WORLD AND THE FOREST APPEAR CLOSED FROM HER THOUGHTS...

...OR SHE WOULD BE AWARE THAT *DEATH* SLOWLY, STEALTHILY CREEPS TOWARD HER!

THEN, WITH A COUGHING SNARL...THE BEAST *LEAPS!*

SO, TOO, DOES *LUKE SKYWALKER!* HE HAS RUN HARD AND FAST TO *PROPEL* HIMSELF INTO THE CREATURE WITH AS MUCH *FORCE* AS POSSIBLE. HARDLY ENOUGH TO *STOP* IT...

...BUT *JUST* ENOUGH TO THROW IT OFF TARGET!

A TOUCH OF *REVULSION* SWEEPS THROUGH LUKE AS THEY CRASH INTO THE WATER. HE HAS LEARNED TO *SWIM* SINCE LEAVING HIS ARID HOME OF *TATOOINE.* BUT IT WILL NEVER SEEM *NATURAL* TO HIM.

THEN, HE IS BUSY SCRAMBLING TO AVOID RAKING, SLASHING *CLAWS*...

...BOLTING TO HIS FEET IN MERCIFULLY *SHALLOW* WATER, KNOWING HE MUST STRIKE *FIRST*...

...OR *DIE!*

BRAAMP!

WET, WEARY, LUKE TURNS...TO FIND HIS VICTORY HAS BEEN WITNESSED. AND OBVIOUSLY *CONDEMNED.*

BROTHERS, SISTERS,...BACK TO THE *TEMPLE.* THE FOREST POOL WILL OBVIOUSLY NOT BE *FIT* FOR OUR DAWN MEDITATION.

LUKE...YOU COULDN'T *KNOW,* BUT THAT SABER CAT WAS A *PET!* HARMLESS... ALLOWED TO ROAM HERE AT WILL!

HARMLESS...?! IT WAS LEAPING TO *KILL* YOU! LET ME GO *AFTER* THEM,... EXPLAIN...!

DON'T...YOU'RE TOO *ANGRY.* YOU MIGHT MAKE THINGS *WORSE,* LUKE.

RELAX. CALM DOWN, I'M *CERTAIN* THAT WHEN WE MEET WITH THE ELDERS ...ALL WILL GO AS IT *SHOULD.*

IT'S *GOT* TO, SISTER DOMINA,...! THIS IS TOO *IMPORTANT* FOR ME TO FOUL UP!

I'LL SEE YOU BACK AT THE *TEMPLE...* AFTER I'VE CLEANED UP.

I COULD ALMOST FEEL *SORRY* FOR HIM. HE'S SO *NAIVE... TRUSTING.*

BUT I TRUST YOU THEN REMEMBER, *HE--* AND HIS REBEL FRIENDS-- ARE RESPONSIBLE FOR THE DEATH OF YOUR *BROTHER...* BARON ORMAN TAGGE!

THE HOUSE OF TAGGE *AVENGES* ITS OWN, LORD VADER... EVEN WITH MY UPBRINGING AS A PRIESTESS OF THE SACRED CIRCLE, I COULD *NEVER* FORGET THAT.

IT IS THE *REASON* I AM ALLIED WITH YOU... I WON'T *WEAKEN.*

WITHIN THE DARK PRISON OF HIS BREATHMASK... THE LORD OF THE SITH SMILES. THE GAME STILL GOES AS PLANNED.

IT IS AN **INTRICATE** GAME. ONE IN WHICH HE MOVES FORMER **RIVALS** FOR THE EMPEROR'S FAVOR LIKE **PAWNS**. RIVALS SUCH AS **BARON TAGGE**...

...WHO HAS BEEN **RESCUED** FROM NEAR-DEATH ABOARD A REBEL-DESTROYED SHIP.* NOW, ELABORATE **LIFE-SUPPORT CAPSULES** SUSTAIN HIM AND HIS SCIENTIST BROTHER...

*AS ESTABLISHED **LAST ISSUE**--ARCHIE.

LIFE SUPPORT CAPSULES... AND THE **WHIM** OF DARTH VADER.

A CHANGE IN THE BARON'S **CONDITION**...? CAPTAIN **WERMIS** SHOULD BE NOTIFIED, SINCE LORD VADER IS ABSENT--

-- BUT HE'S BUSY EXAMINING THAT **FREIGHTER** WE CAPTURED.

AND THAT EXAMINATION IS NOT GOING AS **PLANNED**...

I-IT **CAN'T BE**...! LORD VADER WAS **CERTAIN** THE ALLIANCE WOULD WANT PRINCESS LEIA **NEARBY** TO THE SITUATION ON MONASTERY...!

SHE MAY **BE**, SIR... BUT NOT ON THIS **SHIP**-- AND NOT IN THESE HIDDEN **STORAGE BINS**!

WE COULD BRING IN A **SCANNING TEAM** BUT--

A WASTE OF **TIME**! ALL LIKELY PLACES HAVE BEEN **THOROUGHLY** EXAMINED!

ANYONE CAN MAKE A **MISTAKE**, CAPTAIN... MY MATE AND I UNDERSTAND THE **PRESSURES** UPON AN IMPERIAL OFFICER.

RATHER THAN REPORT THIS FALSE SEARCH AND SEIZURE TO YOUR **SUPERIORS**... WE'LL JUST GO QUIETLY ON OUR WAY AS IF **NOTHING** HAD HAPPENED.

THE ONLY PLACE YOU AND THAT MOUNTAIN OF *FUR* ARE GOING, CORELLIAN... IS TO A *DETENTION CELL!*

TAKE THEM *AWAY!* TELL THE OTHER GUARDS IN THE BAY TO GET BACK TO THEIR REGULAR DUTIES... *LORD VADER* WILL DEAL WITH THIS PAIR WHEN HE *RETURNS!*

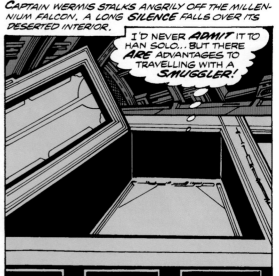

CAPTAIN WERMIS STALKS ANGRILY OFF THE MILLENNIUM FALCON. A LONG *SILENCE* FALLS OVER ITS DESERTED INTERIOR.

I'D NEVER *ADMIT* IT TO HAN SOLO... BUT THERE *ARE* ADVANTAGES TO TRAVELLING WITH A *SMUGGLER!*

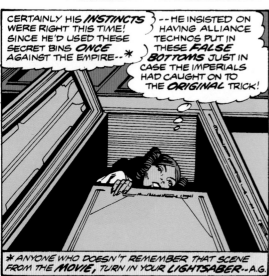

CERTAINLY HIS *INSTINCTS* WERE RIGHT THIS TIME! SINCE HE'D USED THESE SECRET BINS *ONCE* AGAINST THE EMPIRE-- *

--HE INSISTED ON HAVING ALLIANCE TECHNOS PUT IN THESE *FALSE BOTTOMS* JUST IN CASE THE IMPERIALS HAD CAUGHT ON TO THE *ORIGINAL* TRICK!

* ANYONE WHO DOESN'T REMEMBER THAT SCENE FROM THE *MOVIE,* TURN IN YOUR *LIGHTSABER*--A.G.

THREEPIO! WAKE UP! WE'VE GOT TO USE THE *LASERWAVE LINK* TO *WARN* LUKE THAT DARTH VADER IS UP TO *MORE* IN THIS SYSTEM THAN PLAYING *DIPLOMAT!*

OH,... *EXCUSE* ME, YOUR HIGHNESS. THE STORMTROOPERS ORDERED ME TO *SHUT DOWN.* I THOUGHT IT BEST TO *COMPLY* SO THEY WOULDN'T *REMOVE* ME FROM THE SHIP.

AND, MOMENTS LATER, ON *MONASTERY...*

LUKE...! LISTEN *CAREFULLY!* THREEPIO HAS PATCHED MY *VOICE* THROUGH ARTOO'S AUDIO-AMPLIFICATION SYSTEM--

--BUT I CAN'T TALK *LONG* WITHOUT BEING *TRACED!*

LEIA...?!

318

WHAT'S GOING *ON...?* I THOUGHT I WAS WORKING *ALONE...*

GENERAL DODONNA WANTED ME ABLE TO GIVE YOU *ADVICE* IF THE DIPLOMATIC SITUATION TURNED STICKY... BUT WE THOUGHT IF WE TOLD YOU ABOUT THIS, IT MIGHT *INHIBIT* YOU FROM ACTING ON YOUR OWN.

I DON'T KNOW... MAYBE I COULD *USE* A LITTLE INHIBITING. THINGS HAVE BEEN HAPPENING HERE THAT--

BE *ALERT*, LUKE! I'VE GOT TO SEE WHAT I CAN DO FOR HAN AND CHEWBACCA... WE'RE ON LORD VADER'S CRUISER!

HE OBVIOUSLY HAS SOME SCHEME TO TRAP US *ALL*... BUT HE'S CLOSEST TO *YOU!* MAYBE THE ORDER OF THE SACRED CIRCLE CAN HELP...!

WITH A CLICK, PRINCESS LEIA SIGNS OFF, BUT BEFORE LUKE CAN TAKE ACTION...

IT'S TIME TO MEET WITH THE TEMPLE *ELDERS.*

SISTER DOMINA, I'VE GOT TO *TALK* WITH YOU! DARTH VADER IS--

--ALREADY ON HIS WAY TO THE GATHERING CHAMBER. ANYTHING YOU WISH TO BRING UP CAN BE SETTLED *THERE*, LUKE.

SWIFTLY, THE PRIESTESS MOVES INTO THE CORRIDOR BEFORE LUKE CAN SAY MORE...

...AND, AS SHE LEADS THE WAY TO THE MEETING, DOMINA TAGGE *SMILES.* IT IS HER FIRST GENUINE SMILE SINCE THE DAY HER *BROTHER* VISITED...

... HER YOUNGEST BROTHER, ULRIC, THE IMPERIAL GENERAL. HE CAME IN PLACE OF THE ONE BROTHER DOMINA TRULY LOVED; THE HEAD OF THE FAMILY... *BARON ORMAN TAGGE.*

HE CAME, BARELY CONCEALING HIS *NEW* PRIDE IN BEING THE *NEW* BARON, TO EXPLAIN HOW ORMAN HAD DIED BECAUSE OF THE REBELS AND ONE LUKE SKYWALKER IN PARTICULAR...

...AND TO SUGGEST THAT IF *RETRIBUTION* INTERESTED HER, THE BEST HOPE WAS TO MAKE *PEACE* WITH THE LORD OF THE SITH.

SKYWALKER IS *MINE*, DOMINA TAGGE. BUT YOU'LL HAVE THE PLEASURE OF KNOWING YOU DELIVERED HIM TO ME...AND OF DEALING A GREAT *BLOW* TO HIS CAUSE!

IT WASN'T AS MUCH AS SHE WOULD HAVE LIKED... BUT IT WAS ENOUGH. NOW DARTH VADER BECAME THE ONE REGULAR VISITOR SHE WAS ALLOWED IN THE MONASTERY'S CLOISTERED SECLUSION. UNTIL...

YOU ARE *READY.* I HAVE IMPARTED ENOUGH KNOWLEDGE AND SKILL TO YOU TO DO WHAT MUST BE DONE *WITHIN*...

THEN LET'S SEE THIS THING *FINISHED,* MY LORD!

AND ONLY IN WEAKER MOMENTS WOULD SHE RECALL AN INCIDENT FROM LONG, LONG AGO, BEFORE SHE *ENTERED* THE ORDER OF THE SACRED CIRCLE AND THE PROTECTED EXISTENCE IT OFFERED...

MARRY INTO THE IMPERIAL FAMILY WHEN SHE'S OLD ENOUGH...?! SILAS, I'LL *KILL* YOU IF YOU EVER SUGGEST ANYTHING LIKE THAT AGAIN!

DOMINA'S THE ONE PURE AND INNOCENT THING IN THE TAGGE FAMILY... I WON'T SEE HER CORRUPTED IN *ANY* WAY! *EVER!*

SISTER DOMINA SIGHS. THAT INNOCENCE IS LONG GONE NOW, SACRIFICED TO THE NEED FOR VENGEANCE. PERHAPS IF ORMAN HAD BEEN LESS PROTECTIVE, SHE WOULDN'T HAVE FELT HIS LOSS SO STRONGLY. BUT FEEL IT SHE *DOES*...

...AND *NOTHING* WILL STAND IN THE WAY OF MAKING THOSE RESPONSIBLE PAY!

WAIT HERE, LUKE... UNTIL WE SUMMON YOU.

THE PRIESTESS OF THE SACRED CIRCLE DISAPPEARS INTO THE GREAT CHAMBER BEYOND. LONG, ANXIOUS MOMENTS PASS FOR AN ALREADY NERVOUS FIGHTER PILOT TURNED UNLIKELY DIPLOMAT...

ALL CIRCUITS *FUNCTIONING*, ARTOO...? NO PROBLEM WITH THE HOLOGRAPHIC *EVIDENCE* YOU'LL BE PROJECTING...?

THEN WE OUGHTTA BE ALL RIGHT. WHATEVER DARTH VADER'S UP TO, HE CAN'T PULL ANYTHING IN THIS MEETING WITHOUT LOOKING BAD HIMSEL--

THEY ARE *READY* FOR YOU, REBEL.

BUT WHAT WAITS BEHIND THE CHAMBER DOORS IS NOT *QUITE* WHAT THE STAR WARRIOR FROM TATOOINE *EXPECTED*!

YOU ARE ENTITLED TO *SURPRISE*, LUKE SKYWALKER. THE MEMBERS OF THE ORDER HAVE JUST VOTED TO *REVOKE* THE CIRCLE OF ELDER'S AUTHORITY...

...AND NAMED *ME* AS ALL-HIGH PRIESTESS!

AND MY FIRST DUTY IS TO SEE THAT *YOU* AND THE REBEL ALLIANCE ARE *ELIMINATED* AS THREATS TO THE NATURAL CYCLE OF GALACTIC LIFE!

BLEE-T-DA-DEEP!

W-WHAT...? YOU ENCOURAGED ME TO *COME* HERE...! SEEMED TO *LIKE* ME....!

PROOF OF THE *DANGER* YOU POSE...THE DANGER OF ONE WHO RADIATES THE UNNATURAL POWER OF THE *FORCE!*

THE *ELDERS* INSISTED ON INVITING AN ALLIANCE REPRESENTATIVE...I LED THE *OPPOSITION* TO DOING SO!

AND SINCE YOUR ARRIVAL... I'VE BEEN PROVEN *RIGHT!* FROM THE MOMENT YOU SET FOOT ON MONASTERY... THERE HAVE BEEN *DISRUPTIONS* IN THE SACRED CIRCLE OF LIFE!

I TRIED TO BE FAIR AND OPENMINDED BY BEING ONE OF THOSE WHO *BROUGHT* YOU HERE...

...BUT WITH THE INCIDENT IN THE MEDITATION GROVE THIS MORNING, I AND THE ORDER'S MEMBERS HAVE SEEN *ENOUGH!*

YOU'RE A *MENACE,* LUKE SKYWALKER...AND BY PROCLAIMING YOU A *HERO,* THE REBELS CONDEMN THEIR WHOLE CAUSE!

WAIT A MINUTE! THE *FORCE* IS AT WORK HERE ALL RIGHT...WITHOUT YOU CHARMING AND DISTRACTING ME, I CAN *SENSE* IT NOW!

IT'S BEEN USED TO SLOWLY CORRUPT AND WEAKEN THE JUDGMENT OF EVERYONE HERE! AND THE ONLY ONE WHO WOULD USE IT IN *THAT* WAY--

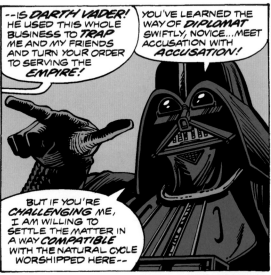

--IS *DARTH VADER!* HE USED THIS WHOLE BUSINESS TO *TRAP* ME AND MY FRIENDS AND TURN YOUR ORDER TO SERVING THE *EMPIRE!*

YOU'VE LEARNED THE WAY OF *DIPLOMAT* SWIFTLY, NOVICE...MEET ACCUSATION WITH *ACCUSATION!*

BUT IF YOU'RE *CHALLENGING* ME, I AM WILLING TO SETTLE THE MATTER IN A WAY *COMPATIBLE* WITH THE NATURAL CYCLE WORSHIPPED HERE--

...FOR WHAT IS MORE *NATURAL* IN THE GREAT CIRCLE OF LIFE... THAN *DEATH?*

YOURS OR MINE, PUPPY....! LET NATURE AND THE CLASH OF OUR *LIGHTSABERS* DECIDE!

CAPTAIN WERMIS! WE'VE HAD *EXPLOSIONS* IN SUPPLY HOLDS E AND F! THEY HELD HIGHLY *INCENDIARY* STOCK...FIRE'S *SPREADING!*

GET ALL AVAILABLE PERSONNEL DOWN THERE TO *FIGHT* IT!

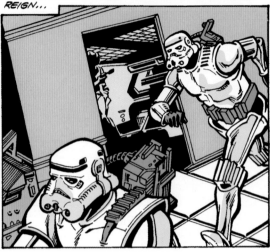

ALARMS SOUND THROUGHOUT THE GIANT STAR DESTROYER. ITS STERILE CORRIDORS ECHO WITH THE CLATTER OF MANY FEET. CONFUSION AND FRENZY REIGN...

...*EXCEPT IN ONE SHADOWED ALCOVE.*

THOSE TIMED CHARGES ON THE *PROTON GRENADES* I TOOK FROM THE BAY GUARDS I SURPRISED DID THE *TRICK...!*

NOW, WHILE EVERYONE'S DIVERTED TO *ONE* PART OF THE SHIP--

--I CAN STRIKE AT *ANOTHER!*

AND THIS STRIKE FREES THE CONTROL PANEL, CRUCIAL TO THE ESCAPE PLANS LEIA ORGANA *FOR HER FRIENDS...*

...BUT HER ACTIONS HAVE ALREADY HAD EFFECT *BEYOND* HER PLANS.

CONCUSSION FROM THOSE BLASTS *SHATTERED* THE LIFE SUPPORT CAPSULES! *SILAS* TAGGE IS STILL UNCONSCIOUS, B-BUT...

...*WHERE'S* THE *BARON?!*

SIR, COULD IT BE THE HOUSE OF TAGGE HAD *AGENTS* ABOARD... DELIBERATELY SABOTAGED US TO *FREE* HIM?

WE *KNOW* IT CAN'T BE REBELS... THE ONLY ONES ON THAT SHIP WE CAPTURED ARE *LOCKED* AWAY!

TROOPER, YOU JUST VOICED MY VERY *OWN* SUSPICIONS!

ACTUALLY, CAPTAIN WERMIS HAD NO SUCH SUSPICION... BUT IT SOUNDS REASONABLE ENOUGH TO BE TRUE. HE PRAYS IT WILL SOUND REASONABLE TO LORD VADER. HE IS STILL TRYING TO DECIDE HOW BEST TO FRAME HIS REPORT SO AS TO ESCAPE BLAME...

...WHEN *NEW* DISASTER FALLS!

SOMETHING'S HAPPENED TO THE *ARTIFICIAL GRAVITY!*

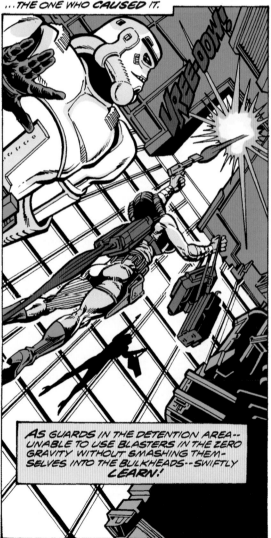

ONE PERSON ABOARD THE MASSIVE EMPIRE VESSEL IS *PREPARED* FOR THIS TURN OF EVENTS ...THE ONE WHO *CAUSED* IT.

VKROOM

AS GUARDS IN THE DETENTION AREA-- UNABLE TO USE BLASTERS IN THE ZERO GRAVITY WITHOUT SMASHING THEM- SELVES INTO THE BULKHEADS--SWIFTLY *LEARN!*

HAN! CHEWBACCA! UNLESS YOU'VE GOTTEN FOND OF THE EMPIRE'S BRAND OF *FOOD PASTE*... STRAP THESE PROPULSION PACKS ON! *QUICKLY!*

GEE, YOUR MAJESTICNESS...YOU THOUGHT OF *EVERY-THING!*

CERTAINLY! I HAD THAT ESCAPE YOU AND LUKE IMPROVISED FROM THE *DEATH STAR* TO REMIND ME WHAT IT WOULD BE LIKE IF *I DIDN'T!*

I HAVE FOND MEMORIES OF THAT ESCAPE, OF COURSE... I GOT *PAID* FOR IT.

DO YOU *REALLY* THINK WE'RE GONNA GET OUT OF HERE WITH-OUT ANY *TROUBLE?* WHAT ABOUT THE *TRACTOR BEAM?*

THERE IS TROUBLE... BUT NONE OF IT INSURMOUNTABLE. AND BY THE TIME WERMIS'S CREW BECOMES AWARE OF WHAT'S HAPPENING AND ACTIVATES THE TRACTOR BEAM...IT IS TOO LATE.

YOU PULLED IT *OFF,* PRINCESS! BUT I STILL CAN'T BELIEVE THERE'S NOT A *KICKER* SOMEWHERE.

WE HAD A LOT IN OUR *FAVOR,* HAN... PARTICULARLY *SUR-PRISE.* THE CRUISER'S *CAPTAIN* DIDN'T REACT TO IT VERY WELL--

I'D BET FROM THE CONFUSED WAY HE HAD HIS TROOPS RUSHING AROUND... HE HASN'T HAD MUCH *BATTLE* EXPERIENCE.

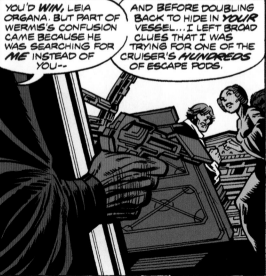

YOU'D *WIN,* LEIA ORGANA. BUT PART OF WERMIS'S CONFUSION CAME BECAUSE HE WAS SEARCHING FOR *ME* INSTEAD OF YOU--

AND BEFORE DOUBLING BACK TO HIDE IN *YOUR* VESSEL...I LEFT BROAD CLUES THAT I WAS TRYING FOR ONE OF THE CRUISER'S *HUNDREDS* OF ESCAPE PODS.

DON'T *STARE*, PRINCESS... SURELY YOU REMEMBER *BARON TAGGE?* IT HASN'T BEEN SO LONG SINCE WE *CLASHED* ON METALORN.*

NOW, HOWEVER, WE'RE TRAVELING COMPANIONS... STRAIGHT DOWN TO *MONASTERY!* I OVERHEARD ENOUGH OF THIS DROID SPEAKING WITH HIS *CONTACT* THERE...TO KNOW I'M *NEEDED!*

N-NO....! THAT WILL VIOLATE THEIR *CLOISTER*...WHATEVER TROUBLE *LUKE* IS IN, THAT MIGHT BE ENOUGH TO *FINISH* HIM!

*STAR WARS #30 --ARCHIE.

SKYWALKER...?! HIS FATE IS NO MORE MY CONCERN THAN *BLASTING* YOU WILL BE, IF YOU SHOULD *DELAY* ME!

EASY, YOUR HIGHNESS... THIS COCKPIT IS NO PLACE FOR A *FIREFIGHT.* TRUST AN OLD SMUGGLING HAND TO GET US DOWN *UNNOTICED*...

SUNDOWN! A PROCESSION SETS OUT FROM THE TEMPLE OF THE SACRED CIRCLE... MOVING TOWARD WHAT WILL BE A *KILLING GROUND.*

DARTH VADER HAS TAUGHT HER *WELL*, DOMINA TAGGE THINKS. *TOO* WELL, PERHAPS, FOR IN LETTING HER DECIDE THE *SITE* FOR THE DUEL...

...HE HAS GIVEN HER THE OPPORTUNITY TO SEE THAT NOT *ONE* BUT *TWO* OF HER FAMILY'S ENEMIES WILL PERISH! WHY SETTLE FOR THE *REBEL* WHEN SHE CAN BRING DOWN THE *SITH LORD* AS WELL?!

NEXT ISSUE: IN MORTAL COMBAT!

WITH NO SOUND BUT THE HISS OF HIS BREATHMASK, THE HUM OF HIS LIGHTSABER, THE SITH LORD STRIDES INSTANTLY FORWARD...

...HIS DARK THOUGHTS SOLELY HIS OWN.

YOUR TURN, REBEL.

YEAH...

...AFTER ALL THE FANCY *MANIPULATING* YOU AND VADER PUT ME THROUGH TO BRING THIS ABOUT--

--A LITTLE HONEST *FIGHTING* WILL BE A PLEASURE!

VLITTA DOOP

I...I'M SORRY, ARTOO. YOU CAN'T GO WITH ME, NOT *THIS* TIME.

DOMINA TAGGE SMILES. EVERYTHING HAS GONE PERFECTLY. BY COOPERATING WITH LORD VADER SHE HAS GAINED THE *POWER* SHE NEEDED...

HIS INFLUENCE HAS MADE ME *LEADER* OF THE ORDER--

--AND, AS AGREED, I'VE SANCTIONED THIS COMBAT.

BUT HE CARELESSLY LET *ME* CHOOSE THE SITE, AND DOWN *THERE*... NO ONE CAN SURVIVE.

INSTEAD OF SETTLING FOR VENGEANCE ON *ONE* ENEMY OF MY BROTHER--

--I'LL SEE THEM *BOTH* DESTROYED!

TWISTING, TURNING, THE PATH DRAWS LUKE STEADILY DOWNWARD THROUGH EVENING MISTS HEAVY WITH DAMPNESS.

WELL, NOW I KNOW WHY THIS IS CALLED THE *CRYSTAL VALLEY.*

THEY COVER THE PLACE LIKE *TREES*--

--OR MAYBE *GRAVE MARKERS.* MUSTN'T GET SO BUSY SIGHT-SEEING THAT I FORGET *DARTH VADER* IS SOMEWHERE AHEAD!

HE'S HAD EVERYTHING TOO MUCH HIS WAY AS IS--

--MANAGING TO SNARE LEIA, HAN, AND THE GANG WHILE THEY WERE MONITORING *MY* TROUBLES DOWN HERE! *

*LAST ISSUE --ARCHIE

DON'T EVEN KNOW IF THEY'RE STILL *TRAPPED* ON HIS CRUISER OR--

THE *GROUND...!* TREMBLING UNDER MY FEET! L-LIKE--

T-THAT *CRYSTAL*...! SEEMED TO *BURST* FROM THE GROUND!

MOISTURE FROM THIS HEAVY DEW AND MIST MUST CAUSE SOME SORT OF *CHEMICAL REACTION*--

-- MAKES THEM GROW *FAST*... ALMOST *EXPLOSIVELY*!

AND THE FORCE OF THE NEW ONES THRUSTING UP... MAKES THE OLD ONES NEARBY *SHATTER* AND *FALL*!

KR-KOW!

EITHER COULD GET YOU FATALLY *SKEWERED*--

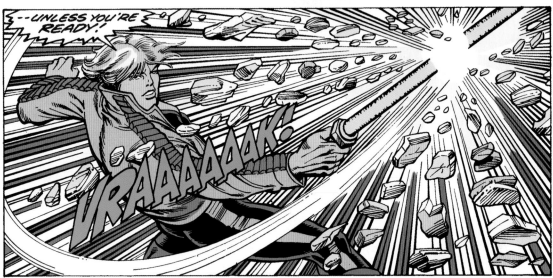

--UNLESS YOU'RE *READY*!

VRAAAAAAK!

BUT HOW READY CAN YOU *STAY* WHEN ONE OF THESE CRYSTALS CAN THRUST UP OR CRASH DOWN--

WROOOM!

-- FROM ANY *PLACE* AT ANY *MOMENT*?!

UNLESS THE FORCE IS WITH *BOTH* OF US... DARTH VADER AND I MAY NOT *LIVE* TO BATTLE EACH OTHER!

BUT THE DARK LORD HAS *HALTED* HIS DESCENT INTO THE VALLEY. HE STANDS WAITING...

...PATIENTLY, EXPECTANTLY, WAITING. UNTIL IN MONASTERY'S TWILIGHT SKY...

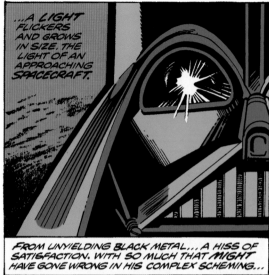

...A *LIGHT* FLICKERS AND GROWS IN SIZE. THE LIGHT OF AN APPROACHING *SPACECRAFT.*

FROM UNYIELDING BLACK METAL... A HISS OF SATISFACTION. WITH SO MUCH THAT *MIGHT* HAVE GONE WRONG IN HIS COMPLEX SCHEMING...

...EVENTS *STILL* HUE CLOSELY TO HIS MASTER PLAN!

UH OH, KIDS! APPEARS THIS SECLUDED VALLEY ISN'T THE GREAT *LANDING SPOT* I FIGURED IT TO BE!

ALL THAT MIST MUST HAVE AFFECTED THE SCANNERS.

BUT HAVE NO FEAR! BEYOND THE CRYSTAL FOREST IS A SMALL *CLEARING...* I'LL TRY FOR THAT.

IF YOU'RE *UP* TO SOMETHING, CORELLIAN... IT'LL BE YOUR *LAST* TRICK!

NOTHING STANDS IN MY WAY... NOT WITH MY *SISTER* IN JEOPARDY!

DESPITE MY FAMILY'S *RIVALRY* WITH DARTH VADER FOR THE EMPEROR'S FAVOR... DOMINA HAS REMAINED INNOCENT, PROTECTED. I'LL *KILL* TO SEE THAT DOESN'T CHANGE!

UNLESS YOU'RE A LOT *NICER* TO ME, BARON OL' BUDDY... YOU WON'T GET THE CHANCE.

THE MIDDLE OF A TOUGH *LANDING* IS NO PLACE TO THREATEN THE *PILOT!*

I *REST* MY CASE! LEAN ON THOSE *RETROS*, CHEWIE--

KWAM

--HARD!

IT IS A TASK THE MILLENNIUM FALCON'S WOOKIEE FIRST MATE CARRIES OUT WELL...

...IF SOMEWHAT JARRINGLY! PARTICULARLY WHERE BARON ORMAN TAGGE IS CONCERNED!

HAN! WHILE HE'S *OFF BALANCE*--

I'VE GOT HIS *BLASTER*--

AND I'VE GOT *HIM!*

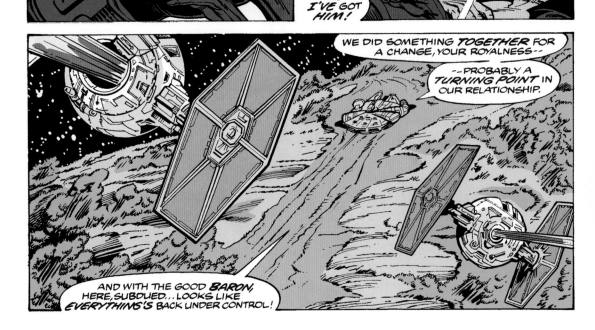

WE DID SOMETHING *TOGETHER* FOR A CHANGE, YOUR ROYALNESS--

--PROBABLY A *TURNING POINT* IN OUR RELATIONSHIP.

AND WITH THE GOOD *BARON*, HERE, SUBDUED...LOOKS LIKE *EVERYTHING'S* BACK UNDER CONTROL!

BOWRK!

WATTA YOU MEAN I'D BETTER LOOK AGAIN? WE JUST--

OH, THOSE *TIE FIGHTERS.* WELL...NOBODY'S PERFECT.

CAPTAIN SOLO? I STILL HAVE THE LASERWAVE LINK *OPEN* TO ARTOO-DETOO.

THE LITTLE FELLOW REPORTS--

NOT *NOW,* THREEPIO...OR WE MAY NOT BE *AROUND* FOR ANY REPORTS!

THEN HAN IS AT THE FALCON'S QUAD LASER CANNON...

...JUST AS THE TWO IMPERIAL SHIPS ARE AT THE FALCON!

PA-KWOM

URA-DOW!

I GUESS THE CAPTAIN OF DARTH VADER'S *CRUISER* TOOK OUR *ESCAPE* PRETTY HARD--

--VIOLATING A RELIGIOUS ORDER'S *CLOISTER* LIKE THIS! IT'S SURE TO BE A *DIPLOMATIC SCANDAL.*

OF COURSE, WE MAY BE TOO LONG *VAPORIZED* TO ENJOY THE EMPIRE'S EMBARRASSMENT!

I DON'T SUPPOSE THIS IS THE TIME TO POINT OUT TO THE CAPTAIN THAT WE, *TOO*, ARE IN VIOLATION.

THE IRONY *MIGHT* ELUDE HIM--

"--JUST AS THAT REMAINING *TIE FIGHTER* SEEMS TO BE DOING!"

I *HEARD* THAT, YOUR *WORSHIP*--

AND IF I DIDN'T *KNOW* THESE LITTLE DIGS WERE JUST YOUR WAY OF DISGUISING YOUR *TRUE* FEELINGS--

--I *MIGHT* BE *INSULTED!*

KA-WOOM

I KNOW THAT KIND OF SHARPSHOOTING LEAVES YOU *STUNNED*, KIDS, BUT RELAX--

--IT'S OKAY TO *CHEER.*

EXCEPT THAT WHILE EVERYTHING *ELSE* WAS BREAKING LOOSE--

"...SO WAS *BARON TAGGE!* HE'S RACING TOWARD THAT FOREST OF CRYSTAL RIGHT NOW!"

"THEN MAYBE THE JOKE'S ON *HIM*, PRINCESS. 'CAUSE ACCORDING TO THE SCOPES..."

"...THE PLACE IS IN A CONSTANT STATE OF *ERUPTION!* ANYONE WHO GETS HIMSELF IN THERE BETTER BE UNNATURALLY *LUCKY*...OR POSITIVELY *INVINCIBLE.*"

"PREFERABLY *BOTH!*"

KRAKOW

AND JUST AS LUKE IS REACHING THE *SAME* CONCLUSION...

ARTOO! YOU FOLLOWED ME AFTER ALL...?! THAT'S--

LESS *RISKY* THAN YOU MIGHT IMAGINE, SIR... GIVEN HIS COMPUTERIZED SENSORY SYSTEM.

STILL...IT'S FAR FROM *FLAWLESS.* THAT'S WHY *I'M* SPEAKING UP VIA THE LASERWAVE LINK--

WE'RE *NEARBY,* SIR! AND BY HOMING IN ON ME, ARTOO CAN *LEAD* YOU TO US, GIVEN YOUR PREDICAMENT... IT'S THE ONLY HOPE!

NO, THREEPIO!

DARTH VADER'S PLAYED US ALL FOR *PAWNS,* BUT I'VE GOT THE CHANCE TO *FIGHT* HIM HERE--

AND WHATEVER THE CONSEQUENCES... I'M GOING TO *DO* IT!

LUKE! THAT MAY BE *EXACTLY* WHAT HE--

I'M SORRY, YOUR HIGHNESS, HE'S BROKEN TRANSMISSION!

MEANWHILE...

WRRAK

T-THE *CRYSTAL!*

CAN'T MOVE *FAST* ENOUGH ...IT'S GOING TO--

CRUSH YOU, ORMAN TAGGE...? NO, ITS GREAT BULK IS GOING TO STOP INCHES SHORT OF THAT--

IT WILL PRESS YOU DOWN... DRIVING YOU FINALLY ONTO YOUR BACK!

IT'S NOT P-POSSIBLE...!

TO A MASTER OF THE FORCE... ALL THINGS ARE POSSIBLE.

INCLUDING LURING YOU HERE... TO THIS SPOT, AT THIS TIME.

IN THE EMPEROR'S NAME... WHY? YOU COULD HAVE SLAIN ME LONG AGO!

AN UNIMAGINATIVE VENGEANCE, BARON... YOU'VE TROUBLED ME ENOUGH TO DESERVE BETTER.

FOR INSTANCE: THIS FATE THAT'S BEFALLEN YOU--

--IS ACTUALLY WHAT YOUR DEAR LITTLE SISTER PLANNED TO HAVE HAPPEN TO ME.

DOMINA...? B-BUT... SHE'S NOT LIKE THAT! SHE'S INNOCENT ... BEYOND SUCH SCHEMING!

NO MORE, TAGGE.

WITH A BIT OF -GUIDANCE FROM ME, ANXIOUS TO AVENGE WHAT SHE THINKS IS YOUR DEATH... SHE'S CHANGED! AS THIS VISI-CUBE SHOWS--

N-NO...! THE ONE UNSULLIED, UNCORRUPTED THING IN OUR ENTIRE LINE...!

FINISH ME, VADER! YOU'VE RUINED THE ONLY PERSON IN THIS GALAXY I LOVED! FINISH ME NOW!

SOON. BUT FIRST... YOU'LL FULFILL A FINAL TASK.

THE SUN IS GONE. NIGHT ON MONASTERY IS MADE BEAUTIFUL BY ITS SOFTLY GLOWING RING OF MOONS, BUT THAT BEAUTY IS LOST ON TWO FIGURES URGENTLY, DESPERATELY SKIRTING THE CRYSTAL VALLEY...

FASTER, HAN! FROM WHAT THREEPIO LEARNED FROM ARTOO... WE CAN STILL STOP THIS DUEL!

BUT WE'VE GOT TO LET DOMINA TAGGE KNOW HER BROTHER IS ALIVE... THAT LUKE DIDN'T CAUSE HIS DEATH, AS DARTH VADER MADE HER BELIEVE!

HAN DOESN'T VOICE A RESPONSE THAT OCCURS TO HIM. IT'S NO DOUBT IN LEIA'S MIND AS WELL...

THEIR EFFORT COULD ALREADY BE TOO LATE TO SAVE LUKE FROM THE VALLEY...

...OR WORSE!

THAT SHARD...! IT DIDN'T FALL OR ERUPT--

I-IT... HURTLED THROUGH THE AIR...! ALMOST AS IF IT WERE THROWN--

WAAMP

-- BY THE FORCE!

NO OTHER WORDS ARE SPOKEN. FOR PERHAPS A HEARTBEAT... BOTH FIGURES ARE STILL.

THEN...THEY MOVE!

SHDAAAAAKKKK!

SWIFTLY, INEVITABLY... LIKE *LIGHTNING* STRIKING!

AND IN THE STRAINING PRESS OF COMBAT... A *TRUTH* COMES TO LUKE SKYWALKER.

I CAN *FEEL* THE FORCE AROUND VADER... IT'S SO *STRONG!* SURROUNDS HIM LIKE A *WALL!* B-BUT... *BEYOND* THAT... I SENSE SOMETHING ELSE... *FEAR!*

H-HE'S ACTUALLY *AFRAID* OF ME! IF THAT'S SO... *I CAN WIN!* IT WON'T BE EASY... BUT I CAN *DO* IT!

BUT IN HIS PROBING OF THE ONE HE FIGHTS...

...THE YOUNG WARRIOR FORGETS *ANOTHER* FACTOR! HE FALLS...

FWAM!

...HIS FOE DOES *NOT!*

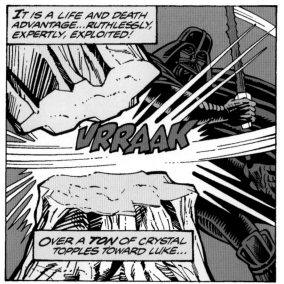

IT IS A LIFE AND DEATH ADVANTAGE...RUTHLESSLY, EXPERTLY, EXPLOITED!

VRRAAK

OVER A *TON* OF CRYSTAL TOPPLES TOWARD LUKE...

WOM

BUT THE LESSONS OF BEN KENOBI ARE *WITH* HIM...

HIS ACTIONS GROW FROM INSTINCT, FROM FEELING, FROM HIS INNER SELF...

ZAMP!

...FROM THE *FORCE!*

HIS ARMORED ENEMY MOVES WITH SKILL, WITH DARING...

...BUT NOW IT IS THE YOUNGER MAN WHO PRESSES THE BATTLE!

HE'S OUT TO *FLATTEN* ME...!

BUT IF I FALL BACK *WITH* HIS KICK AND COME UP *FAST*--

SHRRAAAKK

THE BLADE HITS GLANCINGLY... NOT A KILLING STROKE, MERELY A *DEVASTATING* ONE!

341

THEN, FROM OUT OF THE SURROUNDING CRYSTALS...

VADJOT DABIP WRRT

ARTOO?! YOU'RE SUPPOSED TO BE MAKING YOUR WAY BACK TO THE *FALCON!*

NO ONE EVER HAD A MORE *LOYAL* FRIEND--

BUT I CAN'T AFFORD *ANY* DISTRACTION NOW--

--NOT WHEN I NEED ALL MY CONCENTRATION TO *FINISH* DARTH VADER!

THREEPIO ON THE *LINKUP,* SIR! ARTOO IS FRANTIC BECAUSE HIS SENSORY RECEPTORS *DETECT* SOMETHING--

--YOUR HUMAN VISION APPARENTLY *CAN'T!* HE FEARS--

MY MIND'S BEING *CLOUDED* BY THE *FORCE!* NOW THAT I'M NOT *FIGHTING,* I CAN *SENSE* IT! AND I CAN TELL--

AN ALARMED *SCREECH* ERUPTS FROM THE LITTLE DROID!

NO! THIS DOESN'T HAVE TO BE! DON'T MAKE ME--

THE LOOMING FIGURE'S LIGHTSABER *SWINGS*... AND LUKE HAS NO CHOICE!

WAAAMP

HIS ONLY DEFENSE IS... A *FATAL THRUST!*

THE SITH LORD'S TOWERING FORM *SAGS*... BEGINS TO FALL...

...BUT IT IS *BARON ORMAN TAGGE* WHO CRASHES TO THE GROUND!

I KNEW IT...! BUT I REALIZED IT TOO LATE! IT'S THE REASON I SENSED *FEAR* EARLIER! TAGGE DUELED ME BEFORE....✱ HE LOST THEN, HE FEARED IT MIGHT HAPPEN AGAIN!

B-BUT...THAT *STILL* DOESN'T EXPLAIN--

THE *PURPOSE* OF THE ILLUSION...? THE *REASON* HE WAS MADE TO FIGHT IN *MY* PLACE?

✱ *STAR WARS #33* --ARCHIE.

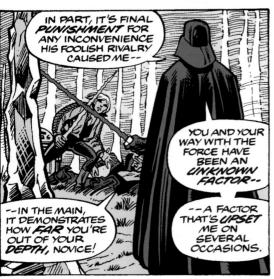

IN PART, IT'S FINAL *PUNISHMENT* FOR ANY INCONVENIENCE HIS FOOLISH RIVALRY CAUSED ME--

YOU AND YOUR WAY WITH THE FORCE HAVE BEEN AN *UNKNOWN FACTOR*--

--A FACTOR THAT'S *UPSET* ME ON SEVERAL OCCASIONS.

--IN THE MAIN, IT DEMONSTRATES HOW *FAR* YOU'RE OUT OF YOUR *DEPTH*, NOVICE!

NO *MORE*, LUKE SKYWALKER! I'VE THOROUGHLY *TESTED* YOU... MADE YOU PERFORM IN A HOSTILE ENVIRONMENT... PROBED YOUR EMOTIONS BY PLACING YOUR FRIENDS IN JEOPARDY. I NOW KNOW YOUR LIMITS...AND YOUR LIMITATIONS!

THEN YOU KNOW SOMETHING *ELSE*. I'M LEARNING...! I CAN *CHANGE*... I CAN *GROW!*

WHEN YOUR ONLY *INSTRUCTOR* IS DEAD...BY MY HANDS?

AN *AMUSING* NOTION, PUPPY. HAVE YOU THE *COURAGE* TO PURSUE IT?

COME! ONLY A FEW *STEPS* SEPARATE US.

I'LL *GIVE* YOU THE FIRST BLOW!

RAGE FLARES WITHIN LUKE, HE TENSES TO CHARGE, THEN INSTEAD...LEAPS BACK!

LOOK *OUT*, ARTOO! HE MEANT TO TRICK ME *INTO* THAT!

KTOOM!

NOW I'LL SHOW WHAT I'VE LEARNED--

THE ONLY WAY TO WIN THIS BATTLE... IS TO STOP PLAYING DARTH VADER'S OWN GAME!

MOVE IT, LITTLE FRIEND... WE'RE GETTING OUT OF HERE!

WHILE ABOVE THE VALLEY... INFORMATION HAS BEEN DELIVERED, INTENSE ARGUMENTS MADE!

YOU WASTE WORDS, LEIA ORGANA! THE SITH LORD MAY HAVE PLAYED ME FOR A FOOL AS YOU SAY--

BUT ALONG WITH MY BROTHER AND YOUR YOUNG REBEL--

--HE'S DOOMED HIMSELF! THERE'S NO WAY TO BRING AID INTO THE CRYSTAL FOREST... OR FOR HIM TO GET OUT!

SOMEONE FORGOT TO TELL VADER...!

THE UNIQUE TIE FIGHTER DISAPPEARS INTO THE HEAVENS, LEAVING SILENCE IN ITS WAKE... SOME SHOCKED, SOME ANGRY.

THEN...

KID...! LUKE...! YOU MADE IT!

THE FORCE WAS WITH ME, HAN. UNFORTUNATELY... IT WAS WITH DARTH VADER TOO!

B-BUT... MY BROTHER! IF YOU COULD SAVE YOURSELF--

--WHY COULDN'T YOU SAVE HIM?!

LUKE TRIES TO EXPLAIN. BUT UNDERSTANDING NEVER LIGHTS THE EYES OF DOMINA TAGGE... ONLY COLD FURY.

LORD VADER'S CORRUPTIVE TOUCH RUNS DEEP, EVEN THE TRUTH CAN'T SHAKE IT.

GO! I'M FINISHED AS ALL-HIGH PRIESTESS... BUT I CAN NEVER FORGET OR FORGIVE THE DEATH OF MY BROTHER, NO MATTER WHAT THE CIRCUMSTANCES

THE ORDER OF THE SACRED CIRCLE WON'T TURN ITS INFLUENCE AGAINST THE REBEL ALLIANCE NOW--

--BUT MY WRATH WILL ALWAYS BE AGAINST YOU, LUKE SKYWALKER!

AND SHORTLY, LIKE THE *IMPERIAL* CRAFT BEFORE IT... THE *MILLENNIUM FALCON* SOARS TOWARD SPACE.

FRANKLY, KID... I DON'T *GET* IT! SEEMS TO ME VADER WENT TO A LOT OF TROUBLE FOR *NOTHING.*

NOT IF YOU REGARD THE *FORCE* AS THE GREATEST POWER IN THE GALAXY, AS *HE* DOES, HAN... IT'S WORTH *ANYTHING* TO LEARN HOW MUCH OF IT HE *SHARES* WITH ME.

UNTIL *CERTAIN,* HE HAD TO BE CAUTIOUS... OUR PAST ENCOUNTERS PROVED THAT. SO THIS TIME, THROUGH HIS CONTROL OF DOMINA TAGGE, HE ARRANGED THE PHYSICAL DISTRACTIONS LIKE MY DUEL--

--ALONG WITH THE *MENTAL* ONES OF MY MISSION GOING WRONG AND ALL OF YOU BEING IN DANGER.

THANKS TO ARTOO... I CAUGHT ON BEFORE HE LURED ME INTO A *FINAL FIGHT* I'M NOT *READY* FOR!

BUT, WITH ALL HE LEARNED... HE WON'T HAVE TO BE *CAUTIOUS* AGAIN.

I'M AFRAID THAT MEANS ROUGH TIMES AHEAD... FOR ME *AND* THE REBEL ALLIANCE!

YOU MEAN UP TILL NOW IT'S BEEN *EASY?* I'M NO BEN KENOBI, LUKE... BUT I'VE GOT SOME *PHILOSOPHY* FOR YOU.

WORRYIN' ABOUT THE FUTURE CAN BE A LOT WORSE--

--THAN *LIVIN'* IT AS IT COMES!

AND IF YOU'VE GOT AN OLD CYNIC LIKE *ME* SPOUTING WISDOM... YOU MUST HAVE A *LOT* MORE GOIN' FOR YOU THAN YOU THINK!

EPILOGUE: IN THE DISTANT, ISOLATED DREXEL SYSTEM... A DERELICT HAS BEEN DISCOVERED.

NO MISTAKE! IT'S CRIMSON JACK'S *PIRATE SHIP!* I'D KNOW THAT CONVERTED IMPERIAL CRUISER ANYWHERE.

MAYBE THE BOARDING CREW WILL SALVAGE *SOMETHING*... BUT FROM HERE IT LOOKS LIKE WE'LL BE RETURNING HOME WITH VERY *BAD* NEWS.

* WE SAW IT *PUT* IN THIS SHAPE BACK IN *STAR WARS* #15 --ARCH.

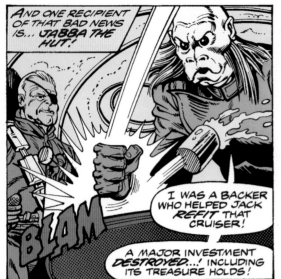

AND ONE RECIPIENT OF THAT BAD NEWS IS... JABBA THE HUT!

BLAM

I WAS A BACKER WHO HELPED JACK REFIT THAT CRUISER!

A MAJOR INVESTMENT DESTROYED...! INCLUDING ITS TREASURE HOLDS!

AT LEAST THE SHIP'S LOG SURVIVED... AND MAKES CLEAR WHO DID THIS!

HARD TO BELIEVE ONE MAN COULD CONTINUALLY BRING ME SO MUCH GRIEF! HARSH ACTION IS REQUIRED!

ONCE REQUIRED... IT IS NOT LONG BEGINNING!

CRAZY BOUNTY HUNTER!

JABBA TOOK THE PRICE OFF OUR HEADS WEEKS AGO...!*

* FOR REASONS RECOUNTED IN STAR WARS #28—ARCH AGAIN.

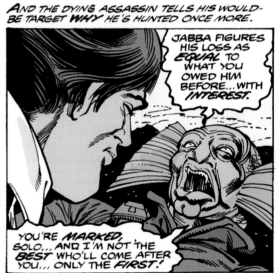

AND THE DYING ASSASSIN TELLS HIS WOULD-BE TARGET WHY HE'S HUNTED ONCE MORE.

JABBA FIGURES HIS LOSS AS EQUAL TO WHAT YOU OWED HIM BEFORE... WITH INTEREST.

YOU'RE MARKED, SOLO... AND I'M NOT THE BEST WHO'LL COME AFTER YOU... ONLY THE FIRST!

WELL, CHEWIE... LOOKS LIKE THE ONLY PLACE WE'RE WELCOME IS WITH THE REBELS.

NOT THE SAFEST OF SPOTS, WITH DARTH VADER AND THE EMPIRE AROUND.

BUT YA GOTTA ADMIT... IT WON'T BE DULL!

NEXT: THE MOST EAGERLY AWAITED SAGA OF THEM ALL BEGINS! MARVEL'S ADAPTATION OF...

THE EMPIRE STRIKES BACK!

YOUR SHIP HAS BEEN *REPAIRED*... YOU SHOULD HAVE NO FURTHER TROUBLE.

BUT WHAT ABOUT *YOU*...?

THIS IS A BIG GALAXY. WHY NOT STAY *HERE*?

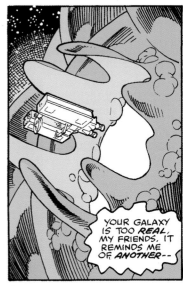

YOUR GALAXY IS TOO *REAL*, MY FRIENDS. IT REMINDS ME OF *ANOTHER*--

--WHICH I TRAVELED LIGHT YEARS TO *ESCAPE*. I WISH YOU WELL...BUT I SEE NOW I *BELONG* TO THE VOID.

RIDING...ME, THE SHIP, THE COMPUTER, OUR GAMES.

MAY YOU IN TIME WIN *HAPPINESS* HERE! MINE... OURS...IS *OUT THERE*.

AND LAUGHTER RISES FROM THE COMMUNICATOR. PERHAPS MAD. PERHAPS NOT.

IT IS DIFFICULT TO TELL...

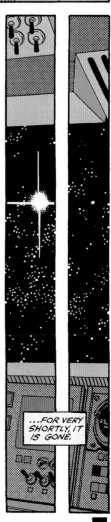

...FOR VERY SHORTLY, IT IS GONE.

NEXT THE **EMPIRE** STRIKES BACK!

STAR WARS *TIMELINE*

GRAPHIC NOVELS AND TRADE PAPERBACKS FROM DARK HORSE COMICS

For more information go to www.darkhorse.com

TALES OF THE SITH ERA
25,000-1000 YEARS BEFORE STAR WARS: A NEW HOPE

TALES OF THE JEDI
THE GOLDEN AGE OF THE SITH
Anderson • Carrasco, Jr. • Gossett
ISBN: 1-56971-229-8 $16.95
FALL OF THE SITH EMPIRE
Anderson • Heike • Carrasco, Jr.
ISBN: 1-56971-320-0 $14 .95
KNIGHTS OF THE OLD REPUBLIC
Veitch • Gossett
ISBN: 1-56971-020-1 $14.95
THE FREEDON NADD UPRISING
Veitch • Akins • Rodier
ISBN: 1-56971-307-3 $5.95
DARK LORDS OF THE SITH
Veitch • Anderson • Gossett
ISBN: 1-56971-095-3 $17.95
THE SITH WAR
Anderson • Carrasco, Jr.
ISBN: 1-56971-173-9 $17.95

*REDEMPTION
Anderson • Gossett • Pepoy • McDaniel
ISBN: 1-56971-535-1 $14.95

*JEDI VS. SITH
Macan • Bachs • Fernandez
ISBN: 1-56971-649-8 $15.95

PREQUEL ERA 1000-0 YEARS BEFORE STAR WARS: A NEW HOPE

*JEDI COUNCIL
ACTS OF WAR
Stradley • Fabbri • Vecchia
ISBN: 1-56971-539-4 $12.95

*DARTH MAUL
Marz • Duursema • Magyar • Struzan
ISBN: 1-56971-542-4 $12.95

PRELUDE TO REBELLION
Strnad • Winn • Jones
ISBN: 1-56971-448-7 $14.95
OUTLANDER
Truman • Leonardi • Rio
ISBN: 1-56971-514-9 $14.95
*JEDI COUNCIL
EMMISSARIES TO MALASTARE
Truman • Duursema • Others
ISBN: 1-56971-545-9 $15.95

STAR WARS: TWILIGHT
Ostrander • Duursema • Magyar
ISBN: 1-56971-558-0 $12.95
EPISODE 1 —
THE PHANTOM MENACE
Gilroy • Damaggio • Williamson
ISBN: 1-56971-359-6 $12.95
EPISODE 1 —
THE PHANTOM MENACE ADVENTURES
ISBN: 1-56971-443-6 $12.95

MANGA EDITIONS
Translated into English
EPISODE 1 —
THE PHANTOM MENACE
George Lucas • Kia Asamiya
VOLUME 1
ISBN: 1-56971-483-5 $9.95
VOLUME 2
ISBN: 1-56971-484-3 $9.95

*JANGO FETT
Marz • Fowler
ISBN: 1-56971-623-4 $5.95

*ZAM WESELL
Marz • Naifeh
ISBN: 1-56971-624-2 $5.95

EPISODE 2 —
ATTACK OF THE CLONES
Gilroy • Duursema • Kryssing • McCaig
ISBN: 1-56971-609-9 $17.95
DROIDS
THE KALARBA ADVENTURES
Thorsland • Windham • Gibson
ISBN: 1-56971-064-3 $17.95
REBELLION
Windham • Gibson
ISBN: 1-56971-224-7 $14 .95

JABBA THE HUTT
THE ART OF THE DEAL
Woodring • Wetherell • Sheldon
ISBN: 1-56971-310-3 $9.95
*UNDERWORLD
THE YAVIN VASSILIKA
Kennedy • Meglia
ISBN: 1-56971-618-8 $14.95
CLASSIC STAR WARS
HAN SOLO AT STARS' END
Goodwin • Alcala
ISBN: 1-56971-254-9 $6.95
BOBA FETT
ENEMY OF THE EMPIRE
Wagner • Gibson • Nadeau • Ezquerra
ISBN: 1-56971-407-X $12.95

TRILOGY ERA 0-5 YEARS AFTER STAR WARS: A NEW HOPE

A NEW HOPE SPECIAL EDITION
Jones • Barreto • Williamson
ISBN: 1-56971-213-1 $9.95
MANGA EDITIONS
Translated into English
A NEW HOPE
George Lucas • Hisao Tamaki
VOLUME 1
ISBN: 1-56971-362-6 $9.95
VOLUME 2
ISBN: 1-56971-363-4 $9.95
VOLUME 3
ISBN: 1-56971-364-2 $9.95
VOLUME 4
ISBN: 1-56971-365-0 $9.95
VADER'S QUEST
Macan • Gibbons
ISBN: 1-56971-415-0 $11.95

CLASSIC STAR WARS
THE EARLY ADVENTURES
Manning • Hoberg
ISBN: 1-56971-178-X $19.95
SPLINTER OF THE MIND'S EYE
Austin • Sprouse
ISBN: 1-56971-223-9 $14.95
CLASSIC STAR WARS
IN DEADLY PURSUIT
Goodwin • Williamson
ISBN: 1-56971-109-7 $16.95
THE EMPIRE STRIKES BACK SPECIAL EDITION
Goodwin • Williamson
ISBN: 1-56971-234-4 $9.95
MANGA EDITIONS
Translated into English
THE EMPIRE STRIKES BACK
George Lucas • Toshiki Kudo
VOLUME 1
ISBN: 1-56971-390-1 $9.95